· SPOTLIGHT ·
ON LITERACY

Authors, Consultants, and Reviewers

MULTICULTURAL AND EDUCATIONAL CONSULTANTS

Alma Flor Ada, Yvonne Beamer, Joyce Buckner, Helen Gillotte, Cheryl Hudson, Narcita Medina, Lorraine Monroe, James R. Murphy, Sylvia Peña, Joseph B. Rubin, Ramon Santiago, Cliff Trafzer, Hai Tran, Esther Lee Yao

LITERATURE CONSULTANTS

Ashley Bryan, Joan I. Glazer, Paul Janeczko, Margaret H. Lippert

INTERNATIONAL CONSULTANTS

Edward B. Adams, Barbara Johnson, Raymond L. Marshall

MUSIC AND AUDIO CONSULTANTS

John Farrell, Marilyn C. Davidson, Rick and Deborah Witkowski, Eastern Sky Media Services, Inc.

TEACHER REVIEWERS

Terry Baker, Jane Bauer, James Bedi, Nora Bickel, Vernell Bowen, Donald Cason, Jean Chaney, Carolyn Clark, Alan Cox, Kathryn DesCarpentrie, Carol L. Ellis, Roberta Gale, Brenda Huffman, Erma Inscore, Sharon Kidwell, Elizabeth Love, Isabel Marcus, Elaine McCraney, Michelle Moraros, Earlene Parr, Dr. Richard Potts, Jeanette Pulliam, Michael Rubin, Henrietta Sakamaki, Kathleen Cultron Sanders, Belinda Snow, Dr. Jayne Steubing, Margaret Mary Sulentic, Barbara Tate, Seretta Vincent, Willard Waite, Barbara Wilson, Veronica York

Macmillan/McGraw-Hill

A Division of The McGraw-Hill Companies

Macmillan/McGraw-Hill
1221 Avenue of the Americas
New York, New York 10020

Printed in the United States of America

ISBN 0-02-181010-9 / 5, L.11
    9 RRW 02 01

Spotlight on Literacy

AUTHORS

ELAINE MEI AOKI • VIRGINIA ARNOLD • JAMES FLOOD • JAMES V. HOFFMAN • DIANE LAPP

MIRIAM MARTINEZ • ANNEMARIE SULLIVAN PALINCSAR • MICHAEL PRIESTLEY • CARL B. SMITH

WILLIAM H. TEALE • JOSEFINA VILLAMIL TINAJERO • ARNOLD W. WEBB • KAREN D. WOOD

Macmillan/McGraw-Hill

NEW YORK • FARMINGTON

Unit 1
SCENES of WONDER

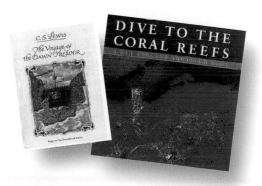

Unit 2

WORLDS *of* CHANGE

7

Unit 3

Winning Attitudes

9

Unit 4
Getting to Know YOU

10

11

Unit 5

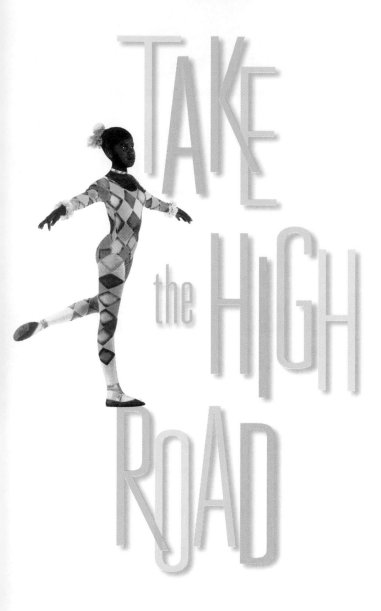

TAKE the HIGH ROAD

Unit 6

ZOOM IN!

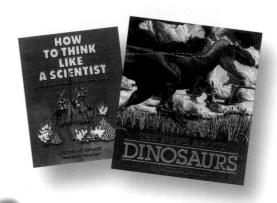

SCENES of WONDER

The Wreck of the Zephyr

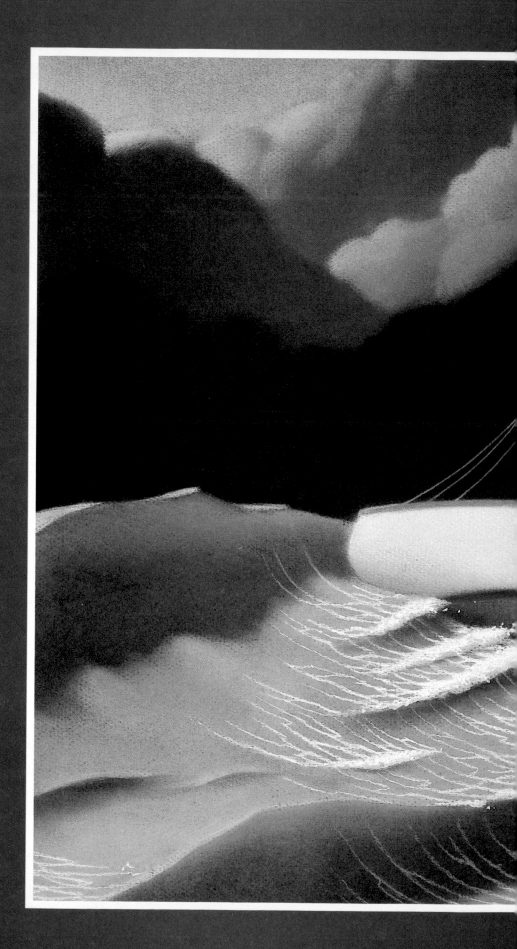

Once, while traveling along the seashore, I stopped at a small fishing village. After eating lunch, I decided to take a walk. I followed a path out of the village, uphill to some cliffs high above the sea. At the edge of these cliffs was a most unusual sight—the wreck of a small sailboat.

An old man was sitting among the broken timbers, smoking a pipe. He seemed to be reading my mind when he said, "Odd, isn't it?"

"Yes," I answered. "How did it get here?"

"Waves carried it up during a storm."

"Really?" I said. "It doesn't seem the waves could ever get that high."

The old man smiled. "Well, there is another story." He invited me to have a seat and listen to his strange tale.

"In our village, years ago," he said, "there was a boy who could sail a boat better than any man in the harbor. He could find a breeze over the flattest sea. When dark clouds kept other boats at anchor, the boy would sail out, ready to prove to the villagers, to the sea itself, how great a sailor he was.

"One morning, under an ominous sky, he prepared to take his boat, the *Zephyr,* out to sea. A fisherman warned the boy to stay in port. Already a strong wind was blowing. 'I'm not afraid,' the boy said, 'because I'm the greatest sailor there is.' The fisherman pointed to a sea gull gliding overhead. 'There's the only sailor who can go out on a day like this.' The boy just laughed as he hoisted his sails into a blustery wind.

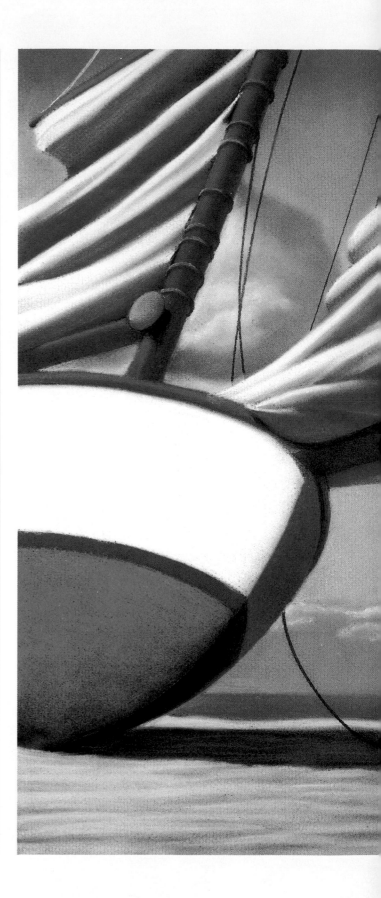

"The wind whistled in the rigging as the *Zephyr* pounded her way through the water. The sky grew black and the waves rose up like mountains. The boy struggled to keep his boat from going over. Suddenly a gust of wind caught the sail. The boom swung around and hit the boy's head. He fell to the cockpit floor and did not move.

"When the boy opened his eyes, he found himself lying on a beach. The *Zephyr* rested behind him, carried there by the storm. The boat was far from the water's edge. The tide would not carry it back to sea. The boy set out to look for help.

"He walked for a long time and was surprised that he didn't recognize the shoreline. He climbed a hill, expecting to see something familiar, but what he saw instead was a strange and unbelievable sight. Before him were two boats, sailing high above the water. Astonished, he watched them glide by. Then a third sailed past, towing the *Zephyr*. The boats entered a bay that was bordered by a large village. There they left the *Zephyr*.

"The boy made his way down to the harbor, to the dock where his boat was tied. He met a sailor who smiled when he saw the boy. Pointing to the *Zephyr* he asked, 'Yours?' The boy nodded. The sailor said they almost never saw strangers on their island. It was surrounded by a treacherous reef. The *Zephyr* must have been carried over the reef by the storm. He told the boy that, later, they would take him and the *Zephyr* back over the reef. But the boy said he would not leave until he learned to sail above the waves. The sailor told him it took years to learn to sail like that. 'Besides,' he said, 'the *Zephyr* does not have the right sails.' The boy insisted. He pleaded with the sailor.

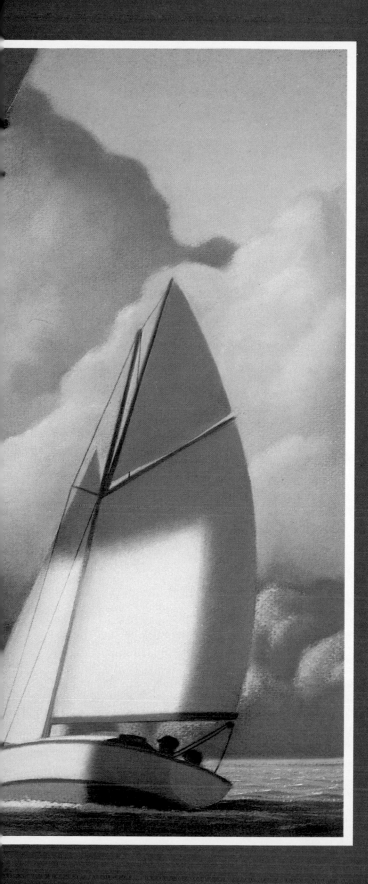

"Finally the sailor said he would try to teach him if the boy promised to leave the next morning. The boy agreed. The sailor went to a shed and got a new set of sails.

"All afternoon they sailed back and forth across the bay. Sometimes the sailor took the tiller, and the boat would magically begin to lift out of the water. But when the boy tried, he could not catch the wind that made boats fly.

"When the sun went down they went back to the harbor. They dropped anchor and a fisherman rowed them to shore. 'In the morning,' the sailor said, 'we'll put your own sails back on the *Zephyr* and send you home.' He took the boy to his house, and the sailor's wife fed them oyster stew.

"After dinner the sailor played the concertina. He sang a song about a man named Samuel Blue, who, long ago, tried to sail his boat over land and crashed:

*'For the wind o'er land's ne'er steady nor true,
   an' all men that sail there'll meet Samuel Blue.'*

"When he was done with his song, the sailor sent the boy to bed. But the boy could not sleep. He knew he could fly his boat if he had another chance. He waited until the sailor and his wife were asleep, then he quietly dressed and went to the harbor. As he rowed out to the *Zephyr*, the boy felt the light evening wind grow stronger and colder.

"Under a full moon, he sailed the *Zephyr* into the bay. He tried to remember everything the sailor had told him. He tried to feel the wind pulling his boat forward, lifting it up. Then, suddenly, the boy felt the *Zephyr* begin to shake. The sound of the water rushing past the hull grew louder. The air filled with spray as the boat sliced through the waves. The bow slowly began to lift. Higher and higher the *Zephyr* rose out of the water, then finally broke free. The sound of rushing water stopped. There was only the sound of wind in the sails. The *Zephyr* was flying.

"Using the stars to guide him, the boy set a course for home. The wind blew very hard, churning the sea below. But that did not matter to the *Zephyr* as she glided through the night sky. When clouds blocked the boy's view of the stars, he trimmed the sails and climbed higher. Surely the men of the island never dared fly so high. Now the boy was certain he was truly the greatest sailor of all.

"He steered well. Before the night was over, he saw the moonlit spire of the church at the edge of his village. As he drew closer to land, an idea took hold of him. He would sail over the village and ring the *Zephyr*'s bell. Then everyone would see him and know that he was the greatest sailor. He flew over the tree-topped cliffs of the shore, but as he reached the church the *Zephyr* began to fall.

"The wind had shifted. The boy pulled as hard as he could on the tiller, but it did no good. The wind shifted again. He steered for the open sea, but the trees at the cliff's edge stood between him and the water. At first there was just the rustle of leaves brushing the hull. Then the air was filled with the sound of breaking branches and ripping sails. The boat fell to the ground. And here she sits today."

"A remarkable tale," I said, as the old man stopped to relight his pipe. "What happened to the boy?"

"He broke his leg that night. Of course, no one believed his story about flying boats. It was easier for them to believe that he was lost in the storm and thrown up here by the waves." The old man laughed.

"No sir, the boy never amounted to much. People thought he was crazy. He just took odd jobs around the harbor. Most of the time he was out sailing, searching for that island and a new set of sails."

A light breeze blew through the trees. The old man looked up. "Wind coming," he said. "I've got some sailing to do." He picked up a cane, and I watched as he limped slowly toward the harbor.

Van Allsburg holding a scene from his book
The Polar Express

Chris Van Allsburg is probably one of the most successful book illustrators in the United States—yet he almost didn't become an illustrator at all. As a child, he loved to draw and was good at it. But by the time he went to college, he wanted to be a lawyer. His talent won out. He took one drawing class "as a lark," and a year later he began serious study to become a professional artist.

His first book, *The Garden of Abdul Gasazi,* won eight book awards, and his second book, *Jumanji,* won a Caldecott Medal, the top award given for children's book illustration. A 1985 book, *The Polar Express,* won another Caldecott Medal—making Van Allsburg the first artist ever to win two.

Part of Van Allsburg's success may have to do with his idea of what an artist should be. "To me, the artist's role is as a magician who can make strange things happen," he explains. "The opportunity to create a small world between two pieces of cardboard . . . is exciting and rewarding." He has turned this fascination into books and illustrations that are both weird and wonderful. In *Jumanji,* a jungle board game comes to life—with frightening results. In the award-winning *The Wreck of the Zephyr,* you saw how Van Allsburg's "magic" turned a simple sailboat into something marvelous to behold.

"For Purple
MOUN

I saw them today.

I saw them.

So many years I have heard them in a song.

It's true. They're purple when you see them.

They rise like kings.

They are mountains.

Suddenly

I know.

I *really* know

What that song is all about.

TAINS'
majesty"

A path to the moon

From my front door there's a path to the moon
that nobody seems to see
tho it's marked with stones & grass & trees
there's nobody sees it but me.

You walk straight ahead for ten trees or so
turn left at the robin's song
follow the sound of the west wind down
past where the deer drink from the pond.

You take a right turn as the river bends
then where the clouds touch the earth
close your left eye & count up to ten
while twirling for all that you're worth.

And if you keep walking right straight ahead
clambering over the clouds
saying your mother's & father's names
over & over out loud

you'll come to the place where moonlight's born
the place where the moonbeams hide
and visit all of the crater sites
on the dark moon's secret side.

From my front door there's a path to the moon
that nobody seems to see
tho it's marked with stones & grass & trees
no one sees it but you & me.

b p Nichol

THE TALKING EGGS

A Folktale from the American South

retold by Robert D. San Souci
pictures by Jerry Pinkney

Back in the old days there was a widow with two daughters named Rose and Blanche. They lived on a farm so poor, it looked like the tail end of bad luck. They raised a few chickens, some beans, and a little cotton to get by.

Rose, the older sister, was cross and mean and didn't know beans from birds' eggs. Blanche was sweet and kind and sharp as forty crickets. But their mother liked Rose the best, because they were alike as two peas in a pod—bad-tempered, sharp-tongued, and always putting on airs.

The mother made Blanche do all the work around the place. She had to iron the clothes each morning using an old iron filled with hot coals, chop cotton in the afternoon, and string the beans for supper. While she'd be doing these chores, her mama and sister would sit side by side in rocking chairs on the shady porch, fanning themselves and talking foolishness about getting rich and moving to the city, where they could go to fancy balls wearing trail-train dresses and lots of jewels.

One hot day the mother sent Blanche to the well to fetch a bucket of water. When the girl got there, she found an old woman wrapped in a raggedy black shawl, near fainting with the heat.

"Please, child, give me a sip of water," the old woman said. "I'm 'bout to die of thirst."

"Yes, aunty," said Blanche, rinsing out her bucket and dipping up some clean, cool well water. "Drink what you need."

"Thank you, child," said the old woman when she'd taken swallow after swallow of water. "You got a spirit of do-right in your soul. God is gonna bless you." Then she walked away down the path that led to the deep woods.

When Blanche got back to the cabin, her mother and sister hollered at her for taking so long.

"This water's so warm, it's near boilin'," shouted Rose, and she dumped the bucket out on the porch.

"Here your poor sister's near dyin' for a drop of cool water," her mother screamed, "and you can't even bring her that little thing."

Then the two of them scolded and hit Blanche until the frightened girl ran away into the woods. She began to cry, since she didn't have anywhere to go, and she was scared to go home.

Suddenly, around a bend in the path came the old woman in the raggedy black shawl. When she saw Blanche, she asked kindly, "What's made you cry so, you poor child?"

"Mama and sister Rose lit into me for something that wasn't my fault," said Blanche, rubbing tears off her cheek. "Now I'm afraid to go home."

"Hush, child! Stop your crying. You come on home with me. I'll give you supper and a clean bed. But you got to promise you won't laugh at anything you see."

Blanche gave her word of honor that she wouldn't laugh. Then the old woman took her by the hand and led her deep into the backwoods. As they walked along the narrow path, bramble bushes and tree branches opened wide in front of them, and closed up behind them.

Soon they came to the old woman's tumble-down shack. A cow with two heads, and horns like corkscrews, peered over a fence at Blanche and brayed like a mule. She reckoned it was a pretty strange sight, but she didn't say anything, not wanting to hurt the old woman's feelings.

Next, she saw that the yard in front of the cabin was filled with chickens of every color. Some were hopping about on one leg, some running about on three or four or even more. These chickens didn't cluck, but whistled like mocking-birds. But strange as all this was, Blanche stuck by her promise not to laugh.

When they got inside the cabin, the old woman said, "Light the fire, child, and cook us some supper." So Blanche fetched kindling from the woodpile outside the back door.

The old woman sat down near the fireplace and took off her head. She set it on her knees like a pumpkin. First she combed out her gray hair, then she plaited it into two long braids. Blanche got pretty scared at this. But the woman had been nothing but kind to her, so she just went on lighting the fire.

After a bit the old woman put her head back on her shoulders and looked at herself in a sliver of mirror nailed to the cabin wall. "Um-m-m-hum!" she said, nodding. "That's better."

Then she gave Blanche an old beef bone and said, "Put this in the pot for supper."

Now Blanche was near starving, and the bone looked like a pretty sad meal for the two of them, but she did what the old woman said. "Shall I boil it for soup, aunty?" she asked.

"Look at the pot, child!" the old woman said, laughing.

The pot was filled with thick stew, bubbling away.

Next the woman gave Blanche only one grain of rice and told her to grind it in the stone mortar. Feeling mighty foolish Blanche began to pound the grain with the heavy stone pestle. In a moment the mortar was overflowing with rice.

When they had finished supper, the old woman said, "It's a fine moonshiny night, child. Come with me."

They sat themselves down on the back porch steps. After a time dozens of rabbits came out of the underbrush and formed a circle in the yard. The men rabbits all had frock-tail coats, and the lady rabbits had little trail-train dresses. They danced, standing on their hind feet, hopping about. One big rabbit played a banjo, and the old woman hummed along with it.

Blanche kept time by clapping along. The rabbits did a square dance, a Virginia reel, and even a cakewalk. The girl felt so happy, she never wanted to leave. She sat and clapped until she fell asleep, and the old woman carried her inside and put her to bed.

When Blanche got up the next morning, the old woman told her, "Go milk my cow."

The girl did what she was told and the two-headed cow with the curly horns gave her a bucket of the sweetest milk she'd ever tasted. They had it with their morning coffee.

"You gotta go home now, child," the old woman said to Blanche, who was washing the breakfast dishes. "But I tell you, things will be better from here on out. And since you are such a good girl, I got a present for you.

"Go out to the chicken house. Any eggs that say, 'Take me,' you go ahead and take. But if you hear any say, 'Don't take me,' you leave them be. When you get near home, throw those eggs one after another over your left shoulder so they break in the road behind you. Then you'll get a surprise."

When Blanche got to the little chicken house, she found all the nests filled with eggs. Half were gold or silver or covered with jewels; half looked no different from the eggs she got from her chickens back home.

All the plain eggs told her, "Take me." All the fancy ones cried, "Don't take me." She wished she could take just *one* gold or silver or jeweled egg, but she did what the old woman told her and only scooped up the plain ones.

She and the old woman waved good-bye to each other, then Blanche went on her way. Partway home she began to toss the eggs one at a time over her left shoulder. All sorts of wonderful things spilled out of those eggs: now diamonds and rubies, now gold and silver coins, now pretty silk dresses and dainty satin shoes. There was even a handsome carriage that grew in a wink from the size of a matchbox—and a fine brown-and-white pony that sprouted from the size of a cricket to draw it.

Blanche loaded all these lovely things into the carriage and rode the rest of the way home like a grand lady.

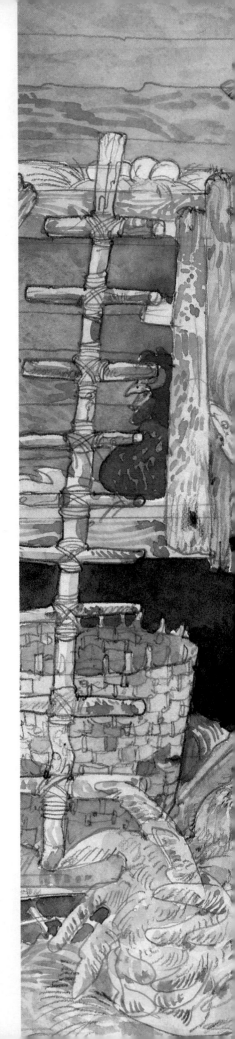

When she got back to the cabin, her mother and sister just gawked at her new finery. "Where did you get all these things?" her mother asked, making Rose help Blanche carry the treasures inside. That evening the mother cooked dinner for the first time since Blanche was old enough to hold a skillet. All the time telling Blanche what a sweet daughter she was, her mama got the girl to tell about the old woman and the cabin in the woods and the talking eggs.

When Blanche was asleep, the mother grabbed Rose and told her, "You gotta go into the woods tomorrow mornin' and find that old aunty. Then you'll get some of those talkin' eggs for yourse'f so's you can have fine dresses and jewels like your sister. When you get back, I'll chase Blanche off and keep her things myse'f. Then we'll go to the city and be fine ladies like we was meant to be."

"Can't we just run her off tonight so's I don't have to go pokin' through the woods lookin' for some crazy ol' aunty?" Rose whined.

"There's not near enough for two," her mother said, getting angry. "You do as I say and don't be so contrary."

So the next morning Rose set out drag-foot into the woods. She dawdled mostly, but soon met the old woman in her raggedy black shawl.

"My sweet little sister Blanche tol' me you got a real pretty house an' all," said Rose. "I'd 'preciate to see it."

"You can come with me if you've a mind to," said the old woman, "but you got to promise not to laugh at whatever you see."

"I swear," said Rose.

So the old woman led her through the bramble bushes and tree branches into the deep woods.

But when they got near the cabin and Rose saw the two-headed cow that brayed like a mule and the funny-looking chickens that sang like mockingbirds, she yelled, "If there ever was a sight, that's one! That's the stupidest thing in the world!" Then she laughed and laughed until she nearly fell down.

"Um-m-m-hum," said the old woman, shaking her head.

Inside, Rose complained when she was asked to start the fire, and she wound up with more smoke than flame. When the old woman gave her an old bone to put in the pot for supper, Rose said crossly, "That's gonna make a mighty poor meal." She dropped it in the pot, but the old bone remained a bone, so they only had thin soup for supper. When the old woman gave her one grain of rice to grind in the mortar, Rose said, "That sad speck won't hardly feed a fly!" She wouldn't lift the pestle, so they had no rice at all.

"Um-m-m-hum!" the old woman muttered.

Rose went to bed hungry. All night long she heard mice scratching under the floor and screech-owls clawing at the window.

In the morning the old woman told her to milk the cow. Rose did, but she made fun of the two-headed creature and all she got was a little sour milk not fit for drinking. So they had their breakfast coffee without cream.

When the old woman lifted her head off her shoulders to brush her hair, quick as a wink Rose grabbed that head and said, "I'm not gonna put you back t'gether 'til you give me presents like my sister got."

"Ah, child, you're a wicked girl," said the old woman's head, "but I got to have my body back, so I'll tell you what to do.

"Go to the chicken house and take those eggs that say, 'Take me.' But leave be the ones that cry, 'Don't take me.' Then you toss those eggs over your right shoulder when you're on your way home."

To be sure the old woman wasn't playing her a trick, Rose set the old woman's head out on the porch while her body sat groping around the cabin. Then she ran to the chicken house. Inside, all the plain eggs cried, "Take me," while all the gold and silver and jeweled ones said, "Don't take me."

"You think I'm fool enough to listen to you and pass up the prettiest ones? Not on your life!" So she grabbed all of the gold and silver and jeweled eggs that kept yelling, "Don't take me," and off she ran into the woods with them.

As soon as she was out of sight of the old woman's cabin, she tossed the eggs over her right shoulder as fast as she could. But out of the shells came clouds of whip snakes, toads, frogs, yellow jackets, and a big, old, gray wolf. These began to chase after her like pigs after a pumpkin.

Hollering bloody murder Rose ran all the way to her mother's cabin. When the woman saw the swarm of things chasing her daughter, she tried to rescue her with a broom. But the wasps and wolf and all the other creatures wouldn't be chased off, so mother and daughter high-tailed it to the woods, with all the animals following.

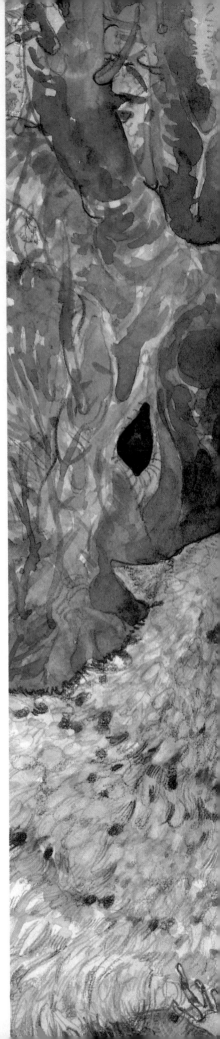

When they returned home, angry and sore and stung and covered with mud, they found Blanche had gone to the city to live like a grand lady—though she remained as kind and generous as always.

For the rest of their lives Rose and her mother tried to find the strange old woman's cabin and the talking eggs, but they never could find that place again.

MEET ROBERT D. SAN SOUCI

When his car broke down in Pecos, Texas, Robert D. San Souci had no idea that it would turn out to be a lucky "break." To escape from the roadside heat, San Souci went into a nearby mission. His first novel, *Emergence,* about Indians of the Southwest, grew out of what he learned there.

San Souci was fascinated by Native American legends and folklore. His first children's book, *The Legend of Scarface,* retold a Blackfoot Indian myth. The book won two awards for the story and another for its illustrator, San Souci's brother, Daniel. The two also worked together on *The Song of Sedna,* based on an Eskimo myth. The brothers have separate projects, too. Jerry Pinkney illustrated *The Talking Eggs* for Robert D. San Souci.

MEET JERRY PINKNEY

If you were to visit the home of artist Jerry Pinkney, you might witness the unusual way in which he plans his work. Before he begins to draw pictures for a book, Jerry and his family and friends put on costumes and act out the events of the book. As they do this, he takes photographs, which he refers to later when doing the actual drawings.

Pinkney is the only artist ever to have illustrated three Coretta Scott King Award-winning books. He has won other awards and prizes, including a Caldecott Honor for *The Talking Eggs.*

71

BOOK REVIEWS

Title: **The Talking Eggs**
Author: **Robert D. San Souci**
Illustrator: **Jerry Pinkney**

Reviewed by:
Tiffany Smart

The Talking Eggs retold by Robert San Souci and illustrated by Jerry Pinkney is a very good story. A young girl named Blanche lived with her mean mother and sister. Blanche had to do all the cooking and cleaning while her mother and sister sat on the porch all day and complained.

One hot day, Blanche met an old lady at the well while getting water for her mother and sister. After she got home with the water, they scared her off into the woods. Blanche, frightened, met the old lady again and she and the old lady had a magical time.

I enjoyed this story because Blanche is a special person. Blanche had a kind heart and she never gave up although her mother and sister were very unkind to her. Also, she did everything that the old lady asked of her and in the end, she truly got what she deserved.

This story is fun for anyone who likes to use his or her imagination. I can imagine every scene in this story! I will recommend this story to my friends and family. This was the first story I have read by Robert San Souci but I look forward to reading more of his work in the future.

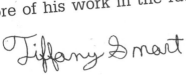

Tiffany Smart

Reviewed by:
Meggie Ito

I liked the way the characters and animals were described by the author. It must have taken a good imagination to come up with a two-headed cow or rainbow-colored chickens. Jerry Pinkney's illustrations helped me to picture the magic in the story. I especially liked the pony and the fancy carriage.

Meggie Ito

Reviewed by:
Emilio Reggianini

What I like about this story is the fine job done by the illustrator. His illustrations show the characters, the animals, and the setting as they are described by the author. The colors chosen for the illustrations are very vivid and real. The only thing that I regret is that it doesn't show one of the most impressive or exciting moments in the story: when the old woman lifts her head from her shoulder.

I wonder how Mr. Pinkney feels about being the only illustrator to win three Coretta Scott King Awards? Will his next book be a little more daring? I strongly recommend this book to someone who likes fairy tales, where magic and good and humane endings mix really well.

Emilio Reggianini

73

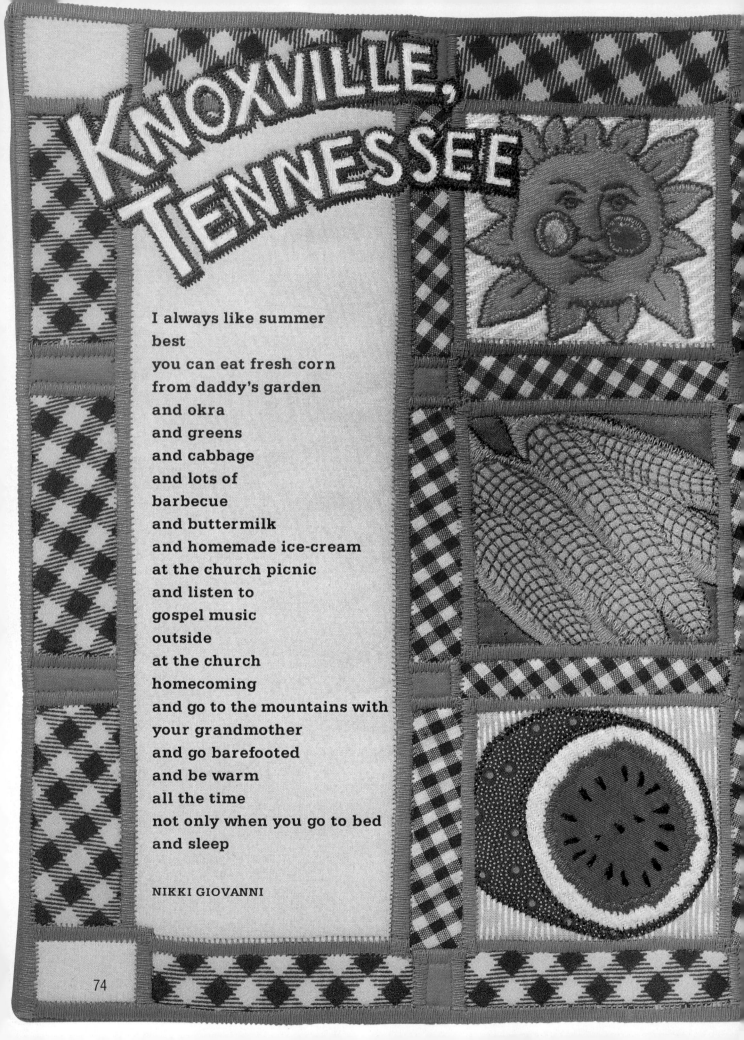

KNOXVILLE, TENNESSEE

I always like summer
best
you can eat fresh corn
from daddy's garden
and okra
and greens
and cabbage
and lots of
barbecue
and buttermilk
and homemade ice-cream
at the church picnic
and listen to
gospel music
outside
at the church
homecoming
and go to the mountains with
your grandmother
and go barefooted
and be warm
all the time
not only when you go to bed
and sleep

NIKKI GIOVANNI

The VOYAGE OF THE DAWN TREADER

By C.S. Lewis
Illustrated by Amy Hill

Cousin Eustace is a rather whiny and annoying boy. Unfortunately, Lucy and Edmund Pevensie must spend the entire summer at his house. They would much rather be in the enchanted land of Narnia, which they have visited twice before.

The land of Narnia is one of literature's most unforgettable places. And the means of getting there are—like Narnia itself—magical, mysterious, and entirely unexpected.

The story begins on an afternoon when Edmund and Lucy were stealing a few precious minutes alone together. And of course they were talking about Narnia, which was the name of their own private and secret country. Most of us, I suppose, have a secret country but for us it is only an imaginary country. Edmund and Lucy were luckier than other people in that respect. Their secret country was real. They had already visited it twice; not in a game or a dream, but in reality. They had got there of course by magic, which is the only way of getting to Narnia. And a promise, or very nearly a promise, had been made them in Narnia itself that they would some day get back. You may imagine that they talked about it a good deal, when they got the chance.

They were in Lucy's room, sitting on the edge of her bed and looking at a picture on the opposite wall. It was the only picture in the house that they liked. Aunt Alberta didn't like it at all (that was why it was put away in a little back room upstairs), but she couldn't get rid of it because it had been a wedding present from someone she did not want to offend.

It was a picture of a ship—a ship sailing nearly straight towards you. Her prow was gilded and shaped like the head of a dragon with wide open mouth. She had only one mast and one large, square sail which was a rich purple. The sides of the ship—what you could see of them where the gilded wings of the dragon ended—were green. She had just run up to the top of one glorious blue wave, and the nearer slope of that wave came down towards you, with streaks and bubbles on it. She was obviously running fast before a gay wind, listing over a little on her port side. (By the way, if you are going to read this story at all, and if you don't know already, you had better get it into your head that the left of a ship when you are looking ahead, is *port,* and the right is *starboard.*) All the sunlight fell on her from that side, and the water on that side was full of greens and purples. On the other, it was darker blue from the shadow of the ship.

"The question is," said Edmund, "whether it doesn't make things worse, *looking* at a Narnian ship when you can't get there."

"Even looking is better than nothing," said Lucy. "And she is such a very Narnian ship."

"Still playing your old game?" said Eustace Clarence, who had been listening outside the door and now came grinning into the room. Last year, when he had been staying with the Pevensies, he had managed to hear them all talking of Narnia and he loved teasing them about it. He thought of course that they were making it all up; and as he was quite incapable of making anything up himself, he did not approve of that.

"You're not wanted here," said Edmund curtly.

"I'm trying to think of a limerick," said Eustace. "Something like this:

> "Some kids who played games about Narnia
> Got gradually balmier and balmier—"

"Well, *Narnia* and *balmier* don't rhyme, to begin with," said Lucy.

"It's an assonance," said Eustace.

"Don't ask him what an assy-thingummy is," said Edmund. "He's only longing to be asked. Say nothing and perhaps he'll go away."

Most boys, on meeting a reception like this, would either have cleared out or flared up. Eustace did neither. He just hung about grinning, and presently began talking again.

"Do you like that picture?" he asked.

"For Heaven's sake don't let him get started about Art and all that," said Edmund hurriedly, but Lucy, who was very truthful, had already said, "Yes, I do. I like it very much."

"It's a rotten picture," said Eustace.

"You won't see it if you step outside," said Edmund.

"Why do you like it?" said Eustace to Lucy.

"Well, for one thing," said Lucy, "I like it because the ship looks as if it was really moving. And the water looks as if it was really wet. And the waves look as if they were really going up and down."

Of course Eustace knew lots of answers to this, but he didn't say anything. The reason was that at that very moment he looked at the waves and saw that they did look very much indeed as if they were going up and down. He had only once been in a ship (and then only as far as the Isle of Wight) and had been horribly seasick. The look of the waves in the picture made him feel sick again. He turned rather green and tried another look. And then all three children were staring with open mouths.

What they were seeing may be hard to believe when you read it in print, but it was almost as hard to believe when you saw it happening. The things in the picture were moving. It didn't look at all like a cinema either; the colours were too real and clean and out-of-door for that. Down went the prow of the ship into the wave and up went a great shock of spray. And then up went the wave behind her, and her stern and her deck became visible for the first time, and then disappeared as the next wave came to meet her and her bows went up again. At the same moment an exercise book which had been lying beside Edmund on the bed flapped, rose and sailed through the air to the wall behind him, and Lucy felt all her hair whipping round her face as it does on a windy day. And this was a windy day; but the wind was blowing out of the picture towards them. And suddenly with the wind came the noises—the swishing of waves and the slap of water against the ship's sides and the creaking and the over-all high, steady roar of air and water. But it was the smell, the wild, briny smell, which really convinced Lucy that she was not dreaming.

"Stop it," came Eustace's voice, squeaky with fright and bad temper. "It's some silly trick you two are playing. Stop it. I'll tell Alberta—ow!"

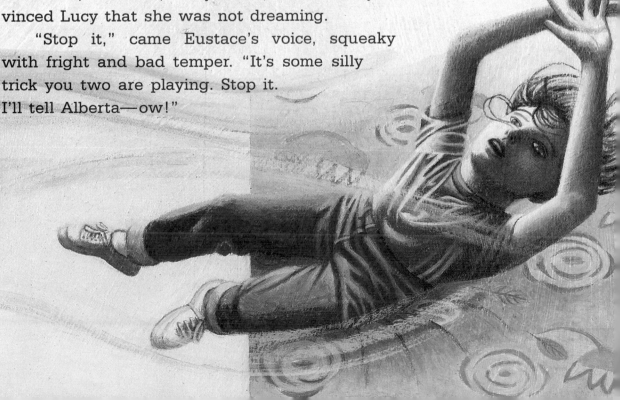

The other two were much more accustomed to adventures, but, just exactly as Eustace Clarence said "Ow," they both said "Ow" too. The reason was that a great cold, salt splash had broken right out of the frame and they were breathless from the smack of it, besides being wet through.

"I'll smash the rotten thing," cried Eustace; and then several things happened at the same time. Eustace rushed towards the picture. Edmund, who knew something about magic, sprang after him, warning him to look out and not to be a fool. Lucy grabbed at him from the other side and was dragged forward. And by this time either they had grown much smaller or the picture had grown bigger. Eustace jumped to try to pull it off the wall and found himself standing on the frame; in front of him was not glass but real sea, and wind and waves rushing up to the frame as they might to a rock. He lost his head and clutched at the other two who had jumped up beside him. There was a second of struggling and shouting, and just as they thought they had got their balance a great blue roller surged up round them, swept them off their feet, and drew them down into the sea. Eustace's despairing cry suddenly ended as the water got into his mouth.

Lucy thanked her stars that she had worked hard at her swimming last summer term. It is true that she would have got on much better if she had used a slower stroke, and also that the water felt a great deal colder than it had looked while it was only a picture. Still, she kept her head and kicked her shoes off, as everyone ought to do who falls into deep water in their clothes. She even kept her mouth shut and her eyes open. They were still quite near the ship; she saw its green side towering high above them, and people looking at her from the

deck. Then, as one might have expected, Eustace clutched at her in a panic and down they both went.

When they came up again she saw a white figure diving off the ship's side. Edmund was close beside her now, treading water, and had caught the arms of the howling Eustace. Then someone else, whose face was vaguely familiar, slipped an arm under her from the other side. There was a lot of shouting going on from the ship, heads crowding together above the bulwarks, ropes being thrown. Edmund and the stranger were fastening ropes round her. After that followed what seemed a very long delay during which her face got blue and her teeth began chattering. In reality the delay was not very long; they were waiting till the moment when she could be got on board the ship without being dashed against its side. Even with all their best endeavours she had a bruised knee when she finally stood, dripping and shivering, on the deck.

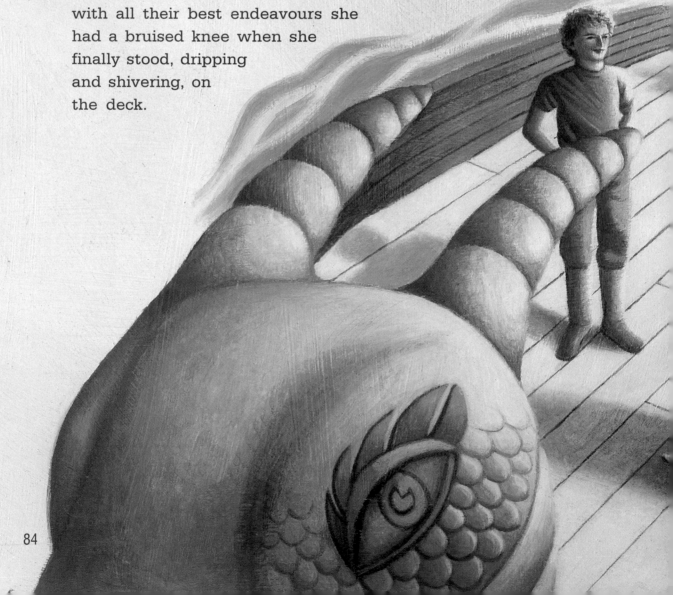

After her Edmund was heaved up, and then the miserable Eustace. Last of all came the stranger—a golden-headed boy some years older than herself.

"Ca—Ca—Caspian!" gasped Lucy as soon as she had breath enough. For Caspian it was; Caspian, the boy king of Narnia whom they had helped to set on the throne during their last visit. Immediately Edmund recognised him too. All three shook hands and clapped one another on the back with great delight.

"But who is your friend?" said Caspian almost at once, turning to Eustace with his cheerful smile. But Eustace was crying much harder than any boy of his age has a right to cry when nothing worse than a wetting has happened to him, and would only yell out, "Let me go. Let me go back. I don't *like* it."

"Let you go?" said Caspian. "But where?"

Eustace rushed to the ship's side, as if he expected to see the picture frame hanging above the sea, and perhaps a glimpse of Lucy's bedroom. What he saw was blue waves flecked with foam, and paler blue sky, both spreading without a break to the horizon. Perhaps we can hardly blame him if his heart sank. He was promptly sick.

"Hey! Rynelf," said Caspian to one of the sailors. "Bring spiced wine for their Majesties. You'll need something to warm you after that dip." He called Edmund and Lucy their Majesties because they and Peter and Susan had all been kings and queens of Narnia long before his time. Narnian time flows differently from ours. If you spent a hundred years in Narnia, you would still come back to our world at the very same hour of the very same day on which you left. And then, if you went back to Narnia after spending a week here, you might find that a thousand Narnian years had passed, or only a day, or no time at all. You never know till you get there. Consequently, when the Pevensie children had returned to Narnia last time for their second visit, it was (for the Narnians) as if King Arthur came back to Britain as some people say he will. And I say the sooner the better.

Rynelf returned with the spiced wine steaming in a flagon and four silver cups. It was just what one wanted, and as Lucy and Edmund sipped it they could feel the warmth going right down to their toes. But Eustace made faces and spluttered and spat it out and was sick again and began to cry again and asked if they hadn't any Plumptree's Vitaminised Nerve Food and could it be made with distilled water and anyway he insisted on being put ashore at the next station.

"This is a merry shipmate you've brought us, Brother," whispered Caspian to Edmund with a chuckle; but before he could say anything more Eustace burst out again.

"Oh! Ugh! What on earth's *that!* Take it away, the horrid thing."

He really had some excuse this time for feeling a little surprised. Something very curious indeed had come out of the cabin in the poop and was slowly approaching them. You might call it—and indeed it was—a Mouse. But then it was a Mouse on its hind legs and stood about two feet high. A thin band of gold passed round its head under one ear and over the other and in this was stuck a long crimson feather. (As the Mouse's fur was very dark, almost black, the effect was bold and striking.) Its left paw rested on the hilt of a sword very nearly as long as its tail. Its balance, as it paced gravely along the swaying deck, was perfect, and its manners courtly. Lucy and Edmund recognised it at once—Reepicheep, the most valiant of all the Talking Beasts of Narnia and the Chief Mouse. It had won undying glory in the second Battle of Beruna. Lucy longed, as she had always done, to take Reepicheep up in her arms and cuddle him. But this, as she well knew, was a pleasure she could never have: it would have offended him deeply. Instead, she went down on one knee to talk to him.

Reepicheep put forward his left leg, drew back his right, bowed, kissed her hand, straightened himself, twirled his whiskers, and said in his shrill, piping voice:

"My humble duty to your Majesty. And to King Edmund, too." (Here he bowed again.) "Nothing except your Majesties' presence was lacking to this glorious venture."

"Ugh, take it away," wailed Eustace. "I hate mice. And I never could bear performing animals. They're silly and vulgar and—and sentimental."

"Am I to understand," said Reepicheep to Lucy after a long stare at Eustace, "that this singularly discourteous person is under your Majesty's protection? Because, if not—"

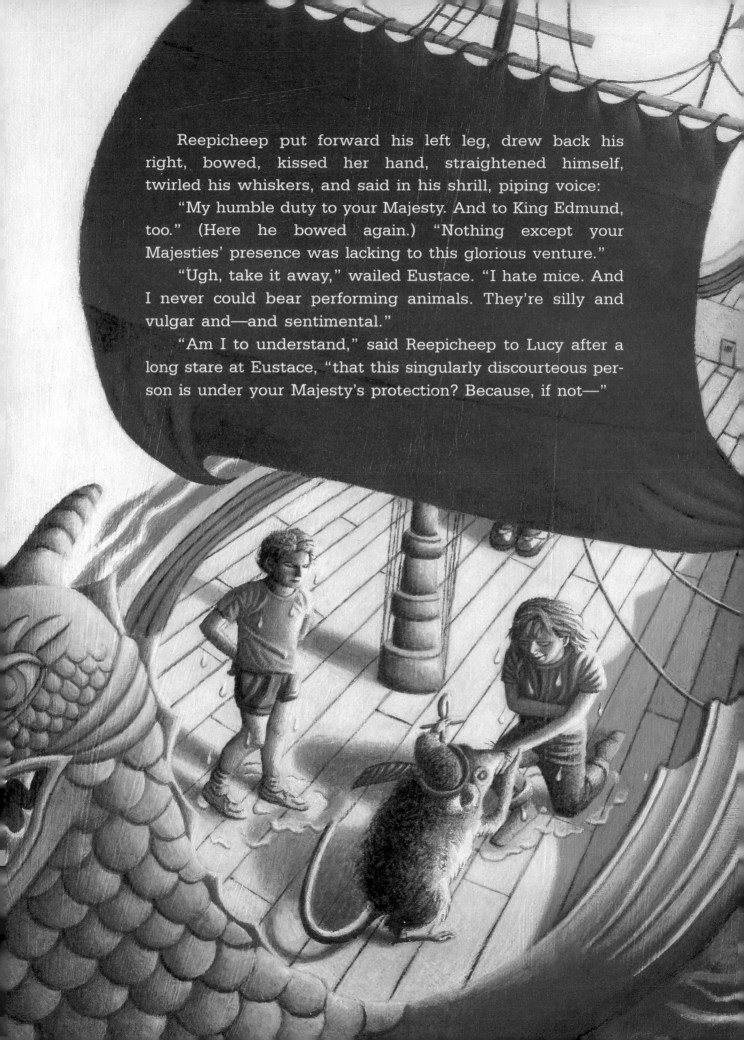

At this moment Lucy and Edmund both sneezed.

"What a fool I am to keep you all standing here in your wet things," said Caspian. "Come on below and get changed. I'll give you my cabin of course, Lucy, but I'm afraid we have no women's clothes on board. You'll have to make do with some of mine. Lead the way, Reepicheep, like a good fellow."

"To the convenience of a lady," said Reepicheep, "even a question of honour must give way—at least for the moment—" and here he looked very hard at Eustace. But Caspian hustled them on and in a few minutes Lucy found herself passing through the door into the stern cabin. She fell in love with it at once—the three square windows that looked out on the blue, swirling water astern, the low cushioned benches round three sides of the table, the swinging silver lamp overhead (Dwarfs' work, she knew at once by its exquisite delicacy) and the flat gold image of Aslan the Lion on the forward wall above the door. All this she took in in a flash, for Caspian immediately opened a door on the starboard side, and said, "This'll be your room, Lucy. I'll just get some dry things for myself"—he was rummaging in one of the lockers while he spoke—"and then leave you to change. If you'll fling your wet things outside the door I'll get them taken to the galley to be dried."

Lucy found herself as much at home as if she had been in Caspian's cabin for weeks, and the motion of the ship did not worry her, for in the old days when she had been a queen in Narnia she had done a good deal of voyaging. The cabin was very tiny but bright with painted panels (all birds and beasts and crimson dragons and vines) and spotlessly clean. Caspian's clothes were too big for her, but she could manage. His shoes, sandals and sea-boots were hopelessly large but she did not mind going barefoot on board ship. When she had finished dressing she looked out of her window at the water rushing past and took a long deep breath. She felt quite sure they were in for a lovely time.

This is only the beginning of the exciting adventures that Lucy, Edmund, and Eustace experience with their friends in the land of Narnia. You can join them on a voyage of the imagination that leads to magical lands and enchanted happenings when you read the series of books called The Chronicles of Narnia.

Meet
C.S. LEWIS

C. S. Lewis grew up with rows and rows of books in every room of his family's house. These books full of stories spurred his imagination. As a child, he created his own stories of an "Animal-Land" inhabited by dressed animals and knights in armor.

When Lewis grew up, he started writing about the adventures of four brave children in a magic land. He planned just one book, *The Lion, the Witch and the Wardrobe,* but he went on to add six more books to his *Chronicles of Narnia.* In these books, which can be read in any order, the saga of Narnia is told through tales of adventure filled with fantastic creatures.

In *The Magician's Nephew,* Lewis tells how the passage between earth and Narnia was created: A tree grown from the magical Narnia apple blew over, and its wood was used to build a wardrobe. Through this wardrobe, the children first enter Narnia, where they help the lord-lion Aslan fight the powers of evil.

Lewis advised one young girl who had written to him, "Write about what really interests you, whether it is real or imaginary things." Following his own advice, Lewis created an entire world for readers.

maggie and milly and molly and may
went down to the beach(to play one day)

and maggie discovered a shell that sang
so sweetly she couldn't remember her troubles,and

milly befriended a stranded star
whose rays five languid fingers were;

and molly was chased by a horrible thing
which raced sideways while blowing bubbles:and

may came home with a smooth round stone
as small as a world and as large as alone.

For whatever we lose(like a you or a me)
it's always ourselves we find in the sea

e. e. cummings

by Elizabeth Tayntor, Paul Erickson, and Les Kaufman

DIVE
TO THE
CORAL
REEFS

A NEW ENGLAND AQUARIUM BOOK

Did you know that there is a city full of fantastic shapes and structures that lies beneath the surface of the sea? It is a city few people have seen because it is so difficult to reach.

Yet it is one of the largest, most colorful, most amazing communities in the world. It is built and inhabited by millions of incredible creatures. It is the living coral reef.

Coral reefs grow in tropical oceans all over the world. The largest, over 1,200 miles long, is the Great Barrier Reef off the coast of Australia. To find out about these underwater coral communities, the New England Aquarium sent a team of scientists and divers to the island of Jamaica in the Caribbean Sea. Their mission: to explore the legendary Pear Tree and Rio Bueno reefs off the island's north coast.

Down here, the coral grows nearly the whole length of the island, from east to west. It rises 40 feet above the sea floor. The divers explored reef growth more than 5,000 years old.

Reefs are built very, very slowly, by corals: tiny animals that actually make up the mounds, boulders, and branches called a coral reef. For example, a mound of brain coral, 3 feet tall, may be 250 years old.

Each coral animal, or polyp, is about the size of a pencil eraser.

A coral polyp has a soft body, stomach, and mouth surrounded by tentacles. Corals are hunters. Like their cousins, the jellyfishes, they use their tentacles to capture their prey, small drifting plants and animals called plankton.

Some people are surprised to find out that corals are animals because many look more like plants. There is something amazing about corals that helps to explain their plantlike shapes. Scientists have discovered that coral animals are also part plant.

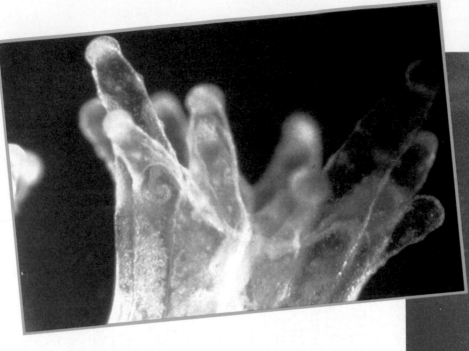

Imagine tiny green plants growing under your skin. Corals have tiny plants, called zooxanthellae, growing inside of them. Like other plants, zooxanthellae use the sun to make food through a process called photosynthesis. Then they pass some of this food on to the coral polyps, and this helps the coral grow.

Each coral polyp uses minerals from seawater to build a limestone skeleton. When disturbed, polyps can pull into the protection of these hard, rocklike homes.

When we think of coral, we often picture the hard white skeletons of corals that have died. Polyps, like people, live close together in colonies. As polyps grow, they move up to build new skeletons on top of the old. And, very slowly, the reef grows with them. It's like a modern city built upon the ruins of an ancient civilization.

Hundreds of individuals make up the forms of the reef. Different species of coral form different shapes.

Staghorn coral looks like deer antlers.

You can see how plate coral gets its name. It is big and flat, like a giant dinner plate.

Brain coral looks like the surface of a human brain with furrows and ridges.

These corals build hard skeletons. . . .

But sea fans, sea whips, and other soft corals have flexible skeletons. In ocean currents, soft corals bend and sway like tree branches in a heavy breeze.

The reef is home to literally millions of plants and animals because it offers good feeding and good places to hide. Small reef dwellers need protection from the many hunters of the reef.

Larger fishes probe cracks and holes in the reef, looking for tasty crabs and worms.

Butterflyfishes are especially good at this because they have long snouts and they can reach into places other fishes can't.

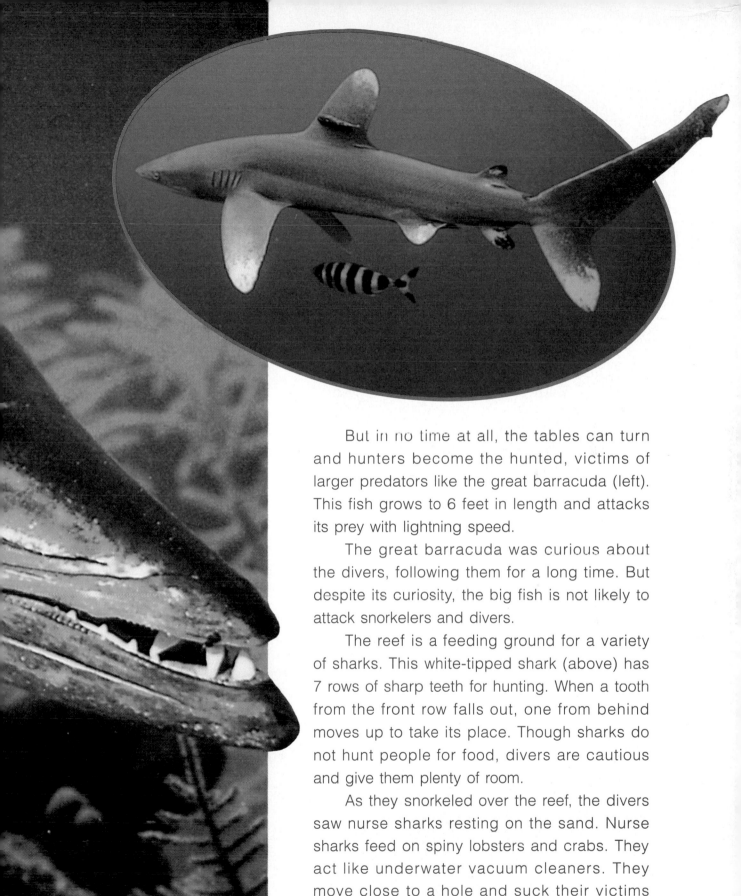

But in no time at all, the tables can turn and hunters become the hunted, victims of larger predators like the great barracuda (left). This fish grows to 6 feet in length and attacks its prey with lightning speed.

The great barracuda was curious about the divers, following them for a long time. But despite its curiosity, the big fish is not likely to attack snorkelers and divers.

The reef is a feeding ground for a variety of sharks. This white-tipped shark (above) has 7 rows of sharp teeth for hunting. When a tooth from the front row falls out, one from behind moves up to take its place. Though sharks do not hunt people for food, divers are cautious and give them plenty of room.

As they snorkeled over the reef, the divers saw nurse sharks resting on the sand. Nurse sharks feed on spiny lobsters and crabs. They act like underwater vacuum cleaners. They move close to a hole and suck their victims right out of hiding places in the reef.

The divers surprised a sea turtle who was sleeping under a ledge. Like humans, sea turtles need to come up for air. But unlike people, these turtles can hold their breath for up to 2 hours.

Animals and plants are everywhere on the reef. Every inch of space is used by living things. Some animals even live inside other animals: shrimp in sponges, and worms in coral.

These snapping shrimp are just two of dozens that were living inside a sponge. To defend itself, the shrimp uses its large claw to make a loud snapping sound that startles nearby hungry predators.

Exploring the shallow reef was just one part of the New England Aquarium dive team's job. Next they dove the deep reef. The divers dropped off the reef edge and descended 100 feet down the reef wall. Special training is required to make a dive like this and it challenges even experts!

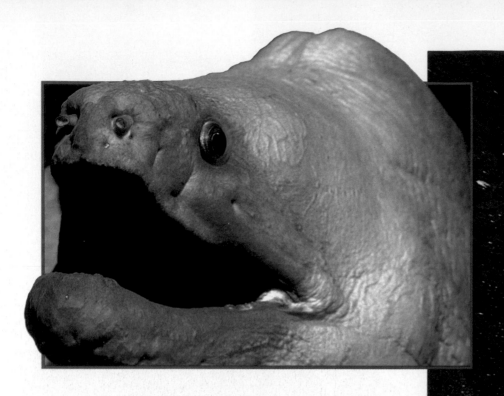

One of the divers describes how it feels to dive the deep reef: "Diving the reef wall is like flying off the side of a mountain with a thousand feet of open water below you."

As the divers went deeper, it got darker.

At about 60 feet, they looked into a crack in the reef, and an octopus came shooting out and draped itself over the corals. Frightened, the octopus changed colors. These camouflage experts are shy animals and it is rare to see one in the open.

At 80 feet down the divers entered a long cave . . . and came out 100 feet below the water's surface.

Here it feels like being on another planet. Enormous sponges grow out of the reef wall. Some are so large a diver can stand inside.

A green moray eel stared out from its underwater cave. By day these fish hide, waiting for something to come a little bit too close. Then they lunge out at it with their sharp teeth. At night they may hunt for octopus and lobsters.

The divers were amazed by the beauty of the reef and the number of organisms that live there. Because everything fits together like a puzzle, one change can create problems for everyone.

In the coral reefs, natural as well as human disasters cause destruction. Dense thickets of staghorn coral are often victims of hurricanes. Despite their hard skeletons, stony corals are surprisingly fragile and easily damaged by anchor-dragging boats. Souvenir collectors destroy living coral that may be decades old.

Probably the greatest threat to corals is coastline development. Offshore oil spills and open ocean dumping may destroy large areas of the reef forever.

Coral reefs can only be preserved through wise ocean management. So maybe someday you, too, can put on scuba tanks and explore this fantastic underwater world.

MEET
LES KAUFMAN,
ELIZABETH TAYNTOR,
and PAUL ERICKSON

Les Kaufman can't remember a time when he wasn't interested in nature and science. A few years ago, when Kaufman headed the New England Aquarium's education department, a new 186,000-gallon exhibit showing a coral reef in the Caribbean Sea was developed. Kaufman worked with his fellow Aquarium staff members Elizabeth Tayntor and Paul Erickson to create a filmstrip that led the three to write *Dive to the Coral Reefs*. The authors wrote the book to help young people gain a sense of the wonder of nature and the value of understanding it.

Kaufman sees science as a tool for understanding nature. "All the horrible things kids are hearing about the world falling apart ecologically are true. What they are not hearing is that these things can be fixed. We've got to clean up about 20 thousand years of damage. We've made a start. It will be up to the kids to continue the work." Kaufman thinks that even if kids who go into marine biology don't solve all the problems, they'll get another kind of payoff: coming to know nature as few people do. Kaufman promises, "The reward is enormous."

Fellow divers and authors Elizabeth Tayntor and Paul Erickson

Human-Made

Sunken objects replace damaged coral reefs

Old airplanes, school buses, and army tanks are getting new use—but not for transportation. Instead, they are being lowered into the ocean to start coral reefs. In fact, those objects are taking the place of many natural coral reefs off the coast of Florida.

Natural coral reefs are colorful undersea structures made up of the skeletons of millions of tiny sea animals. Many of Florida's—and the world's—natural coral reefs have been badly damaged by fishing boats, hurricanes, and tourists who break off pieces of coral.

Replacing damaged coral reefs is important because the reefs are places where tiny plants and animals grow. Those plants and animals become food for larger sea creatures. Reefs also protect young fish from strong currents and provide a place to hide from bigger fish.

Building a Reef
Experts carefully select objects to replace natural coral reefs. Since most natural reefs grow and remain in place for thousands of years, artificial reefs must start on stable objects.

When experts find a good reef-building object, they sink it onto an underwater plain. Millions of tiny plants and animals begin to attach themselves to the sunken object right away. The growth of those plants and animals depends on sunlight, so most artificial reefs rest on ocean floors less than 100 feet below the surface. At such depths, sunlight reaches the artificial reef, causing plants and animals to grow quickly.

▲ A ship is sunk to start a coral reef off the coast of Fort Lauderdale, Florida.

▼ Experts lower an airplane into waters near Miami, Florida. The airplane, will slowly become a thriving coral reef.

Reef Relief

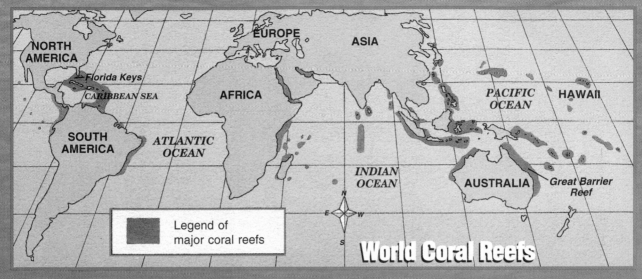

World Coral Reefs

Legend of major coral reefs

▲ Coral reefs are found in warm, shallow waters around the world. Reef-forming coral animals cannot live in water that is colder than 65 degrees Fahrenheit.

In about ten days, the object is completely covered with *algae*, or simple plants. Then, over the following few years, coral creatures attach themselves to the object. When the creatures die, their hard skeletons remain part of the reef. According to artificial coral reef expert Ben Mostkoff, after 30 years the human-made object—whether an airplane, a school bus, or an army tank—is no longer recognizable. Instead, the object becomes a well-developed coral reef, supporting much sea life.

Efforts Around the World

According to Mostkoff, people have been sinking objects to form artificial reefs for hundreds of years. Florida has more than 300 artificial reefs in the waters near its coastline. Artificial reefs also lie in oceans and seas around the world. More than 2,500 have been sunk off the coast of Japan.

Today, many artificial reefs are sunk to increase the number of fish living in certain ocean areas. When a reef is sunk in an area where few fish live, says Mostkoff, the number of fish in that area increases within six months.

Besides attracting fish, artificial coral reefs attract tourists. Many people travel to both natural *and* artificial reef sites all over the world to see corals and other sea plants and animals.

In what ways might the conditions needed for coral growth make it likely that the coral will be damaged?

SCUBA DIVING

The silence of diving.
Slipping through
the water like a
worm sliding
through mud.
Skittering along
the bottom of the
ocean floor like a
hamster.
A big whale flies by like a silent jet.
Giant coral reefs like big
skyscrapers in the sea.
Bubbles coming from a rubber tube
like smoke coming from a factory.
Giant fish floating by like a
submarine.
Giant flippers propelling you further
and further into the ocean.

Stuart Francis, Grade 6
Widsten Elementary School
Wayzata, Minnesota

Unit 2

WORLDS *of* CHANGE

It's Our

World, Too!

Stories of Young People Who Are Making a Difference

by Phillip Hoose

Justin Lebo

Since he was ten, Justin Lebo, fourteen, of Paterson, New Jersey, has been building bicycles out of used parts he finds from old junkers. When he finishes, he gives them away to kids who are homeless or sick. He plows most of his allowance into the project and often works on nights and weekends. Why does he do it? The answer is surprising. "In part," he says, "I do it for myself."

Something about the battered old bicycle at the garage sale caught ten-year-old Justin Lebo's eye. What a wreck! It was like looking at a few big bones in the dust and trying to figure out what kind of dinosaur they had once belonged to.

It was a BMX bike with a twenty-inch frame. Its original color was buried beneath five or six coats of gunky paint. Now it showed up as sort of a rusted red. Everything—the grips, the pedals, the brakes, the seat, the spokes—were bent or broken, twisted and rusted. Justin stood back as if he were inspecting a painting for sale at an auction. Then he made his final judgment: perfect.

Justin talked the owner down to $6.50 and asked his mother, Diane, to help him load the bike into the back of their car.

When he got it home, he wheeled the junker into the garage and showed it proudly to his father. "Will you help me fix it up?" he asked. Justin's hobby was bike racing, a passion the two of them shared. Their garage barely had room for the car anymore.

It was more like a bike shop. Tires and frames hung from hooks on the ceiling, and bike wrenches dangled from the walls.

After every race, Justin and his father would adjust the brakes and realign the wheels of his two racing bikes. This was a lot of work, since Justin raced flat out, challenging every gear and part to perform to its fullest. He had learned to handle almost every repair his father could and maybe even a few things he couldn't. When Justin got really stuck, he went to see Mel, the owner of the best bike shop in town. Mel let him hang out and watch, and he even grunted a few syllables of advice from between the spokes of a wheel now and then.

"It is by spending one's self that one becomes rich."

Sarah Bernhardt

Now Justin and his father cleared out a work space in the garage and put the old junker up on a rack. They poured alcohol on the frame and rubbed until the old paint began to yield, layer by layer. They replaced the broken pedal, tightened down a new seat, and restored the grips. In about a week, it looked brand new.

Justin wheeled it out of the garage, leapt aboard, and started off around the block. He stood up and mashed down on the pedals, straining for speed. It was a good, steady ride, but not much of a thrill compared to his racers.

Soon he forgot about the bike. But the very next week, he bought another junker at a yard sale and fixed it up, too. After a while it bothered him that he wasn't really using either bike. Then he realized that what he loved about the old bikes wasn't riding them: it was the challenge of making something new and useful out of something old and broken.

Justin wondered what he should do with them. They were just taking up space in the garage. He

remembered that when he was younger, he used to live near a large brick building called the Kilbarchan Home for Boys. It was a place for boys whose parents couldn't care for them for one reason or another.

He found "Kilbarchan" in the phone book and called the director, who said the boys would be thrilled to get two bicycles. The next day when Justin and his mother unloaded the bikes at the home, two boys raced out to greet them. They leapt aboard the bikes and started tooling around the semicircular driveway, doing wheelies and pirouettes, laughing and shouting.

The Lebos watched them for a while, then started to climb into their car to go home. The boys cried after them, "Wait a minute! You forgot your bikes!" Justin explained that the bikes were for them to keep.

"They were so happy," Justin remembers. "It was like they couldn't believe it. It made me feel good just to see them happy."

On the way home, Justin was silent. His mother assumed he was lost in a feeling of satisfaction. But he was thinking about what would happen once those bikes got wheeled inside and everyone saw them. How would all those kids decide who got the bikes? Two bikes could cause more trouble than they would solve. Actually, they hadn't been that hard to build. It was fun. Maybe he could do more. . . .

"Mom," Justin said as they turned onto their street, "I've got an idea. I'm going to make a bike for every boy at Kilbarchan for Christmas." Diane Lebo looked at Justin out of the corner of her eye. She had rarely seen him so determined.

When they got home, Justin called Kilbarchan to find out how many boys lived there. There were twenty-one. It was already June. He had six months to make nineteen bikes. That was almost a bike a week. Justin called the home back to tell them of his plan. "I could tell they didn't think I could do it," Justin remembers. "I knew I could."

"It just snowballed."

Justin knew his best chance was to build bikes almost the way GM or Ford builds cars: in an assembly line. He would start with frames from three-speed, twenty-four-inch BMX bicycles. They were common bikes, and all the parts were interchangeable. If he could find enough decent frames, he could take parts off broken bikes and fasten them onto the good frames. He figured it would take three or four junkers to produce enough parts to make one good bike. That meant sixty to eighty bikes. Where would he get them?

Garage sales seemed to be the only hope. It was June, and there would be garage sales all summer

long. But even if he could find that many bikes, how could he ever pay for them? That was hundreds of dollars.

He went to his parents with a proposal. "When Justin was younger, say five or six," says his mother, "he used to give some of his allowance away to help others in need. His father and I would donate a dollar for every dollar Justin donated. So he asked us if it could be like the old days, if we'd match every dollar he put into buying old bikes. We said yes."

Justin and his mother spent most of June and July hunting for cheap bikes at garage sales and thrift shops. They would haul the bikes home, and Justin would start stripping them down in the yard.

Justin Lebo, who has built hundreds of bikes and given them away to kids who are orphaned, ill, or homeless.

But by the beginning of August, he had managed to make only ten bikes. Summer vacation was almost over, and school and homework would soon cut into his time. Garage sales would dry up when it got colder, and Justin was out of money. Still, he was determined to find a way.

At the end of August, Justin got a break. A neighbor wrote a letter to the local newspaper describing Justin's project, and an editor thought it would make a good story. One day a reporter entered the Lebo garage. Stepping gingerly through the tires and frames that covered the floor, she found a boy with cut fingers and dirty nails, banging a seat onto a frame. His clothes were covered with grease. In her admiring article about a boy who was devoting his summer to help kids he didn't even know, she said Justin needed bikes and money, and she printed his home phone number.

Overnight, everything changed. "There must have been a hundred calls," Justin says. "People would call me up and ask me to come over and pick up their old bike. Or I'd be working in the garage, and a station wagon would pull up. The driver would leave a couple of bikes by the curb. It just snowballed."

By the start of school, the garage was overflowing with BMX frames. Pyramids of pedals and seats rose in the corners. Soon bike parts filled a toolshed in the backyard and then spilled out into the small yard itself, wearing away the lawn.

More and more writers and television and radio reporters called for interviews. Each time he told his story, Justin asked for bikes and money. "The first few interviews were fun," Justin says, "but it reached a point where I really didn't like doing them. The publicity was necessary, though. I had to keep doing interviews to get the donations I needed."

By the time school opened, he was working on ten bikes at a time. There were so many calls now that he was beginning to refuse offers that weren't the exact bikes he needed.

As checks came pouring in, Justin's money problems disappeared. He set up a bank account and began to make bulk orders of common parts

> "I don't think you can ever really do anything to help anybody else if it doesn't make you happy."
>
> Justin Lebo

from Mel's bike shop. Mel seemed delighted to see him. Sometimes, if Justin brought a bike by the shop, Mel would help him fix it. When Justin tried to talk him into a lower price for big orders, Mel smiled and gave in. He respected another good businessman. They became friends.

"Why do you do it?"

The week before Christmas Justin delivered the last of the twenty-one bikes to Kilbarchan. Once again, the boys poured out of the home and leapt aboard the bikes, tearing around the snow.

And once again, their joy inspired Justin. They reminded him how important bikes were to him. Wheels meant freedom. He thought how much more the freedom to ride must mean to boys like these who had so little freedom in their lives. He decided to keep on building.

"First I made eleven bikes for the children in a foster home my mother told me about. Then I made bikes for all the women in a battered women's shelter. Then I made ten little bikes and tricycles for the kids in a home for children with AIDS. Then I made twenty-three bikes for the Paterson Housing Coalition."

In the four years since he started, Justin Lebo has made between 150 and 200 bikes and given them all away. He has been careful to leave time for his homework, his friends, his coin collection, his new interest in marine biology, and of course his own bikes.

Reporters and interviewers have asked Justin Lebo the same question over and over: "Why do you do it?" The question seems to make him uncomfortable. It's as if they want him to say what a great person he is. Their stories always make him seem like a saint, which he knows he isn't. "Sure it's nice of me to make the bikes," he says, "because I don't have to. But I want to. In part, I do it for myself. I don't think you can ever really do anything to help anybody else if it doesn't make you happy.

"Once I overheard a kid who got one of my bikes say, 'A bike is like a book; it opens up a whole new world.' That's how I feel, too. It made me happy to know that kid felt that way. That's why I do it."

Dwaina Brooks

On Friday nights, Dwaina Brooks, eleven, and as many as twenty-six of her friends and relatives, turn her mother's kitchen into a meal factory for the homeless of Dallas. With the radio set to 100.3—the rap station—and with mayonnaise up to their elbows, they have produced as many as three hundred meals in a night.

*E*ach morning on her way to school, Dwaina Brooks saw the line of men and women outside a homeless shelter and soup kitchen in Dallas. Many looked cold and sleepy. Sometimes one man stood in the street carrying a sign that said, "I Will Work for Food to Feed My Children." No one ever stopped to talk to him. How could they just pass him by?

At school, her fourth-grade class was doing a unit on homelessness. Once a week, students telephoned a shelter and talked with someone who was staying there. Dwaina would ask the person on the other end of the phone, "How'd you wind up on the streets?" "Do you want to be there?" "What did you do before?" She listened carefully.

Most people's lives had been going along okay, and then something bad had happened. They got fired. The family broke up. They couldn't make a rent payment.

Always she asked, "What do you

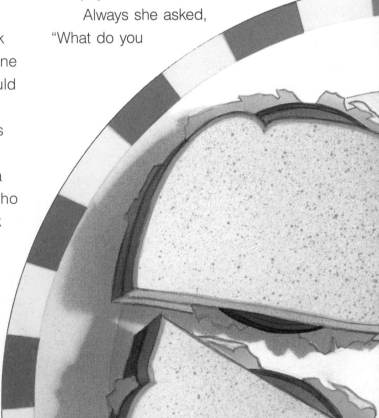

need?" The answer was always "a home," or "a job." It never seemed as though she could do much more than keep sending her lunch money to the shelter. Then one afternoon, Dwaina talked with a young man who had been without a home for a long time.

"What do you need?" she asked him.

"I need a job and a permanent home," he replied.

"Well, I can't give you that," she answered impatiently. "I don't have a job either. Don't you need anything else?"

"Yeah. I would love a really good meal again."

"Well, now," said Dwaina, brightening. "I *can* cook."

"*Even when she was a baby, Dwaina couldn't stand to see anyone hurt . . .*"

Gail Brooks

Why not?

Dwaina tore into the house that night after school and found her mother, Gail. As usual, she was in the kitchen. "Mama," she said. "I need you to help me fix some stuff to take down to that shelter we call at school. Let's make up as much as we can. Sandwiches and chicken. Let's get everyone to do it. C'mon."

Gail Brooks looked at her daughter. All of her children were generous, but Dwaina had always been a little different. Even when she was a baby, Dwaina couldn't stand to see anyone hurt or left out. If she only took one doll to bed with her, pretty soon she would start wondering if all the others felt bad. The next morning, there would be a bed full of dolls and Dwaina on the floor.

Make food for the homeless? Well, why not? They decided to prepare meals on Friday night. They spent the next three days shopping and preparing. Counting Dwaina's lunch money, which she decided to donate to the cause, they figured they had about sixty dollars to spend. Their challenge was how to make that stretch into as many meals as possible.

Coupons helped cut the prices for sandwich wrapping, cookies, and mayonnaise. Dwaina's uncle got them discount lunch meats from the store where he used to work. Thursday night was bargain night at the bakery in nearby Lancaster. They drove away with six big loaves of day-old bread for $1.78. "Mama, do you think anyone at the shelter will really eat day-old bread?" Dwaina asked. "We eat it," Gail replied. "If it don't kill us, it won't kill them."

The baker gave them twenty free boxes, too, when he heard how they would be used. Dwaina's aunts and uncles brought over huge sacks of chips and big bottles of salad dressing.

When Dwaina got home from school on Friday, the stage was set. Her mother's table was covered with a plastic cloth. The plastic gloves from the dime store were laid out. Mountains of ham, turkey, and cheese were at one end. Two rows of bread went from one end of the table to the other. They looked like piano keys. A huge jar of mayonnaise was open and ready.

Dwaina's sisters, Stephanie, sixteen, and Crystal, nine, already had aprons tied around their waists. Dwaina turned on the radio, and they all formed an assembly line and dug in. Gail threw chicken into three skillets and got them all going at once. Dwaina slapped meat on open slices of bread and covered them with mayo. Crystal wrapped sandwiches and stuffed sacks. Dwaina looked on proudly as the corner of the kitchen began to fill up with sacks. It looked like a lot of meals.

It was after ten when the last sack was stuffed. The kitchen looked like a tornado had ripped through it. They placed 105 carefully wrapped meals in the bakery boxes, loaded them in the Oldsmobile, and headed downtown.

When they got to the shelter, two men came out to the street and helped carry in the boxes. Dwaina set down her first box and looked around the shelter. It was a big, open room with beds along the walls. It was dark, but some men were up front in a lighted area drinking coffee. She wondered if the man who had said he wanted a good meal was still living there. If he was, she thought with pride, he sure enough would have a treat tomorrow.

"Who'll be there?"

After that, nearly every Friday night for a year, Dwaina and her mother and

whatever sisters were around made food for shelters in Dallas. At first they took the food to the shelters themselves, but then their church volunteered to make the deliveries for them.

Always, Dwaina wanted to make more meals. That shelter had hundreds of people; she and her mom alone probably weren't feeding half of them. One Friday evening, she had an idea: she knew where she could get some extra help, and lots of it, too.

The following Monday, she asked her fifth-grade teacher, Mr. Frost, if she could speak to the class while he took roll. Dwaina had been the class leader since the first day of school, when she had told a group of loud boys to shut up so she could hear her teacher. She could be tough or funny or kind. She always seemed to know exactly what would move them.

Now Dwaina smacked both hands on her desk hard to get their attention and stood up. She pushed her glasses up onto her forehead and glared at them for a moment, hands on hips, as if she were about to lecture them:

"Okay, y'all," she began. "We've been reading about the homeless in class, and I can tell you that for some reason it's getting worse and worse." Her eyes swept around the room. "Now, my mama and I been makin' sandwiches this year till we got mayonnaise up to our elbows and we can't make enough. Why should we be up till midnight every Friday night when y'all ain't doin' a thing? Now, listen. I want you to come to my house this Friday night and help. Who'll be there?"

Twenty-three hands went up. When Dwaina excitedly reported this to her mother, Gail Brooks nearly passed out. "Twenty-three kids? Plus *our* family?" "Yeah, Mama, isn't it great! Think how many meals we can make!"

Dwaina Brooks, who organized her family and friends to feed homeless people in Dallas.

Dwaina and Gail advised each participating family about where to get food cheaply. They made a central list of who would bring what and taped it to the refrigerator. All that week, parents drove boxes of food to the Brooks's small house. At school, the kids made bigger and bigger plans each day. Making food for the shelter was shaping up to be the social event of the year.

"Why don't y'all stay over?" asked Dwaina.

"I'll bring popcorn!" said Claire.

"I got a Hammer tape," said Qiana.

"What about boys?" said Christopher. "Can we sleep over, too?"

"Sorry," came a chorus of girls. "Oh, maybe on the kitchen floor."

The next Friday night, twenty-eight people crowded into the Brooks kitchen. They set up one of the world's longest assembly lines, kicked the radio onto 100.3 FM-JAMZ—the rap station—wrapped towels around their waists, and started in. By midnight, the boxes were filled with more than three hundred sacks.

In a little more than two years, Dwaina Brooks, now in sixth grade, has organized several thousand meals for unfortunate people in the Dallas area. She and her mother and the classmates who sometimes still join in have perfected the art of helping others and having fun at the same time. They do it by doing something they already love to do: cooking and putting meals together.

Dwaina hopes to become a doctor and open her own clinic someday, but she thinks it's crazy to wait till then to start caring for others. "Kids should get going," she says. "There aren't enough jobs out there, especially for people without diplomas. Not even at McDonald's. We should try to help. If we don't act, there will be more and more homeless people. Each of us should have some kind of concern in our hearts for other people. And we owe it, too: there isn't a one of us who hasn't been helped by someone."

Meet
Phillip Hoose

Phillip Hoose got the idea for *It's Our World, Too!* from his daughter Hannah. She and some classmates held an art sale at their elementary school in Portland, Maine. They sold their own drawings and paintings. The money raised went to a homeless shelter. Hoose says, "Their good work gave me an idea for a book. Why not look all around the world for great stories of young people reaching out, making a difference, trying to help others?"

Hoose spent the next year searching for young people working for positive change. He ended up talking with over a hundred young activists.

When Hoose is not writing, he himself also works to change the world. He raises money for a group that tries to save prairies, swamps, marshes, and forests from being destroyed.

MAKING A DIFFERENCE

by Tracy Williams Cheney and Connie Eden

This is a story about kids who saved a green space in our neighborhood. We are the two grown-ups who worked with them and want to share their excellent work with you.

We live in the state of Washington. Most people think of tall green trees when they think of our state. But every year, more and more forests disappear to make room for houses and shopping malls. The population of our city, Everett, is expected to be almost twice as big in the next 20 years. We already have 75,000 people and not enough parks or green spaces.

On a map of our neighborhood, we had discovered some wooded land owned by the city. We checked and found that there was no money, time, or staff to make or take care of a new park. We tried to interest the adults at our neighborhood meetings, but no one seemed to care.

Then, a classroom of students at View Ridge Elementary School and their teacher jumped in and helped us.

For many years, neighbors had dumped yard clippings and garbage on this property. There is a creek that runs through here only during heavy rain— and then it flows into a salmon stream. A developer planned to build 15 houses squeezed between this land and our grade school. His plans would mean oily water running off the new streets and driveways into the creek.

The class did some investigating. They took a boat trip and saw how human activities on land can cause problems for aquatic animals and fish. For example, clear-cutting trees causes muddy streams because rain washes huge amounts of dirt down the bare hillsides. This clogs the air supply for fish, and salmon can't survive. The class visited the Public Works Department to learn

The kids learned about native plants and "invaders" such as holly. Natives are the original plants in a region. Invaders were brought in by people and animals. In Everett, there's lots of holly. Birds eat the berries and spread the seeds through their droppings.

how water is controlled and filtered in a city. When the developer realized people cared about the creek, he paid for a new design for collecting dirty water on his property.

The students divided into teams. Adults with special knowledge about wildlife, plants, and water came to school to talk to the children. The class collected this information and made a scrapbook for future classes.

Each student adopted a tree, named it, drew pictures of it, and wrote poems about it. They listened through stethoscopes to the sap running.

Next came the trash cleanup—a week-long job. The kids found everything from fake fingernails to chunks of concrete. Then, on a Saturday morning, 44 people, including neighbors and parents, joined in to fill a dumpster. The city paid for removing tons of garbage and provided a machine to cut up fallen trees. The kids spread fresh wood chips along the pathways.

The project was humongous.

Finally, it was time to name the park. The class discovered that two women— Gertrude Johnston and Cora Kelly— had donated the land for a park in the 1920s. The land had been forgotten and neglected all this time. All fourth and fifth graders at the school voted. The winning name was "Johnston/Kelly Environmental Park."

A group of students presented the name at our neighborhood meeting and it was approved. Next, they needed to convince

Kids, parents, neighbors, teachers, and city workers pitched in on the day of the cleanup. They gathered tons of garbage.

the park board, the city council, and the mayor. Two boys spent hours investigating records at the library, county courthouse, and even the cemetery to help show that these two women's names should be used for the park.

The developer now gives money to help protect the park. With this money, the class will put up signs identifying plant species. They will plant native plants, buy guide books, and make a space for an outdoor classroom. Our neighborhood organization will pay for a sign that says "Johnston/Kelly Environmental Park."

Here in Everett, kids did what grown-ups wouldn't do. They saved a wildlife area and green space. And they gave a life-long gift to our neighborhood.

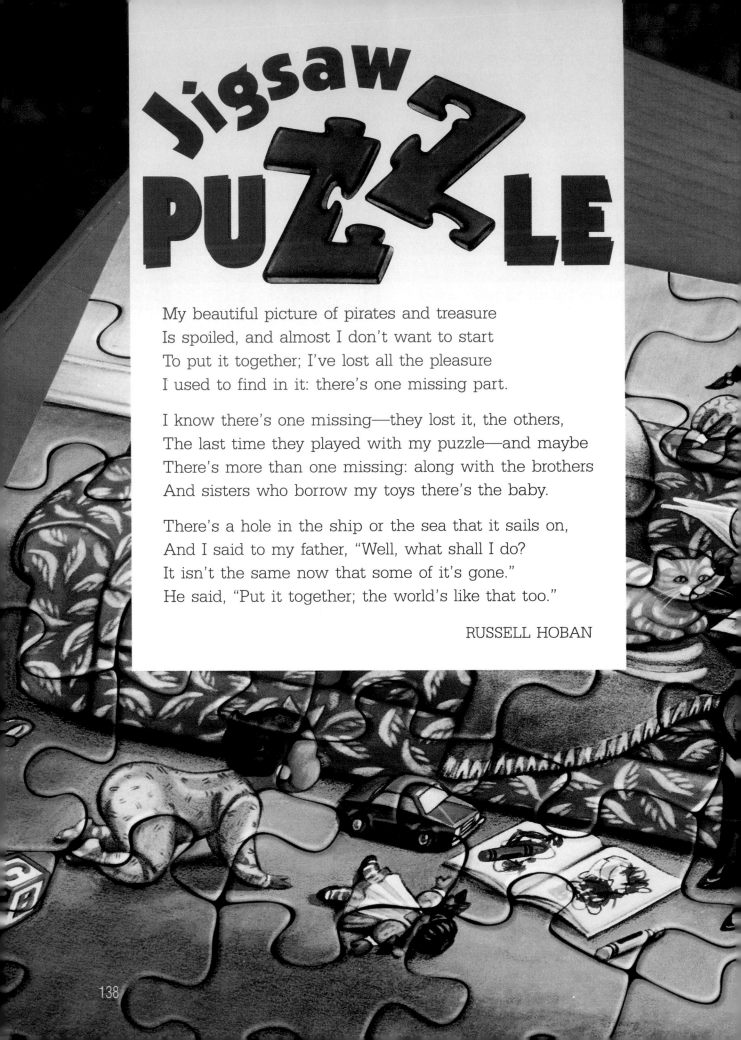

Jigsaw PUZZLE

My beautiful picture of pirates and treasure
Is spoiled, and almost I don't want to start
To put it together; I've lost all the pleasure
I used to find in it: there's one missing part.

I know there's one missing—they lost it, the others,
The last time they played with my puzzle—and maybe
There's more than one missing: along with the brothers
And sisters who borrow my toys there's the baby.

There's a hole in the ship or the sea that it sails on,
And I said to my father, "Well, what shall I do?
It isn't the same now that some of it's gone."
He said, "Put it together; the world's like that too."

RUSSELL HOBAN

New Pro

vidence

by Renata von Tscharner and Ronald Lee Fleming

a changing cityscape

illustrated by Denis Orloff

10 1910 1910 1910 1910 19
1910 1
10 191
10 191
1910 1
10 191
1910 1

1910

Put the city up; tear the city down;
put it up again; let us find a city. . . .

—Carl Sandburg

New Providence is thriving. Cobblestone streets bustle with activity—Model T Fords, streetcars, and horse-drawn carts carrying meat, milk, and ice. There is no concert in the band-stand today, but a crowd has gathered in the square in front of the Town Hall and the Tenebo County Courthouse. A fountain has been built in commemoration of Chief Tenebo, a Native American from a local tribe. The statue is about to be unveiled. Around the

base of the fountain is an inscription: GOOD CITIZENS ARE THE RICHES OF A CITY.

New Providence's good citizens—women in long skirts and men in hats—buy fruit at the sidewalk stand in front of the grocery and most of their clothing and household items at Getz & McClure's, the largest store in town. They shop for shoes and jewelry and office supplies and have supper at Gilman's or at the Butler House Cafe.

The rural hillsides surrounding the city are lush, with comfortable Victorian homes dotting the landscape and the Bloom mill and worker housing in the distance. The large red brick schoolhouse is attended by all school-age children in the region. A flock of birds flies peacefully overhead.

143

1935

As a mist rolls into New Providence, effects of the Great Depression are visible; the city has fallen on hard times. Gone is the bandstand from the courthouse square, where homeless men now huddle over trash can fires for warmth. A WPA sign publicizes the Works Progress Administration, a jobs program funded by the government. A line of jobless men waits for free bread outside the post office, and hoboes are taking a free ride out of the city on trains. Many buildings are in need of repair.

But even in times such as these, life goes on. A Charlie Chaplin movie is playing at the Strand Theater. A huge Coca-Cola advertisement goes up on the side of a building. A streetlight now controls automobile traffic. The Bloom mill—expanded before the stock market crash—is still in operation, the grocery has become a shoe store, and the dry goods store, a jeweler's. The Colonel Fleming House now accommodates three small businesses. Art Deco chrome and glass streamline some of the storefronts, contrasting with the older styles of the upper stories. A modern yellow apartment building squats on the hillside, while a biplane and a blimp cruise the skies.

1955

A postwar prosperity settles over New Providence, although there are signs that downtown is deteriorating.

The night sky glows with neon, Christmas lights, and lighted billboards advertising bread, used cars, and cigarettes. Part of the courthouse square is now paved with asphalt to make room for more and larger cars. Buses have replaced streetcars. Franchises like Rexall's and Woolworth's have moved into town, and the Alpine Motel attracts traveling businessmen. Walt Disney's *Lady and the Tramp* is playing at the Strand.

The elegant Butler House is now a liquor store and a boarding house for transients. Next to it, a Victorian cast-iron building
is being covered with prefabricated siding. Getz & McClure's has
already been sheathed with stark metal grillwork and a currently
popular style of lettering. Two of the small businesses in the
Colonel Fleming House are boarded up. Behind it, a bland new
building has been erected to house Monarch Insurance. The old
slate roof of the Town Hall has been replaced by asphalt shingles.
A fire is raging at the train station, while the citizens of New
Providence go about their holiday shopping.

1970

By 1970, downtown New Providence is an uninspired jumble of old and new. To attract people from thriving suburbia, part of Main Street has been converted into a pedestrian mall, dominated by a harsh concrete fountain. But there is less traffic than ever in the city center, and fewer people actually live there.

A number of people in town today are gathered outside the courthouse, taking part in a protest march against the Vietnam War. Across the newly sunken and cemented square, a mugging is in progress. Graffiti mars the area, as do more and more billboards— advertising beer, cigarettes, whiskey, and an Army/Navy surplus

store. The post office and several other buildings have been demolished and turned into parking lots, the Bloom mill is for rent, and the train station tower remains burnt out.

The Alpine Motel is now a Holiday Inn, a Fotomat has opened, and the Beatles' *Let It Be* is playing at the Strand. A day school has opened, complete with colorful murals and giant toadstools. The Colonel Fleming House seems about to be rescued by a preservation group. Victorian homes in the hills are disappearing to make room for highways, look-alike suburban housing, and another addition to the school. In the afternoon sky, a jet flies over the increasing number of powerlines strung across the horizon.

149

1980

Ten years later, there are signs that downtown New Providence is sadly in need of recovery—and also signs that help is on the way.

Chief Tenebo's statue has been vandalized; debris blows around its dry base and across the square. Graffiti is everywhere, street lamps are smashed, and a police box has appeared. The Colonel Fleming House has been moved across the street, but its placement does not look permanent. In its old location are a Cor-Ten steel sculpture and Monarch Insurance's new highrise, which bears no architectural relationship to the buildings around it.

But the streets seem more populated, and people are again living—even barbecuing—downtown in the new red brick infill structure next to McDonald's. The only billboard in town advertises health food and a cultural event. The old Strand Theater is being expanded into a Cultural Center. And although the Butler House has been all but abandoned, a sign shows that rehabilitation is being planned. A superhighway now cuts through the hillside, making downtown more accessible to summer holiday travelers. A large parking structure has been built, and well-tended plantings soften the mall.

151

1992

It is wisdom to think the people are the city. . . .
—*Carl Sandburg*

In the sunny afternoon sky a flock of birds heads back to its winter home. Below, people have returned to the city—living, shopping, working, playing. New Providence has never looked better. Sidewalk vendors sell their produce once more, and traffic again flows through handsomely paved streets. Buses are made to look like old-fashioned trolleys. Chief Tenebo has been restored, and the bandstand is back, a concert in full swing. Gone are graffiti, billboards, and harsh sculptures. Plants and fall flowers are everywhere—even the parking structure has been elegantly camouflaged.

All of the old building facades have been renovated, and the condition of most buildings is strikingly similar to what it was in 1910. The Town Hall's slate roof has been restored, and the air-raid siren is gone. Street furniture is comfortable and compatible with the architecture. The circular clock is back in front of the Butler House, now beautifully refurbished. An arcaded building where people live and work occupies the site of the controversial tower, serving as an entry into the restored train station, and an atrium full of plants softens the Monarch Insurance skyscraper. A Fitness Center has replaced the Feminist Health Center, and a film festival is in progress at the Strand Cultural Center.

The good citizens of New Providence have worked hard to make the city livable again—and true to its heritage.

*N*ew Providence, a small American city, will not be found on any map. It is the creation of a team of architectural historians and designers, and yet its fictional cityscape is truly authentic. The buildings, the signs, even the street furniture can be found somewhere in urban America. Almost every detail was discovered in old photographs and assembled by the design team at The Townscape Institute.

Baltimore, Maryland
(McDonald's building and
H$_2$O fountain)

Binghamton, New York
(courthouse lights)

Boston, Massachusetts
(church in center and
1970 concrete plaza)

Brookline, Massachusetts
(church)

Cambridge, Massachusetts
(signs)

Chelsea, Massachusetts
(storefront)

Chicago, Illinois
(metal awning on the Butler House)

Cincinnati, Ohio
(1987 City Identity System booth)

Denver, Colorado
(building across the street from
courthouse in 1910)

Eugene, Oregon
(1970 modern concrete fountain)

Flint, Michigan
(1910 shoe sign and street awnings)

Fresno, California
(1970-80 sculptural clock tower)

Garland, Utah
(Bloom mill)

Grand Rapids, Michigan
(City Hall)

Heber City, Utah
(water tower)

Junction City, Kansas
(corner bank)

Knoxville, Tennessee
(billboard)

Los Angeles, California
(Getz & McClure building)

Milwaukee, Wisconsin
(suburban villas)

Montclair, New Jersey
(Colonel Fleming House)

Montgomery, Alabama
(Victorian cast-iron building)

New York, New York
(Butler House and train station)

Portland, Oregon
(fountain base)

Richmond, Virginia
(signs on Reiter's shoe store)

Salem, Ohio
(cornice on Main Street)

San Diego, California
(circular clock)

Scottsdale, Arizona
(parking structure with plantings)

Staunton, Virginia
(stained glass in McDonald's building)

Syracuse, New York
(layout of courthouse square)

Topeka, Kansas
(Alpine Motel sign)

Townsend, Massachusetts
(bandstand)

Traverse City, Michigan
(mansard roof on Butler House)

Upper Sandusky, Ohio
(horse fountain and pavilion)

Waltham, Massachusetts
(bench)

Washington, D.C.
(Masonic building)

Westerville, Ohio
(gas station)

Wilkes-Barre, Pennsylvania
(park outline)

Wilmington, Delaware
(1970 metal Main Street shelters)

Winooski, Vermont
(Main Street building)

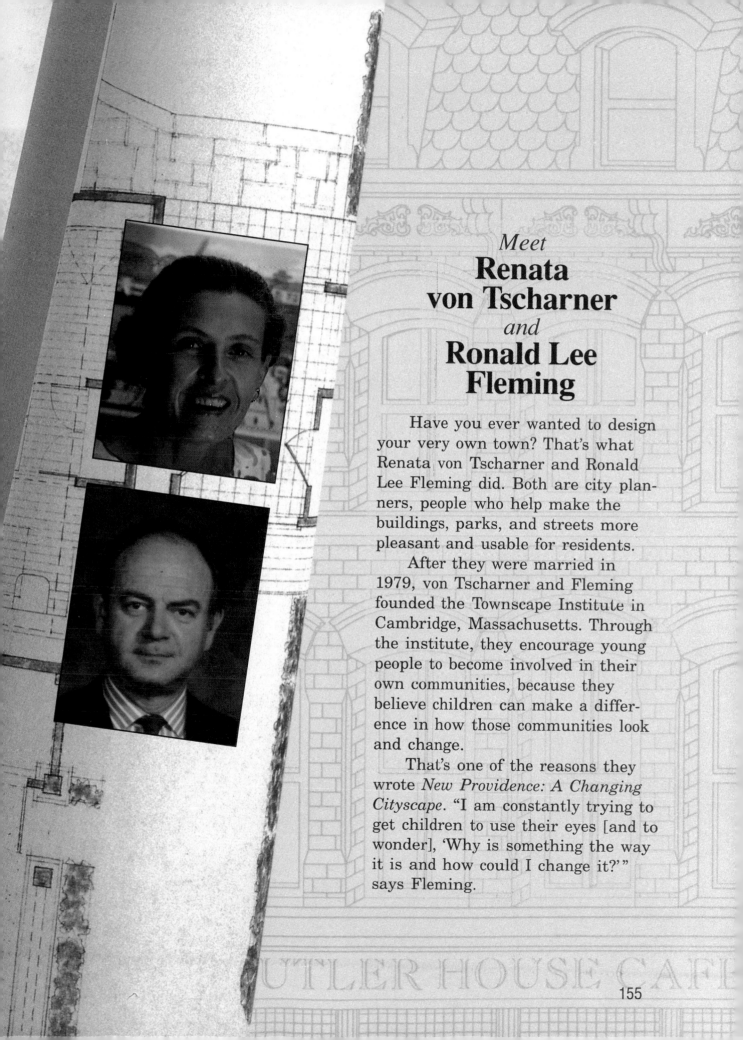

Meet
Renata
von Tscharner
and
Ronald Lee
Fleming

Have you ever wanted to design your very own town? That's what Renata von Tscharner and Ronald Lee Fleming did. Both are city planners, people who help make the buildings, parks, and streets more pleasant and usable for residents.

After they were married in 1979, von Tscharner and Fleming founded the Townscape Institute in Cambridge, Massachusetts. Through the institute, they encourage young people to become involved in their own communities, because they believe children can make a difference in how those communities look and change.

That's one of the reasons they wrote *New Providence: A Changing Cityscape*. "I am constantly trying to get children to use their eyes [and to wonder], 'Why is something the way it is and how could I change it?'" says Fleming.

CITY

In the morning the city
Spreads its wings
Making a song
In stone that sings.

In the evening the city
Goes to bed
Hanging lights
About its head.

Langston Hughes

Meet
Alma Flor Ada

"Most of my stories I told aloud before I ever wrote them down," says Alma Flor Ada. "And it was other people listening and other people being interested that gave me a motivation to write them."

Listening to other people's stories has also influenced Ada's writing. *The Gold Coin* is based in part on a story her grandfather told her when she was about fifteen. In the story, a rich man had to choose between going away to save his fortune or staying with his dying wife. That man was Alma Flor Ada's grandfather—and he told her he never regretted choosing to stay with his wife. "[Money] should never rule your life," he told her.

Alma Flor Ada grew up in Cuba and today lives in California, where she is a professor of multicultural education at the University of San Francisco. She has written many children's books published in Mexico, Peru, Argentina, and Spain.

THE GOLD COIN

by Alma Flor Ada

illustrated by Neil Waldman

translated from the Spanish by Bernice Randall

Juan had been a thief for many years. Because he did his stealing by night, his skin had become pale and sickly. Because he spent his time either hiding or sneaking about, his body had become shriveled and bent. And because he had neither friend nor relative to make him smile, his face was always twisted into an angry frown.

One night, drawn by a light shining through the trees, Juan came upon a hut. He crept up to the door and through a crack saw an old woman sitting at a plain, wooden table.

What was that shining in her hand? Juan wondered. He could not believe his eyes: It was a gold coin. Then he heard the woman say to herself, "I must be the richest person in the world."

Juan decided instantly that all the woman's gold must be his. He thought that the easiest thing to do was to watch until the woman left. Juan hid in the bushes and huddled under his poncho, waiting for the right moment to enter the hut.

Juan was half asleep when he heard knocking at the door and the sound of insistent voices. A few minutes later, he saw the woman, wrapped in a black cloak, leave the hut with two men at her side.

Here's my chance! Juan thought. And, forcing open a window, he climbed into the empty hut.

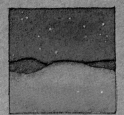

161

He looked about eagerly for the gold. He looked under the bed. It wasn't there. He looked in the cupboard. It wasn't there, either. Where could it be? Close to despair, Juan tore away some beams supporting the thatch roof.

Finally, he gave up. There was simply no gold in the hut.

All I can do, he thought, is to find the old woman and make her tell me where she's hidden it.

So he set out along the path that she and her two companions had taken.

It was daylight by the time Juan reached the river. The countryside had been deserted, but here, along the riverbank, were two huts. Nearby, a man and his son were hard at work, hoeing potatoes.

It had been a long, long time since Juan had spoken to another human being. Yet his desire to find the woman was so strong that he went up to the farmers and asked, in a hoarse, raspy voice, "Have you seen a short, gray-haired woman, wearing a black cloak?"

"Oh, you must be looking for Doña Josefa," the young boy said. "Yes, we've seen her. We went to fetch her this morning, because my grandfather had another attack of—"

"Where is she now?" Juan broke in.

"She is long gone," said the father with a smile. "Some people from across the river came looking for her, because someone in their family is sick."

"How can I get across the river?" Juan asked anxiously.

"Only by boat," the boy answered. "We'll row you across later, if you'd like." Then turning back to his work, he added, "But first we must finish digging up the potatoes."

The thief muttered, "Thanks." But he quickly grew impatient. He grabbed a hoe and began to help the pair of farmers. The sooner we finish, the sooner we'll get across the river, he thought. And the sooner I'll get to my gold!

It was dusk when they finally laid down their hoes. The soil had been turned, and the wicker baskets were brimming with potatoes.

"Now can you row me across?" Juan asked the father anxiously.

"Certainly," the man said. "But let's eat supper first."

Juan had forgotten the taste of a home-cooked meal and the pleasure that comes from sharing it with others. As he sopped up the last of the stew with a chunk of dark bread, memories of other meals came back to him from far away and long ago.

By the light of the moon, father and son guided their boat across the river.

"What a wonderful healer Doña Josefa is!" the boy told Juan. "All she had to do to make Abuelo better was give him a cup of her special tea."

"Yes, and not only that," his father added, "she brought him a gold coin."

Juan was stunned. It was one thing for Doña Josefa to go around helping people. But how could she go around handing out gold coins—*his gold coins?*

When the threesome finally reached the other side of the river, they saw a young man sitting outside his hut.

"This fellow is looking for Doña Josefa," the father said, pointing to Juan.

"Oh, she left some time ago," the young man said.

"Where to?" Juan asked tensely.

"Over to the other side of the mountain," the young man replied, pointing to the vague outline of mountains in the night sky.

"How did she get there?" Juan asked, trying to hide his impatience.

"By horse," the young man answered. "They came on horseback to get her because someone had broken his leg."

"Well, then, I need a horse, too," Juan said urgently.

"Tomorrow," the young man replied softly. "Perhaps I can take you tomorrow, maybe the next day. First I must finish harvesting the corn."

So Juan spent the next day in the fields, bathed in sweat from sunup to sundown.

Yet each ear of corn that he picked seemed to bring him closer to his treasure. And later that evening, when he helped the young man husk several ears so they could boil them for supper, the yellow kernels glittered like gold coins.

While they were eating, Juan thought about Doña Josefa. Why, he wondered, would someone who said she was the world's richest woman spend her time taking care of every sick person for miles around?

The following day, the two set off at dawn. Juan could not recall when he last had noticed the beauty of the sunrise. He felt strangely moved by the sight of the mountains, barely lit by the faint rays of the morning sun.

As they neared the foothills, the young man said, "I'm not surprised you're looking for Doña Josefa. The whole countryside needs her. I went for her because my wife had been running a high fever. In no time at all, Doña Josefa had her on the road to recovery. And what's more, my friend, she brought her a gold coin!"

Juan groaned inwardly. To think that someone could hand out gold so freely! What a strange woman Doña Josefa is, Juan thought. Not only is she willing to help one person after another, but she doesn't mind traveling all over the countryside to do it!

"Well, my friend," said the young man finally, "this is where I must leave you. But you don't have far to walk. See that house over there? It belongs to the man who broke his leg."

The young man stretched out his hand to say good-bye. Juan stared at it for a moment. It had been a long, long time since the thief had shaken hands with anyone. Slowly, he pulled out a hand from under his poncho. When his companion grasped it firmly in his own, Juan felt suddenly warmed, as if by the rays of the sun.

But after he thanked the young man, Juan ran down the road. He was still eager to catch up with Doña Josefa. When he reached the house, a woman and a child were stepping down from a wagon.

"Have you seen Doña Josefa?" Juan asked.

"We've just taken her to Don Teodosio's," the woman said. "His wife is sick, you know—"

"How do I get there?" Juan broke in. "I've got to see her."

"It's too far to walk," the woman said amiably. "If you'd like, I'll take you there tomorrow. But first I must gather my squash and beans."

So Juan spent yet another long day in the fields. Working beneath the summer sun, Juan noticed that his skin had begun to tan. And although he had to stoop down to pick the squash, he found that he could now stretch his body. His back had begun to straighten, too.

Later, when the little girl took him by the hand to show him a family of rabbits burrowed under a fallen tree, Juan's face broke into a smile. It had been a long, long time since Juan had smiled.

Yet his thoughts kept coming back to the gold.

The following day, the wagon carrying Juan and the woman lumbered along a road lined with coffee fields.

The woman said, "I don't know what we would have done without Doña Josefa. I sent my daughter to our neighbor's house, who then brought Doña Josefa on horseback. She set my husband's leg and then showed me how to brew a special tea to lessen the pain."

Getting no reply, she went on. "And, as if that weren't enough, she brought him a gold coin. Can you imagine such a thing?"

Juan could only sigh. No doubt about it, he thought, Doña Josefa is someone special. But Juan didn't know whether to be happy that Doña Josefa had so much gold she could freely hand it out, or angry for her having already given so much of it away.

When they finally reached Don Teodosio's house, Doña Josefa was already gone. But here, too, there was work that needed to be done. . . .

Juan stayed to help with the coffee harvest. As he picked the red berries, he gazed up from time to time at the trees that grew, row upon row, along the hillsides. What a calm, peaceful place this is! he thought.

The next morning, Juan was up at daybreak. Bathed in the soft, dawn light, the mountains seemed to smile at him. When Don Teodosio offered him a lift on horseback, Juan found it difficult to have to say good-bye.

"What a good woman Doña Josefa is!" Don Teodosio said, as they rode down the hill toward the sugarcane fields. "The minute she heard about my wife being sick, she came with her special herbs. And as if that weren't enough, she brought my wife a gold coin!"

In the stifling heat, the kind that often signals the approach of a storm, Juan simply sighed and mopped his brow. The pair continued riding for several hours in silence.

Juan then realized he was back in familiar territory, for they were now on the stretch of road he had traveled only a week ago—though how much longer it now seemed to him. He jumped off Don Teodosio's horse and broke into a run.

This time the gold would not escape him! But he had to move quickly, so he could find shelter before the storm broke.

Out of breath, Juan finally reached Doña Josefa's hut. She was standing by the door, shaking her head slowly as she surveyed the ransacked house.

"So I've caught up with you at last!" Juan shouted, startling the old woman. "Where's the gold?"

"The gold coin?" Doña Josefa said, surprised and looking at Juan intently. "Have you come for the gold coin? I've been trying hard to give it to someone who might need it," Doña Josefa said. "First to an old man who had just gotten over a bad attack. Then to a young woman who had been running a fever. Then to a man with a broken leg. And finally to Don Teodosio's wife. But none of them would take it. They all said, 'Keep it. There must be someone who needs it more.'"

Juan did not say a word.

"You must be the one who needs it," Doña Josefa said.

She took the coin out of her pocket and handed it to him. Juan stared at the coin, speechless.

At that moment a young girl appeared, her long braid bouncing as she ran. "Hurry, Doña Josefa, please!" she said breathlessly. "My mother is all alone, and the baby is due any minute."

"Of course, dear," Doña Josefa replied. But as she glanced up at the sky, she saw nothing but black clouds. The storm was nearly upon them. Doña Josefa sighed deeply.

"But how can I leave now? Look at my house! I don't know what has happened to the roof. The storm will wash the whole place away!"

And there was a deep sadness in her voice.

Juan took in the child's frightened eyes, Doña Josefa's sad, distressed face, and the ransacked hut.

"Go ahead, Doña Josefa," he said. "Don't worry about your house. I'll see that the roof is back in shape, good as new."

The woman nodded gratefully, drew her cloak about her shoulders, and took the child by the hand. As she turned to leave, Juan held out his hand.

"Here, take this," he said, giving her the gold coin. "I'm sure the newborn will need it more than I."

Money, Money, Money

Bartering

A long time ago people didn't need money. They got everything they needed through bartering, or trading. In bartering, you trade something you don't need for something you do need. Bartering is great as long as somebody wants the things that you have.

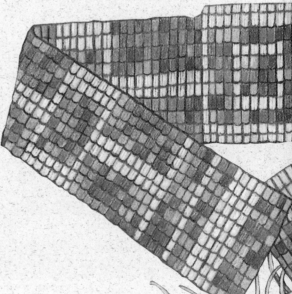

Tobacco
American colonies

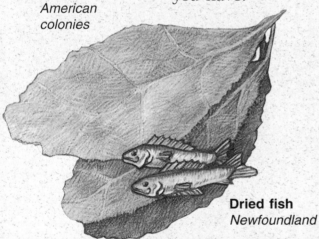

Dried fish
Newfoundland

Whale teeth
Fiji Islands

Money axe
Mexico

Wampum
Native American

Cowrie shells
China

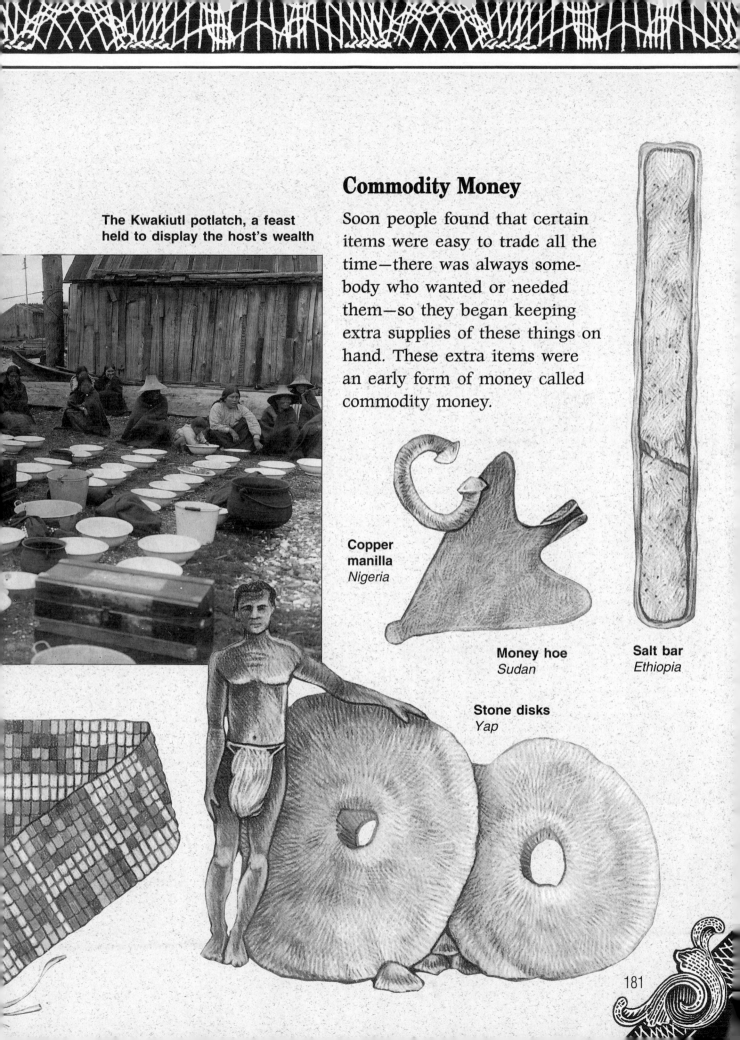

The Kwakiutl potlatch, a feast held to display the host's wealth

Commodity Money

Soon people found that certain items were easy to trade all the time—there was always somebody who wanted or needed them—so they began keeping extra supplies of these things on hand. These extra items were an early form of money called commodity money.

Copper manilla
Nigeria

Money hoe
Sudan

Salt bar
Ethiopia

Stone disks
Yap

Metal Money

After a while people began to use pieces of metal—copper, bronze, iron, silver, and gold—instead of commodities as money. Metal was better to use because:

- it was easier to carry
- it wouldn't rot or spoil
- it was easy to recognize
- it wouldn't wear out easily
- it was scarce enough to be valuable
- it wouldn't break

When people began to use metal for money, they measured it out in lumps, bars, and rings. The heavier the piece of metal, the more a person could buy with it. But that meant that every time you went shopping, someone had to weigh your metal.

Soon someone discovered that you could melt metal down into disks and mark their weight on them, then use them over and over. These disks were the first coins.

Chinese knife-shaped coin

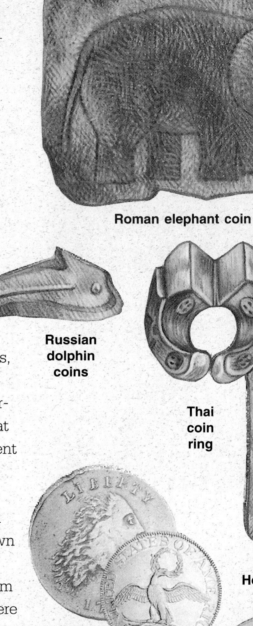

Roman elephant coin

Russian dolphin coins

Thai coin ring

Hoe-shaped coin

Early American coins

Chinese round coin with square hole for stringing

Earliest coin, issued by the King of Lydia

Kenyan hundred-shilling note

Japanese feudal note

Paper Money

Although it was handier to carry a pocketful of coins than commodity money, metal money didn't work as well when you had to buy big items that cost a lot. Large sacks of money were too heavy, too bulky, and too easy to steal.

Paper money was first used in China during the 600s. As its use gradually spread all over the world, governments became involved in printing money, each one printing its own type. The United States has had printed money since 1781.

Paper money has value only when a government declares that people must accept it as payment for things. Bills may be the same size, but have different values according to what is printed on them.

Many people see a tiny white owl or spider in the upper right corner of each one-dollar bill.

Two Roses on a Tablecloth by the 19th-century painter
Édouard Manet.

The Act

There were the roses, in the rain.
Don't cut them, I pleaded.
   They won't last, she said
But they're so beautiful
   where they are.
Agh, we were all beautiful once, she
   said,
and cut them and gave them to me
   in my hand.

WILLIAM CARLOS WILLIAMS

March 31   April 1   April 2

N

Pacific Ocean   Sierra Nevada   Great Basin   Rocky Mountains   Great Plains

Snow   Blizzards   Tornadoes

MEET
BRUCE HISCOCK

Bruce Hiscock began work on *The Big Storm* by calling up weather reporters from the radio. "I had them suggest storms to write about. I wanted a spring storm because they are the most violent and active." Hiscock then studied weather for six months. He felt he had to learn all he could about weather to understand this storm fully. For details, Hiscock read newspaper accounts from towns hit by the storm. He also visited places pictured in his book.

From his cabin in the Adirondack Mountains, Hiscock stays in touch with nature. "I spend time every day in the woods with the birds and the animals. At night I watch the stars with a telescope. . . ." A billion-year-old boulder near his home is the subject of another Hiscock book, *The Big Rock*.

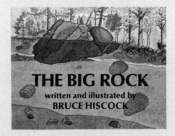

THE BIG ROCK
written and illustrated by
BRUCE HISCOCK

186

April 3 April 4 April 5 April 6 E

Mississippi River
Tornadoes
Rain
Hail Blizzards
Appalachian Mountains
Atlantic Ocean

THE BIG STORM

written and illustrated by Bruce Hiscock

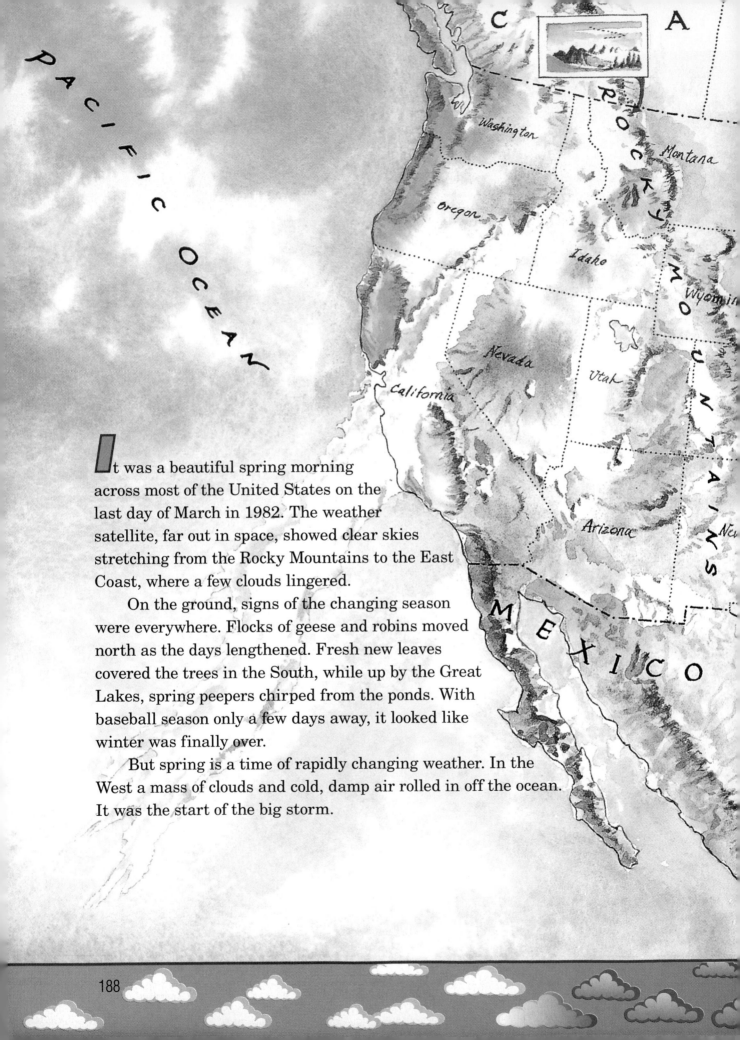

It was a beautiful spring morning across most of the United States on the last day of March in 1982. The weather satellite, far out in space, showed clear skies stretching from the Rocky Mountains to the East Coast, where a few clouds lingered.

On the ground, signs of the changing season were everywhere. Flocks of geese and robins moved north as the days lengthened. Fresh new leaves covered the trees in the South, while up by the Great Lakes, spring peepers chirped from the ponds. With baseball season only a few days away, it looked like winter was finally over.

But spring is a time of rapidly changing weather. In the West a mass of clouds and cold, damp air rolled in off the ocean. It was the start of the big storm.

The clouds brought heavy rain to the Pacific Coast as the gathering storm moved inland. Like most weather systems in North America, it was carried along by the westerlies, the winds that nearly always blow from west to east across the continent.

When the storm ran up against the mountains of the Sierra Nevada range in California, the wind pushed the clouds up the steep slopes. In the cold mountain air the rain changed to snow.

W

E

CALIFORNIA

SIERRA NEVADA
SPANISH
FOR
SNOWY MOUNTAINS

It snowed hard all day in the Sierras. The flakes clung to the tall pines, coating them in heavy layers of white. But near the mountaintops, where no trees grow, the wind piled the snow into great drifts. Soon the drifts became so deep that the slopes would hold no more.

The snow began to slide from the high places, gently at first, then faster and faster, until the slides became huge avalanches. The avalanches roared down the mountains and slammed into buildings. Several people were killed.

Any storm can be dangerous as well as beautiful, but this one was a real powerhouse. And it was just getting started.

The storm moved swiftly over the Rocky Mountains, spreading blizzards from Montana to Arizona. In Colorado fierce winds gusted to 141 miles per hour, overturning vans and campers. In Nebraska the wind blew hard enough to move cow chips around.

The strongest winds came right at the leading edge of the storm. There a cold front marked the boundary between the warm springlike air covering most of the country and the cold, stormy air rushing in. Big masses of warm and cold air do not mix when they meet but instead push each other around. The line where the air masses bump is called a front.

This front was a cold front because the cold air was pushing the warm air away. Strong cold fronts usually bring high winds and sometimes violent weather.

The tremendous power of weather comes from the sun. Our planet is surrounded by a thin layer of air called the atmosphere, which is a mixture of gases, clouds, and dust. Heat from the sun causes the atmosphere to flow and swirl around the earth.

For instance, imagine that your city or county is covered by a blanket of cool, cloudy air. No wind stirs the leaves, and temperatures are the same everywhere.

Now let the clouds open slightly so that sunlight falls on a plowed field or a parking lot at the mall. The sun warms the earth or the pavement, which in turn heats the air right above it. Hot air rises, and soon a huge bubble of warm air is going up like an invisible balloon.

As the warm air rises, cool air flows in along the ground to take its place, causing a breeze. Temperatures begin to change. The sun has made the atmosphere move.

The same sort of uneven heating keeps the atmosphere moving worldwide. Warm air rises from the tropics while cold air flows down from the poles. This heating pattern and others create the vast wind and weather systems of the planet. Of course, these weather systems change with the seasons. The long summer days provide much more sunlight to warm and lift the air than the short, cold days of winter.

The sun moves the weather, but the land and sea affect it too. Ocean currents cool or warm the air. Hills and mountains block the wind. Even the spinning of the earth changes the wind's direction.

In fact, so many things affect the weather that when a storm comes up, it is not easy to predict exactly what it will do.

The big storm grew worse as it swept out over the Great Plains. Flocks of robins huddled on the ground, unable to fly in the blowing snow. Across the Dakotas and Minnesota, weather forecasters watched their barometers as the readings fell to record low levels. A deep low-pressure center was forming.

NATIONAL WEATHER SERVICE

NWS INSTRUMENTS

Barometers measure the pressure of the air directly overhead. Air, like water, has weight, and tons of air press down on the earth. This force, called barometric or atmospheric pressure, changes constantly as the air moves.

Forecasters pay close attention to these changes, for they help predict the weather to come. High pressure usually brings fair skies. Low pressure means storms, and the lower the pressure, the stronger the storm.

As the blizzard raged on, the weather stations in the storm reported the low pressure, the freezing temperatures, and the gusty wind and snow conditions to the National Meteorological Center near Washington, D.C. The data went directly into their huge computers along with data from hundreds of other weather stations, satellites, and instrument-carrying balloons.

The computer gave an overall picture of the weather to the forecasters at the National Center. Then, using more computers, they predicted what the storm would do next. These predictions were sent back to each weather station. There, a detailed forecast was made for the local area.

This work goes on every day, but with a killer storm on the loose, the forecasts were especially important.

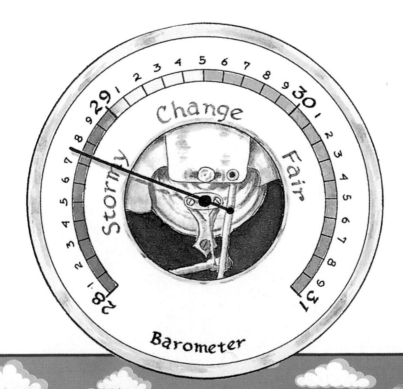

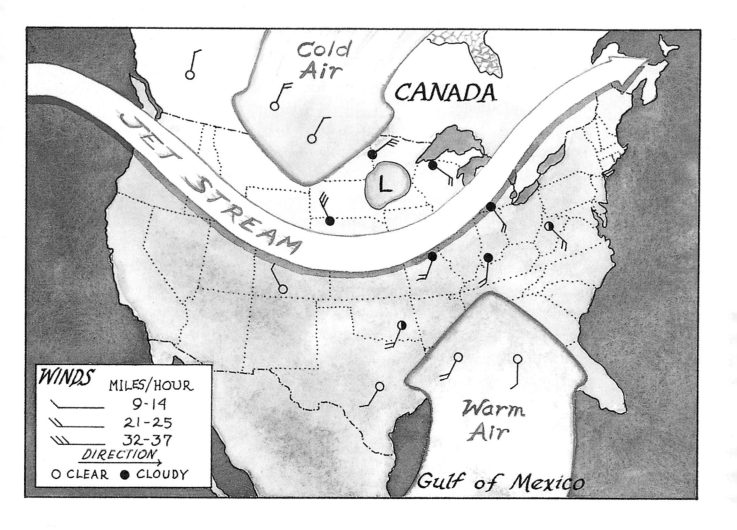

On the morning of Friday, April 2, the weather map showed strong surface winds blowing in toward the low-pressure center. Areas of low pressure push enormous amounts of air upward, causing air near the ground to rush in from all sides, like air rushing into a vacuum cleaner. Far above the surface, the jet stream, a narrow band of high-speed wind that snakes across the continent, formed a giant curve around the low.

All this was creating a huge counterclockwise swirl in the atmosphere typical of big storms. On one side of the swirl warm, moist air from the Gulf of Mexico was being drawn north. On the backside, frigid air was coming down out of Canada.

The National Severe Storm Forecast Center in Kansas City, Missouri, began plotting where these two air masses would meet. Chances were good that the collision would result in a powerful cold front, producing violent thunderstorms and tornadoes.

Local weather stations from Texas to Iowa and east were alerted. A Severe Weather Watch was announced on radio and television to warn that bad weather was possible. Forecasters checked their radar screens constantly, looking for signs of the front. Everyone waited.

The afternoon was warm and humid when a line of towering clouds appeared across the Texas plains. Lightning flashed in the distance. Soon the rumble of thunder was heard. Airports closed. Dogs whined and hid under beds. The clouds came on, churning and billowing. An eerie darkness fell. Then slashing winds hit. Rain and hail poured down. The cold front raced through. Temperatures dropped sharply.

All along the front, police and other spotters watched for tornadoes. Tornadoes are violent whirlwinds, funnel-shaped clouds that may spiral down from thunderstorms. They are extremely dangerous. The spotters watched anxiously, for they knew that weather radar can pinpoint thunderstorms but usually cannot "see" tornadoes. Eyes are better for that.

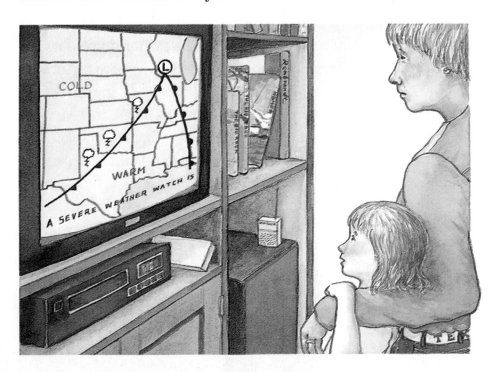

Suddenly a tornado was sighted heading for Paris, Texas. Sirens blew. A Tornado Warning was broadcast. Families rushed for the nearest bathroom, closet, or basement shelter.

The tornado hit with the roar of a freight train. Houses and churches were torn apart. Trees shattered. Cars were tossed around.

The funnel cloud stayed down for twenty minutes, ripping a path through the city two blocks wide and five miles long. Most of the people in the path survived, though many were injured. Ten people were killed.

Tornado Areas April 2-3

More than eighty tornadoes touched down that afternoon and night in Texas, Oklahoma, Arkansas, Missouri, and other states as far east as Ohio. Even with the warning broadcasts, over thirty people died, and the damage was horrendous. The United States has more tornadoes than anyplace else in the world, but this was the worst outbreak since 1974.

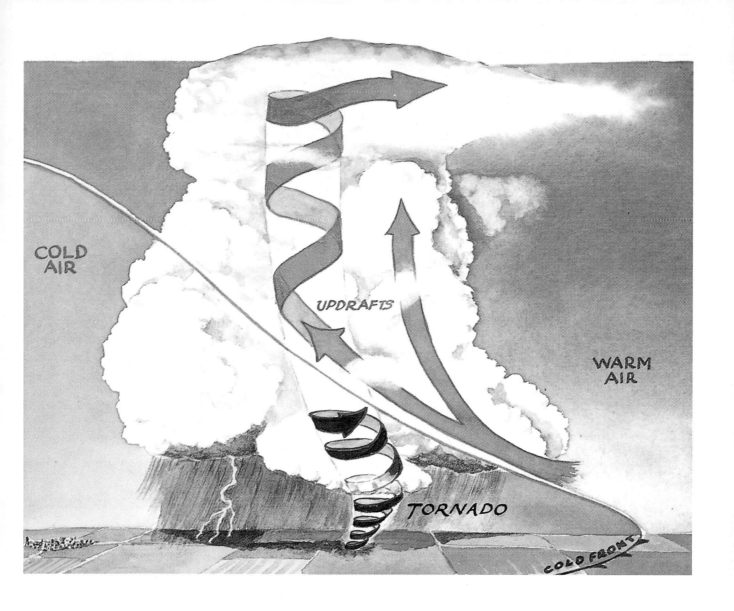

Tornadoes usually form just behind a cold front as the wedge of cold, dense air pushes in, forcing the warm, moist air to rise very quickly. This produces strong updraft winds and huge thunderclouds.

If an updraft begins to spin, it may set off a tornado. Exactly what causes the spinning is not completely understood, but once the twister is formed, it sucks in air, dirt, and anything else it touches with winds of over two hundred miles an hour. Boards, bricks, and glass become deadly flying missiles. Huge funnel clouds can even lift railroad cars.

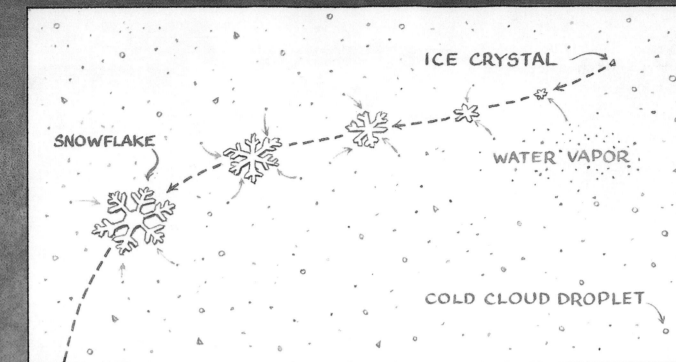

ICE CRYSTAL

SNOWFLAKE

WATER VAPOR

COLD CLOUD DROPLET

RAINDROP

When the front passed, the tornadoes stopped, but thunderstorms continued throughout the South. Heavy rain drenched Alabama and Georgia. Hail the size of golf balls dented cars and broke windows in Kentucky.

Rain and hail are formed from the moisture in clouds, but they are not simply falling bits of mist and ice. The water droplets and tiny ice crystals that make up clouds are far too small to fall by themselves, and so they remain suspended in air like fog.

Surprisingly, most raindrops start out as snowflakes. High in the cloud where the air is very cold, ice crystals gradually grow into snowflakes that are heavy enough to fall. The snowflakes then melt, if it is warm near the ground, and become raindrops. A raindrop is about a million times larger than a cloud droplet.

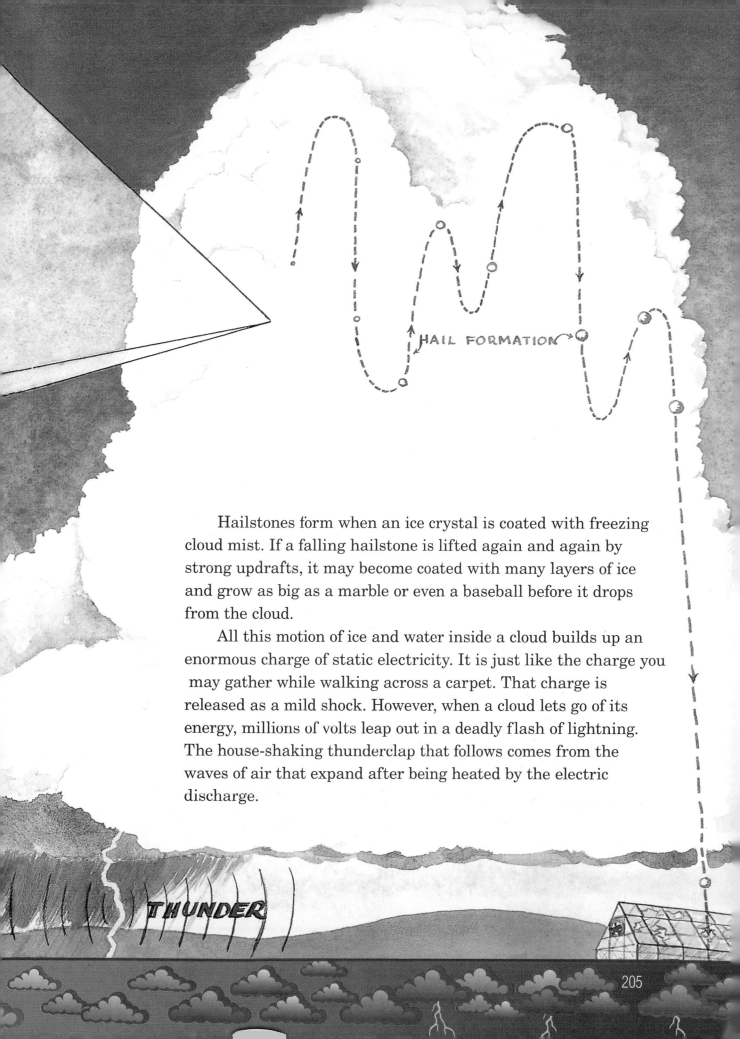

HAIL FORMATION

Hailstones form when an ice crystal is coated with freezing cloud mist. If a falling hailstone is lifted again and again by strong updrafts, it may become coated with many layers of ice and grow as big as a marble or even a baseball before it drops from the cloud.

All this motion of ice and water inside a cloud builds up an enormous charge of static electricity. It is just like the charge you may gather while walking across a carpet. That charge is released as a mild shock. However, when a cloud lets go of its energy, millions of volts leap out in a deadly flash of lightning. The house-shaking thunderclap that follows comes from the waves of air that expand after being heated by the electric discharge.

THUNDER

For the next three days the huge mass of Arctic air behind the cold front brought more snow and high winds to the Midwest. Driving became very dangerous. Five hundred travelers were stranded in Michigan and had to spend the night in school gyms. Rush-hour traffic in Chicago was a tangle of accidents.

The great swirl of clouds around the low was clearly visible from space, and as the swirl drifted east, clear skies and intense cold followed it. With no blanket of clouds at night, the earth rapidly lost heat to outer space. Low temperature records were set from Idaho to the Appalachians. And still the storm was not through!

Tuesday, April 6, was opening day for the baseball season, and the New York Yankees were scheduled to play at home. The main storm center was now out at sea, but still the forecast was not good. Cold air continued to pour in, forming new lows over Pennsylvania and the New Jersey coast.

Around three in the morning, snow began to fall softly on New York City. In the Northeast the great snowstorms often begin very quietly. Soon the wind picked up. By noon it was a howling blizzard. Traffic snarled. Trains were delayed. The pace of the great city slowed to a sloppy walk.

Over a foot of snow fell in New York before the storm moved on to Boston. It was the first blizzard ever to hit New York City in April. The Yankee game was delayed for four days. Many adults said bad things about the weather, but few kids complained. They all had a day off from school.

The big storm finally ended. Snow turned to slush and melted away. People cleaned up their towns. Spring returned. Birds began traveling north again, and the evenings lost their chill.

The storm is just a memory now, but every spring the cycle repeats itself. Warm air from the south meets with cold Arctic air, triggering storms of all sizes and giving the United States one of the most varied and exciting climates on earth.

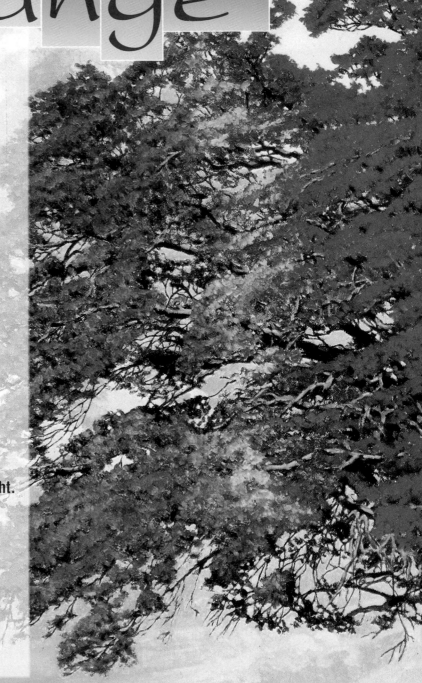

Change

The summer
still hangs
heavy and sweet
with sunlight
as it did last year.

The autumn
still comes
showering gold and crimson
as it did last year.

The winter
still stings
clean and cold and white
as it did last year.

The spring
still comes
like a whisper in the dark night.

It is only I
who have changed.

Charlotte Zolotow

Winning
Attitudes

the MARBLE

by Gary Soto

Illustrated by Ken Spengler

Lupe Medrano, a shy girl who spoke in whispers, was the school's spelling bee champion, winner of the reading contest at the public library three summers in a row, blue ribbon awardee in the science fair, the top student at her piano recital, and the playground grand champion in chess. She was a straight-A student and—not counting kindergarten, when she had been stung by a wasp—never missed one day of elementary school. She had received a small trophy for this honor and had been congratulated by the mayor.

But though Lupe had a razor-sharp mind, she could not make her body, no matter how much she tried, run as fast as the other girls'. She begged her body to move faster, but could never beat anyone in the fifty-yard dash.

The truth was that Lupe was no good in sports. She could not catch a pop-up or figure out in which direction to kick the soccer ball. One time she kicked the ball at her own goal and scored a point for the other team. She was no good at baseball or basketball either, and even had a hard time making a hula hoop stay on her hips.

It wasn't until last year, when she was eleven years old, that she learned how to ride a bike. And even then she had to use training wheels. She could walk in the swimming pool but couldn't swim, and chanced roller skating only when her father held her hand.

"I'll never be good at sports," she fumed one rainy day as she lay on her bed gazing at the shelf her father had made to hold her awards. "I wish I could win something, anything, even marbles."

At the word "marbles," she sat up. "That's it. Maybe I could be good at playing marbles." She hopped out of bed and rummaged through the closet until she found a can full of her brother's marbles. She poured the rich glass treasure on her bed and picked five of the most beautiful marbles.

She smoothed her bedspread and practiced shooting, softly at first so that her aim would be accurate. The marble rolled from her thumb and clicked against the targeted marble. But the target wouldn't budge. She tried

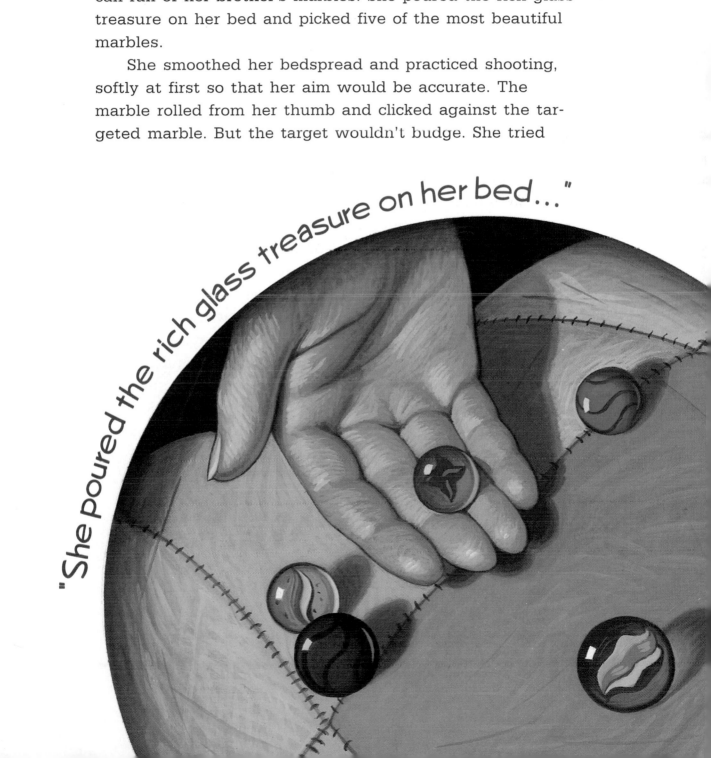

"She poured the rich glass treasure on her bed..."

"...the bedspread was slowing the marbles."

again and again. Her aim became accurate, but the power from her thumb made the marble move only an inch or two. Then she realized that the bedspread was slowing the marbles. She also had to admit that her thumb was weaker than the neck of a newborn chick.

She looked out the window. The rain was letting up, but the ground was too muddy to play. She sat cross-legged on the bed, rolling her five marbles between her palms. Yes, she thought, I could play marbles, and marbles is a sport. At that moment she realized that she had only two weeks to practice. The playground championship, the same one her brother had entered the previous year, was coming up. She had a lot to do.

To strengthen her wrists, she decided to do twenty push-ups on her fingertips, five at a time. "One, two, three . . ." she groaned. By the end of the first set she was breathing hard, and her muscles burned from exhaustion. She did one more set and decided that was enough push-ups for the first day.

She squeezed a rubber eraser one hundred times, hoping it would strengthen her thumb. This seemed to work because the next day her thumb was sore. She could hardly hold a marble in her hand, let alone send it flying with power. So Lupe rested that day and listened to her brother, who gave her tips on how to shoot: get low, aim with one eye, and place one knuckle on the ground.

"Think 'eye and thumb'—and let it rip!" he said.

After school the next day she left her homework in her backpack and practiced three hours straight, taking time only to eat a candy bar for energy. With a popsicle stick, she drew an odd-shaped circle and tossed in four marbles. She used her shooter, a milky agate with hypnotic swirls, to blast them. Her thumb *had* become stronger.

After practice, she squeezed the eraser for an hour. She ate dinner with her left hand to spare her shooting hand and said nothing to her parents about her dreams of athletic glory.

Practice, practice, practice. Squeeze, squeeze, squeeze. Lupe got better and beat her brother and Alfonso, a neighbor kid who was supposed to be a champ.

"Man, she's bad!" Alfonso said. "She can beat the other girls for sure. I think."

The weeks passed quickly. Lupe worked so hard that one day, while she was drying dishes, her mother asked why her thumb was swollen.

"It's muscle," Lupe explained. "I've been practicing for the marbles championship."

"You, honey?" Her mother knew Lupe was no good at sports.

"Yeah. I beat Alfonso, and he's pretty good."

That night, over dinner, Mrs. Medrano said, "Honey, you should see Lupe's thumb."

"Huh?" Mr. Medrano said, wiping his mouth and looking at his daughter.

"Show your father."

"Do I have to?" an embarrassed Lupe asked.

"Go on, show your father."

Reluctantly, Lupe raised her hand and flexed her thumb. You could see the muscle.

The father put down his fork and asked, "What happened?"

"Dad, I've been working out. I've been squeezing an eraser."

"Why?"

"I'm going to enter the marbles championship."

Her father looked at her mother and then back at his daughter. "When is it, honey?"

"This Saturday. Can you come?"

The father had been planning to play racquetball with a friend Saturday, but he said he would be there. He knew his daughter thought she was no good at sports and he wanted to encourage her. He even rigged some lights in the backyard so she could practice after dark. He squatted with one knee on the ground, entranced by the sight of his daughter easily beating her brother.

" ...Lupe raised her hand and flexed her thumb."

The day of the championship began with a cold blustery sky. The sun was a silvery light behind slate clouds.

"I hope it clears up," her father said, rubbing his hands together as he returned from getting the newspaper. They ate breakfast, paced nervously around the house waiting for 10:00 to arrive, and walked the two blocks to the playground (though Mr. Medrano wanted to drive so Lupe wouldn't get tired). She signed up and was assigned her first match on baseball diamond number three.

Lupe, walking between her brother and her father, shook from the cold, not nerves. She took off her mittens, and everyone stared at her thumb. Someone asked, "How can you play with a broken thumb?" Lupe smiled and said nothing.

She beat her first opponent easily, and felt sorry for the girl because she didn't have anyone to cheer for her. Except for her sack of marbles, she was all alone. Lupe invited the girl, whose name was Rachel, to stay with them. She smiled and said, "OK." The four of them walked to a card table in the middle of the outfield, where Lupe was assigned another opponent.

She also beat this girl, a fifth-grader named Yolanda, and asked her to join their group. They proceeded to more matches and more wins, and soon there was a crowd of people following Lupe to the finals to play a girl in a baseball cap. This girl seemed dead serious. She never even looked at Lupe.

"I don't know, Dad, she looks tough."

Rachel hugged Lupe and said, "Go get her."

"You can do it," her father encouraged. "Just think of the marbles, not the girl, and let your thumb do the work."

The other girl broke first and earned one marble. She missed her next shot, and Lupe, one eye closed, her thumb quivering with energy, blasted two marbles out of the circle but missed her next shot. Her opponent earned two more before missing. She stamped her foot and said

"It was now six to six..."

"Shoot!" The score was three to two in favor of Miss Baseball Cap.

The referee stopped the game. "Back up, please, give them room," he shouted. Onlookers had gathered too tightly around the players.

Lupe then earned three marbles and was set to get her fourth when a gust of wind blew dust in her eyes and she missed badly. Her opponent quickly scored two marbles, tying the game, and moved ahead six to five on a lucky shot. Then she missed, and Lupe, whose eyes felt scratchy when she blinked, relied on instinct and thumb muscle to score the tying point. It was now six to six, with only three marbles left. Lupe blew her nose and studied the angles. She dropped to one knee, steadied her hand, and shot so hard she cracked two marbles from the circle. She was the winner!

"I did it!" Lupe said under her breath. She rose from her knees, which hurt from bending all day, and hugged her father. He hugged her back and smiled.

Everyone clapped, except Miss Baseball Cap, who made a face and stared at the ground. Lupe told her she was a great player, and they shook hands. A newspaper photographer took pictures of the two girls standing shoulder-to-shoulder, with Lupe holding the bigger trophy.

Lupe then played the winner of the boys' division, and after a poor start beat him eleven to four. She blasted the marbles, shattering one into sparkling slivers of glass. Her opponent looked on glumly as Lupe did what she did best—win!

"...she displayed her trophies..."

The head referee and the President of the Fresno Marble Association stood with Lupe as she displayed her trophies for the newspaper photographer. Lupe shook hands with everyone, including a dog who had come over to see what the commotion was all about.

That night, the family went out for pizza and set the two trophies on the table for everyone in the restaurant to see. People came up to congratulate Lupe, and she felt a little embarrassed, but her father said the trophies belonged there.

Back home, in the privacy of her bedroom, she placed the trophies on her shelf and was happy. She had always earned honors because of her brains, but winning in sports was a new experience. She thanked her tired thumb. "You did it, thumb. You made me champion." As its reward, Lupe went to the bathroom, filled the bathroom sink with warm water, and let her thumb swim and splash as it pleased. Then she climbed into bed and drifted into a hard-won sleep.

meet gary Soto

Gary Soto grew up in Fresno, California—the town where "The Marble Champ" takes place—in the agricultural Central Valley. Many of the other stories in his book *Baseball in April and Other Stories* are also based on his youth and Mexican heritage. In simple, realistic language, he tells how it feels to grow up Chicano in California. Soto has also begun making short films based on his stories.

Though he hopes his work speaks to everybody, Soto has a specific audience in mind. "My target is Mexican children," he says. "It's really to make them feel that their story is as important as anyone else's story."

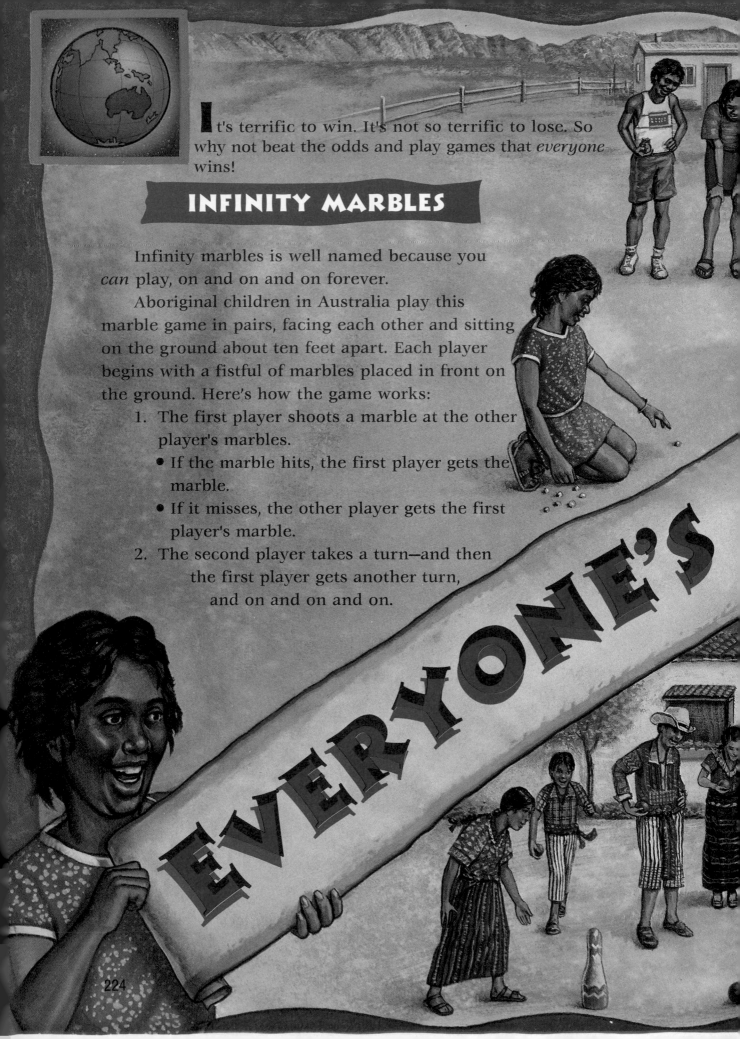

It's terrific to win. It's not so terrific to lose. So why not beat the odds and play games that *everyone* wins!

INFINITY MARBLES

Infinity marbles is well named because you *can* play, on and on and on forever.

Aboriginal children in Australia play this marble game in pairs, facing each other and sitting on the ground about ten feet apart. Each player begins with a fistful of marbles placed in front on the ground. Here's how the game works:

1. The first player shoots a marble at the other player's marbles.
   - If the marble hits, the first player gets the marble.
   - If it misses, the other player gets the first player's marble.
2. The second player takes a turn—and then the first player gets another turn, and on and on and on.

EVERYONE'S

A WINNER!

PIN

To play this game, you need:

- several players to make up your team
- one ball for *each* team member
- a throwing line—even a scratch in the dirt—behind which the team members stand
- a wooden pin, set up at an agreed-upon distance from the throwing line

Here's how the Indian children in Guatemala play Pin:

1. The first player rolls a ball (the lead ball) at the pin.
2. The other team members take turns rolling their balls at the lead ball to make it knock down the pin.
3. The player whose ball makes the lead ball knock down the pin gets to throw the lead ball in the next game.

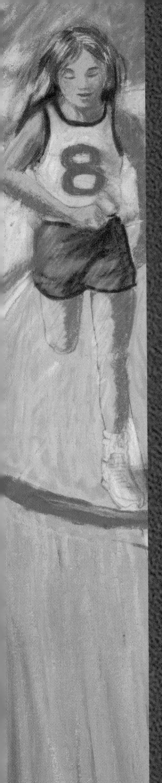

CRYSTAL ROWE
(TRACK STAR)

by Mel Glenn

Allthegirlsarebunched
togetheratthestarting
_____ line _____

But

When the gun goes off

I
J
U
M
P

out ahead and
never look back
and
HIT
the

__T__A__P__E__

a
WINNER!

Try, Try Again

T. H. Palmer

'Tis a lesson you should heed,
    Try, try again;
If at first you don't succeed,
    Try, try again;
Then your courage should appear,
For, if you will persevere,
You will conquer, never fear;
    Try, try again.

BREAKER'S BRIDGE

by Laurence Yep

illustrated by David Wisniewski

There was once a boy who was always breaking things. He didn't do it on purpose. He just had very clumsy hands. No matter how careful he tried to be, he always dropped whatever he picked up. His family soon learned not to let him set the table or send him for eggs. Everyone in the village called him Breaker.

But Breaker was as clever as he was clumsy. When he grew up, he managed to outlive his nickname. He could design a bridge to cross any obstacle. No canyon was too wide. No river was too deep. Somehow the clever man always found a way to bridge them all.

Eventually the emperor heard about this clever builder and sent for him.

"There is a river in the hills," the emperor said to him. "Everyone tells me it is too swift and deep to span. So I have to go a long way around it to get to my hunting palace. But you're famous for doing the impossible."

The kneeling man bowed his head to the floor. "So far I have been lucky. But there is always a first time when you can't do something."

The emperor frowned. "I didn't think you were lazy like my other bridge builders. You can have all the workers and all the materials you need. Build

the bridge and you'll have your weight in gold. Fail and I'll have your head."

There was nothing for Breaker to do but thank the emperor and leave. He went right away to see the river. He had to take a steep road that wound upward through the hills toward the emperor's hunting palace.

It was really more than a palace, for it included a park the size of a district, and only the emperor could hunt the wildlife. The road to it had to snake through high, steep mountains. Although the road was well kept, the land became wilder and wilder. Pointed boulders thrust up like fangs, and the trees grew in twisted, writhing clumps.

Breaker became uneasy. "This is a place that doesn't like people very much."

The road twisted suddenly to the left when it came to a deep river gorge. On the other side of the gorge, the many trees of the palace looked like a dark-green sea. The yellow-tiled roofs looked like golden rafts floating on its top. Dark mountains, their tops capped with snow all year round, loomed behind the palace like monstrous guards.

Breaker carefully sidled to the edge of the gorge and looked down. Far below, he saw the river. When the snow melted in the distant mountains, the water flowed together to form this river. It raced faster than a tiger and stronger than a thousand buffalo. When it splashed against a rock, it threw up sheets of white spray like an ocean wave.

Breaker shook his head in dismay. "The emperor might as well have commanded me to bridge the sea."

But his failure would mean the loss of his head, so the next day Breaker set to work. The river was too wide to span with a simple bridge. Breaker would have to construct two piers in the middle of the river. The piers would support the bridge like miniature stone islands.

From the forests of the south came huge logs that were as tough and heavy as iron. From the quarries of the west came large, heavy stones of granite. The workers braved the cold water to sink the logs in the muddy riverbed. Breaker had to change the teams of workers often. The cold numbed anyone who stayed too long in the river.

Once the logs had been pounded into the mud, he tried to set the stones on top of the logs. But the river did not want to be tamed. It bucked and fought like a herd of wild stallions. It crushed the piles of stones into pebbles. It dug up the logs and smashed them against the rocky sides until they were mounds of soggy toothpicks.

Over the next month, Breaker tried every trick he knew; and each time the river defeated him. With each new failure, Breaker suspected more and more that he had met his match. The river flowed hard and strong and fast like the lifeblood of the earth itself. Breaker might as well have tried to tame the mountains.

In desperation, he finally tried to build a dam to hold back the river while he constructed the biggest and strongest piers yet. As he was supervising the construction, an official came by from the emperor.

"This bridge has already cost a lot of money," he announced to the workers. "What do you have to show for it?"

Breaker pointed to the two piers. They rose like twin towers toward the top of the gorge. "With a little luck, the emperor will have his bridge."

Suddenly, they heard a distant roar. The official looked up at the sky. "It sounds like thunder, but I don't see a cloud in the sky."

Breaker cupped his hands around his mouth to amplify his voice. "Get out," he shouted to his men. "Get out. The river must have broken our dam."

His men slipped and slid on the muddy riverbed, but they all managed to scramble out just as a wall of water rolled down the gorge. The river swept around the two piers, pulling and tugging at the stones.

Everyone held their breath. Slowly the two piers began to rock back and forth on their foundations until they toppled over with a crash into the river. Water splashed in huge sheets over everyone, and when the spray finally fell back into the river, not one sign of the piers remained.

"All this time and all this money, and you have nothing to show for it." The official took a soggy yellow envelope from his sleeve.

Breaker and the other workers recognized the imperial color of the emperor. They instantly dropped to their knees and bowed their heads.

Then, with difficulty, Breaker opened the damp envelope and unfolded the letter. "In one month," it said, "I will have a bridge or I will have your head." It was sealed in red ink with the official seal of the emperor.

Breaker returned the letter and bowed again. "I'll try," he promised.

"You will do more than try," the official snapped. "You will build that bridge for the emperor. Or the executioner will be sharpening his sword." And the official left.

Wet and cold and tired, Breaker made his way along a path toward the room he had taken in an inn. It was getting late, so the surrounding forest was black with shadows. As he walked, Breaker tried to come up with some kind of new scheme, but the dam had been his last resort. In a

month's time, he would feel the "kiss" of the executioner's sword.

"Hee, hee, hee," an old man laughed in a creaky voice that sounded like feet on old, worn steps. "You never liked hats anyway. Now you'll have an excuse not to wear them."

Breaker turned and saw a crooked old man sitting by

the side of the road. He was
dressed in rags, and a gourd
hung from a strap against
his hip. One leg was shorter
than the other.

"How did you know that,
old man?" Breaker wondered.

"Hee, hee, hee. I know a
lot of things: the softness of
clouds underneath my feet,
the sound of souls inside
bodies." And he shook his

gourd so that it rattled as if
there were beans inside. "It
is the law of the universe
that all things must change;
and yet Nature hates change
the most of all."

"The river certainly fits
that description." Although
he was exhausted and wor-
ried, Breaker squatted down
beside the funny old man.
"But you better get inside,

old man. Night's coming on and it gets cold up in these mountains."

"Can't." The old man nodded to his broken crutch.

Breaker looked all around. It was growing dark, and his stomach was aching with hunger. But he couldn't leave the old man stranded in the mountains, so Breaker took out his knife. "If I make you a new crutch, can you reach your home?"

"If you make me a crutch, we'll all have what we want." It was getting so dim that Breaker could not be sure if the old man smiled.

Although it was hard to see, Breaker found a tall, straight sapling and tried to trim the branches from its sides; but being Breaker, he dropped his knife several times and lost it twice among the old leaves on the forest floor. He also cut each of his fingers. By the time he was ready to cut down the sapling, he couldn't even see it. Of course, he cut his fingers even more. And just as he was trimming

the last branch from the sapling, he cut the sapling right in two.

He tried to carve another sapling and broke that one. It was so dark by now that he could not see at all. He had to find the next sapling by feel. This time he managed to cut it down and began to trim it. But halfway through he dropped his knife and broke it. "He'll just have to take it as it is," Breaker said.

When he finally emerged from the forest, the moon had come out. Sucking on his cut fingers, Breaker presented the new crutch to the funny old man.

The old man looked at the branches that grew from the sides of his new crutch. "A little splintery."

Breaker angrily took his cut finger from his mouth. "Don't insult someone who's doing you a favor."

The crooked old man lifted his right arm with difficulty and managed to bring it behind his neck. "Keep that in mind yourself." He began to rub the back of his neck.

Breaker thrust the crutch at the old man. "Here, old man. This is what you wanted."

But the old man kept rubbing the back of his neck. "Rivers are like people: Every now and then, they have to be reminded that change is the law that binds us all."

"It's late. I'm tired and hungry and I have to come up with a new plan. Here's your crutch." And Breaker laid the crutch down beside the old man.

But before Breaker could straighten, the old man's left hand shot out and caught hold of Breaker's wrist. The old man's grip was as strong as iron. "Even the least word from me will remind that river of the law."

Breaker tried to pull away, but as strong as he was, he could not break the old man's hold. "Let me go."

But the crooked old man lowered his right hand so that Breaker could see that he had rubbed some of the dirt and sweat from his skin.

"We are all bound together," the old man murmured, "and by the same laws." He murmured that over and over until he was almost humming like a bee. At the same time, his fingers quickly rolled the dirt and sweat into two round little pellets.

Frightened, Breaker could only stare at the old man. "Ar-ar-are you some mountain spirit?" he stammered.

The old man turned Breaker's palm upward and deposited the two little pellets on it. Then he closed Breaker's fingers over them. "Leave one of these at each spot where you want a pier. Be sure not to lose them."

"Yes, all right, of course," Breaker promised quickly.

The old man picked up the crutch and thrust himself up from the ground. "Then you'll have what you want too." And he hobbled away quickly.

Breaker kept hold of the pellets until he reached the inn. Once he was among the inn's bright lights and could smell a hot meal, he began to laugh at himself. "You've let the emperor's letter upset you so much that you let a harmless old man scare you."

Even so, Breaker didn't throw away the pellets but put them in a little pouch. And the next morning when he returned to the gorge, he took along the pouch.

The canyon widened at one point so that there was a small beach. Breaker kept his supplies of stone and logs there. Figuring that he had nothing to lose, Breaker walked down the steep path. Then he took the boat and rowed out onto the river.

As he sat in the bobbing boat, he thought of the funny old man again. "You and I," he said to the river, "are both part of the same scheme of things. And it's time you faced up to it."

Although it was difficult to row at the same time, he got out the pouch with the two pellets. "I must be even crazier than that old man." He opened the pouch and shook one of the pellets into his hand.

When he was by the spot where the first pier should be, Breaker threw the pellet in. For a moment, nothing happened. There was only the sound of his oars slapping at the water.

And suddenly the surface began to boil. Frantically, he tried to row away, but the water began to whirl and whirl around in circles. Onshore, the workers shouted and ran to higher ground as waves splashed over the logs and stones.

From beneath the river came loud thumps and thuds and the grinding of stone on stone. A rock appeared above the surface. The water rose in another

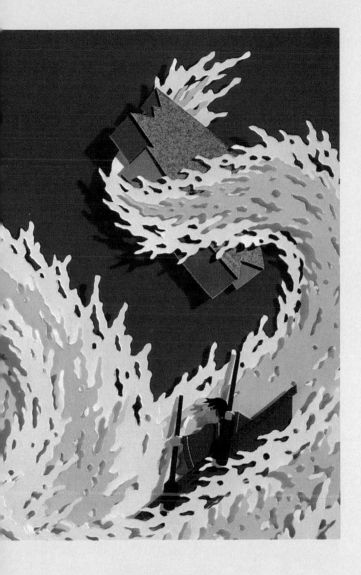

wave. On top of the wave another stone floated as if it were a block of wood. The river laid the first stone by the second.

Open-mouthed, Breaker watched the river lay stone after stone. The watery arms reached higher and higher until the first pier rose to the top of the gorge.

As the waters calmed, Breaker eagerly rowed the boat over to the second spot. At the same time that he tried to row enough to keep himself in the right place, Breaker reached for the pouch and opened it.

But in his hurry, his clumsy fingers crushed part of the pellet. He threw the remainder of the pellet into the water and then shook out the contents of the pouch. But this time, the river only swirled and rippled.

Breaker leaned over the side and peered below. He could just make out the pale, murky shape of a mound, but that was all. Even so, Breaker wasn't upset. His workers could easily build a second pier and meet the emperor's deadline.

So Breaker finished the bridge, and that summer the emperor reached his hunting palace with ease. When the emperor finished hunting and returned to his capital, he showered Breaker with gold and promised him all the work he could ever want.

However, winter brought deep snows once again to the mountains. That spring, when the snow thawed, the river grew strong and wild again. It roared down the gorge and smashed against the first pier. But the first pier was solid as a mountain.

However, the second pier had not been built with magic. The river swept away the second pier as if it were nothing but twigs.

The bridge was repaired before the summer hunting, but the emperor angrily summoned Breaker to his hunting palace. "You were supposed to build a bridge for me," the emperor declared.

"Hee, hee, hee," laughed a creaky old voice. "He did, but you didn't say how long it was supposed to stay up."

Breaker turned around and saw it was the crooked old man. He was leaning on the crutch that Breaker had made for him. "How did you get here?" he asked the old man. But from the corner of his eye, he could see all the court officials kneeling down. And when Breaker looked back at the throne, he saw even the emperor kneeling.

"How can we serve you and the other eight immortals?" the emperor asked the crooked old man.

Meet
LAURENCE YEP

"We are all bound by the same laws," the old man croaked again, and then vanished.

And then Breaker knew the old man for what he truly was—a saint and a powerful magician.

So the emperor spared Breaker and sent him to build other projects all over China. And the emperor never regretted that he had let Breaker keep his head. But every year, the river washed away part of the bridge and every year it was rebuilt. And so things change and yet do not change.

Laurence Yep's first published story was about a nonhuman, written from that character's viewpoint. This probably wasn't difficult for someone who felt "different" for most of his childhood. Yep, who is Chinese American, grew up in an African-American neighborhood in San Francisco. He went to school in Chinatown, but he felt like an outsider there, too, because he could not speak Chinese.

Even the books Yep could find to read were not about Chinese Americans like himself. So he turned to science fiction and fantasy. "In those books, children were taken to other lands and other worlds where they had to learn strange customs and languages," says Yep, "and that was something I did every time I got on and off the bus."

Years later, Yep began to write the stories for which he has won so many awards. The first, *Dragonwings*, described the United States in the early 1900s through the eyes of a newly arrived Chinese boy. "Breaker's Bridge" is from *The Rainbow People*, a book of Chinese tales. Yep still writes science fiction as well.

SUPER SHAPE

The Alcántara (al-KAN-tar-uh) Bridge in Spain was built in the year 98—and is still used today. Tall arches held up the bridge all these years. And the stones in each arch hang together without sticky cement! What keeps them together? Their shape!

Stones in an arch can't fall easily because they hold each other up. Check out the *keystone* — the big block in the top of each arch above. Look closely, and you'll see that the top of a keystone is a little wider than the bottom. This wedge shape keeps the stone from falling down. Instead, it presses out on the stones next to it. In the same way, the other stones push on the ones below

them, and the bottom one presses on the stone pillar. This is why the arch stands up so well to *compression* (pressing) from above. In fact, the arch is one of the strongest shapes in the world.

TRASH TOWERS

The famous Brooklyn Bridge in New York City was built on a garbage dump! Workers climbed into special underwater boxes to dig at the bottom of the East River. One day, they smelled a horrible stink. Some even passed out! They had dug into a dumping spot for city garbage—at the bottom of the river.

Why were they digging to make a superhigh bridge? To find rock, so the towers could rest on something solid. Steel cables hang from the towers, and the road hangs from the cables. (This is called a *suspension bridge*.) That's a lot of weight hanging down! The cables can take it—steel stands up to a lot of *tension* (pulling).

But the towers wouldn't stand if they were resting on the soft river floor—or on garbage!

D G E S

by Laura Allen

OUT-OF-SIGHT BRIDGE

The longest bridge in the world stretches nearly 39 km (24 mi) across Lake *Pontchartrain* (PONT-shur-train) in Louisiana. It's so long that if you stand in the center of the bridge, you can barely see land at all!

To stretch that far, the roadway rests on hundreds of concrete piles, or posts. Not all bridges can use piles. The water might be too rough—and could knock the piles down. Or large boats might need to pass under the bridge. Luckily, Lake Pontchartrain is calm. And the bridge has a drawbridge, so big boats can pass.

FLOATING BRIDGE

No part of this bridge in Mombasa, Kenya, ever rests on the ground. Instead, the bridge floats on *pontoons*, floating pieces of hollowed-out concrete. The pontoons are chained to concrete blocks in the river bottom, so the bridge won't float downstream. Pontoons are handy when the sides and bottom of a river are too soft to hold a bridge.

Why does some concrete sink, while other concrete floats? A solid block of concrete will sink because it's *denser* than water. (That means a cup of concrete weighs more than a cup of water.) But if you hollow out the middle, then air will fill the

block. Concrete and air together are less dense than water. So concrete can float!

247

Mr. Amos Ferguson's folk art painting of four men fishing in the Bahamas was the inspiration for the poem by Eloise Greenfield.

248

TO CATCH A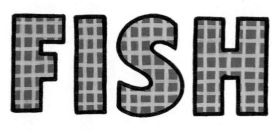

It takes more than a wish
to catch a fish
you take the hook
you add the bait
you concentrate
and then you wait
you wait   you wait
but not a bite
the fish don't have
an appetite
so tell them what
good bait you've got
and how your bait
can hit the spot
this works a whole
lot better than
a wish
if you really
want to catch
a fish

Eloise Greenfield

JILL KREMENTZ

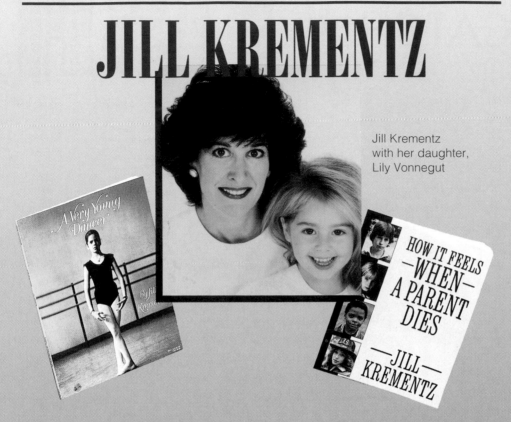

Jill Krementz with her daughter, Lily Vonnegut

Several years ago, Jill Krementz attended the funeral of a friend. There, she spotted her friend's son, a boy of about eight, bravely holding back tears. But when Krementz spoke to him, he let loose a flood of feelings. One of the strongest was his feeling of being alone. "That's when I decided to write *How It Feels When a Parent Dies*," Krementz said. "I wanted kids who have experienced the death of a parent to know that they are not alone."

Since then, Krementz has written three more *How It Feels* books. In each, Krementz tells the children's stories in a writer's voice that sounds like the children's own. For *How It Feels to Fight for Your Life*, she interviewed children who were very ill. Although such a book could be terribly sad, this one isn't. Krementz's interviews bring out the children's hopes, their courage—and their fears.

Krementz has photographed and written children's books on many other topics. The books in her *Very Young* series, including the award-winning *A Very Young Dancer*, look at children working hard to succeed in various fields.

HOW IT FEELS TO
FIGHT FOR YOUR LIFE

Rachel
DeMaster,
age ten

written and photographed
by Jill Krementz

"LAST YEAR
I LEARNED
TO GIVE
MYSELF
INJECTIONS."

I was seven years old when my mom told me I had diabetes. It was a big shock because other than having to go to the bathroom more than usual I was feeling fine. I had gone to my doctor for a regular checkup and he found sugar in my urine. This was a sign that my pancreas wasn't working right.

When my mother explained to me what diabetes was I burst into tears. I was afraid I was going to die. Even after my parents convinced me that this wasn't going to happen, I felt that my life was going to change completely.

My pancreas is in my tummy and it produces insulin. Insulin helps the body to process sugar and turn it into energy. There are two kinds of diabetes, Type One and Type Two. In Type One the pancreas can't produce insulin at all. In Type Two there's nothing wrong with the pancreas but the cells in the rest of the body don't respond to the insulin. Type One used to be called juvenile onset diabetes because it occurred most frequently among kids, but now they've learned that grown-ups can also get Type One. I have Type One, which means that I have to get insulin shots.

I was really lucky that my pediatrician noticed a problem so quickly because we were able to start treatment right away. I was diagnosed in December and a couple of months later, when it was time for me to start taking insulin, I went to the hospital and stayed there for three days. I was in Mount Sinai Hospital in New York City, which has one of the best diabetes programs anywhere. I wasn't sick when I went in—they just wanted to monitor my reaction to the insulin. It was also the best way for them to educate me and my parents. The doctors gave Mom and Dad a book to study and the diabetes team showed them how to take care of me.

While I was in the hospital, a nurse gave me my injections but they also started teaching my parents how to give me my insulin shots and blood tests. I have to have two shots of insulin every day, one when I get up in the morning and one about a half hour before I eat dinner.

I take two different kinds of insulin, a short-acting one and a long-acting one. The amount of each depends on the results of my blood test. I usually have the same amount of the long-acting one and different amounts of the short-acting one, but this also depends on the season and how much exercise I'm planning to get. Things like getting sick also change my insulin dose. For example, when I have the flu I have to take more because my blood sugar level shoots up.

"First, I practiced the whole technique on an old doll."

The first time my mother gave me an insulin shot, I could tell she was really scared. We were both afraid it would hurt. After experimenting with a few different kinds of needles we found one that's so sharp it hardly hurts. Last year I learned to give myself injections. First, I practiced the whole technique on an old doll. In the beginning I was scared that it would hurt more if I did it. Now I'm scared it'll hurt more when my mother does it.

Some people use air guns without a needle for giving insulin. I've heard that the air pressure coming out of the gun hurts as much as getting a needle so I still take injections.

Insulin shots keep the amount of sugar in my blood at the right level but only on a temporary basis. That's why I have to give myself blood tests to make sure everything is okay. The blood test is more annoying than painful—just a tiny little finger prick. The first time I had to have one I was so scared I hid in my father's closet. I sat there behind his shoes and wouldn't come out. My parents talked to me for a while and finally I agreed to let them do the test. I was so nervous that I think I made it hurt more than it should have. Nowadays I'm so used to it that I can do it in the morning without even getting out of bed. I take turns with my fingers. I never use my thumbs or pinkies. I have callouses on my pointer fingers, middle fingers, and ring fingers because I've stuck myself so many times.

In the nurse's office at school I have a special machine that tests my blood for me. If I'm not feeling well I'll go and have a test. My teacher also checks to make sure that if I'm going to exercise I have some Life Savers or juice with me in case I have a low.

Lows happen when you overdo things that keep your blood sugar low, like taking too much insulin or getting too much exercise. When I get a

"... I have a special machine that tests my blood for me."

low I feel shaky and dizzy and blah. Sometimes it gives me a slight headache, too. All I can do is sit. I don't have lows every day but there are days when I have two or three. Usually it depends on how much exercise I'm getting and how the day is going. Sometimes it's hard to distinguish between having a low and feeling crummy. I might go down to the nurse's office and take my blood test and find I'm not low at all.

If I'm having a low and don't do anything for it for a couple of minutes, it won't do any damage. But if I don't get some sugar into my system quickly it can be dangerous. I've never fainted during a low but that's because I always treat it in time. I wear a Medic Alert necklace that tells people I'm an insulin-dependent diabetic. It has phone numbers on it for them to call in case of an emergency. That way, if I'm somewhere alone and I have a problem, people who don't know what's wrong with me will be able to get me help immediately.

My brother, Neil, is great about helping me with my lows. When I'm feeling shaky he'll get me some food so I don't have to get up and move around. He knows that if it's not too bad I should have milk and crackers and that I should drink orange juice if the low is more serious.

For me, the worst part of having diabetes is not being able to eat whatever I want. Unless I'm having a low I can't eat any sugar except the natural type that's in fruit. The sugar that's in candy and cake makes my blood sugar level very high for a long time after I eat it. Once in a while, on

"I GO TO THE SUPERMARKET WITH MY MOTHER AND HELP HER WITH THE SHOPPING."

"MY FAVORITE EXERCISE IS JOGGING WITH MY FATHER."

special occasions like my birthday, I have cake, but I'm basically not supposed to eat sweets. I feel bad when all my friends are eating candy and I can't have any. Neil is very considerate about not eating candy or cookies in front of me. He's older than I am and if he wants to eat sweets he usually waits until after I've gone to bed. There's one good thing about not eating sugar, which is that I don't have any cavities! My dentist is really proud of me.

On Halloween, my parents and I go trick or treating like everyone else, but since I can't eat the candy my parents buy it from me. They give me five cents for every piece of candy I get and I buy myself a stuffed animal. I have a great collection now. Neil used to eat all of my candy but since he got braces my parents have been buying his candy too.

I would have to say that I miss maple syrup the most of all the things I'm not allowed to eat. I go to the supermarket with my mother and help her with the shopping. We get stuff like diet soda and sugar-free hot chocolate so I don't miss sweet things too much. We spend a long time reading the labels on everything. It's amazing how many foods that don't taste sweet actually have sugar in them.

The worst thing about my diet is that I have to eat so much! Besides breakfast, lunch, and dinner, I have three snacks every day. People with diabetes have to eat a certain amount of carbohydrates and more protein than most people. This is a pain because I'm not a big eater and especially because I don't like protein. The morning snack we have at school is at just the right time for my first snack of the day. I always have milk and a carbohydrate. When I get home at three-thirty my mom gives me chips or crackers. I like Goldfish a lot because they come in lots of flavors. I'm allowed to eat ice cream because it doesn't have that much sugar and it has fat and protein to balance the sugar, so that's what I have for my evening snack. In the morning, after I get my insulin shot, my mother asks me what I want for breakfast. I usually say, "Pig's feet, please." But I end up eating mozzarella cheese or eggs with toast, fruit, and milk. For lunch, I like to have some peanut butter to take care of the protein. And for dinner I have to eat a protein, a starch, a vegetable, a fruit, and a glass of milk. Our family eats together and we all eat the same food.

I have to be extremely punctual about my meals and snacks so that the food can interact with the insulin properly. This means that my parents always make sure I have food and juice with me when we're on a trip in case we get stuck in traffic. I can never sleep late, even on weekends and holidays, because I have to have my blood tested and take my insulin the first thing in the morning. I also have to eat half an hour after my insulin shot.

Exercise is good for everybody but it's especially good for me. This is because if my blood sugar is high I can lower it by exercising instead of taking insulin. When I want to exercise, I tell my mother in advance and she gives me a smaller dose of insulin. I'm one of the most athletic girls in my class and I've won trophies for swimming and soccer. There are lots of famous athletes who have diabetes. The ones I know about are Bill Talbert and Ham Richardson, who are both great tennis

"There are lots of famous athletes who have diabetes."

players. Curt Fraser plays hockey for the Minnesota North Stars. My favorite exercise is jogging with my father. We go to the park near our house and we have a great time together.

Besides my regular pediatrician, I see a special doctor for my diabetes every three months. Her name is Dr. Fredda Ginsberg and she's at Mount Sinai Hospital. People come from all over the world to see her because she's so good. She asks me how much I've been exercising and whether I've been having lots of lows. I also have to have some blood tests when I see her. She lets me take my own blood pressure, which is fun. Dr. Ginsberg is much more than my doctor. She's my friend. I made her a paperweight out of rocks and shells and I crocheted her a little triangle that she pinned on her wall.

Having diabetes hasn't changed my relationships with my friends. However, when I go to play at other people's houses, I usually don't stay for dinner. If I sleep over at a neighbor's house my mom will come over and give me my shot. One time I went to my friend's house and did all my shots myself. Mom gave me instructions about how much insulin I should take so it wasn't hard at all.

Sometimes my friends from school watch to see how I do my blood tests. My brother's friend Mike always covers his eyes and yells "Mommy!" when I stick myself. My friend Dana, who wants to be a scientist when he grows up, likes to keep track of my blood sugar level so that he can tell me how I'm doing.

"Having diabetes hasn't changed my relationships with my friends."

261

I have only one friend with diabetes. Her name is Tory and she's nine years old. Dr. Ginsberg introduced us at the hospital and we go to each other's house. If Tory hadn't taken a blood test with me, I never would have thought she had diabetes. She seems very healthy and she doesn't talk about it very much. I don't like to talk about diabetes either but I do like to know all about it. My family subscribes to a magazine called *Forecast,* which has all the latest news about machines and shots and what's going on medically. The best thing about *Forecast* is the section called "Making Friends." You can write to other people with diabetes. It has separate sections for people of all different ages and there's one section called "Friendly People 12 and Under." I think it would be fun to have a pen pal.

I also think it would be fun to go away to a special sleep-away camp for kids with diabetes. I can't go this year because my parents say I'm not old enough but I hope I can next year.

Sometimes I wonder if when I grow up anyone will want to marry me because my children may have diabetes. I worry that it's hereditary because my grandfather had it. My mother told me that it wouldn't be a problem because when people are really in love, the relationship comes first. My brother says that I shouldn't even be thinking about marriage for another fifteen years. He's right! Besides, by then there may be a cure for diabetes. In the meantime, things are okay because no matter what happens, I'm still me.

"...NO
MATTER WHAT
HAPPENS, I'M
STILL ME."

_____

For POETS

by Al Young

Stay beautiful
but dont stay down underground
   too long
Dont turn into a mole
or a worm
or a root
or a stone

Come on out into the sunlight
Breathe in trees
Knock out mountains
Commune with snakes
& be the very hero of birds

Dont forget to poke your head up
& blink
think
Walk all around
Swim upstream

Dont forget to fly

MEET ROSEBUD YELLOW ROBE

When Rosebud Yellow Robe was young, her parents told her the stories of her people, the Lakota-oyate. Children were expected to memorize the stories and pass them on to their own children.

Yellow Robe, however, has passed these tales on to a much wider audience. Through her books *Tonweya and the Eagles and Other Lakota Indian Tales* and *The Album of the American Indian*, through her appearances on radio and television, and through her visits to schools and libraries, she has shared her stories with the world.

TONWEYA AND THE EAGLES

Native Americans crafted many items of both beauty and utility. At far left, an Oglala Sioux love flute shaped like the bird whose song it echoes. Next to it, a Sioux painted shield. On this page, the teepee of Old Bull is covered with a winter count, and below is shown a scene from High Hawk's Winter Count. A winter count shows a pictorial history of the Sioux.

RETOLD BY
ROSEBUD YELLOW ROBE
ILLUSTRATIONS BY
RICHARD RED OWL

FOREWORD

This story was told to me by my father, Canowicakte. Canowicakte was the boy Chano. Chano was a shortened name used for him. The *c* is pronounced like a *ch,* and the *a* as in *ah.*

My father was born in the southern part of what is now Montana. He lived with his people, the Lakota-oyate, or Sioux nation, roaming the Plains of what are now South Dakota, North Dakota, Nebraska, Wyoming, and Montana. My grandfather was named Tasinagi, or Yellow Robe. He was the son of a hereditary chief. He had won his title to chieftainship as a fearless warrior and great hunter. He too

267

was a leader of his people. My grandmother was named Tahcawin, meaning fawn or female deer. My father was her favorite child because he was her firstborn.

When my father was an infant, my grandfather Tasinagi and my grandmother Tahcawin gave a huge feast for the great men of the tribe in his honor. At that time he was named Canowicakte, meaning kill-in-the-woods. The lobes of both his ears were pierced so that he might wear earrings. Tasinagi gave away two of his best ponies.

Canowicakte spent many hours in the tipi of his grandfather and grandmother. They were his tutors in legends and history of the tribe. He was expected to memorize all these stories so that he in turn would be able to relate them to his children. He was taught respect and reverence for Wakan-tanka, the Great Mystery. He learned of the great and inspiring deeds of the famous chiefs, warriors, and medicine men. He was trained in the old customs of how to make bows and arrows for hunting and for wars. He learned to ride ponies bareback. He learned how to hunt deer and buffalo. He enjoyed wrestling, swimming, and foot-racing with his companions.

Often Canowicakte followed his father on his hunting trips and learned how to kill a deer or elk and drag it back to camp over the prairie.

Living so close to nature he became familiar with the characteristics and habits of the animals and birds. He knew that his people did not kill buffalo or other game for pleasure. They killed only for use.

He saw his first white man when his parents made camp near one of the trading posts along the Missouri River. He was playing near the camp with his brother when he saw a creature coming toward them. It had long fair hair and a beard and was wearing a large hat and a fringed buckskin suit. It carried a musket on its shoulder. Chano couldn't decide if it was a man or an animal of some kind. As the creature came near the boys, Chano decided it was an evil spirit. For the first time in his life his bravery failed him. He screamed, and leaving his brother behind, he ran to his father in the tipi. His father laughed when he heard the story of the evil spirit. He told Chano he had seen a white man. He told the boys not to go

Standing proudly is the father of Chano, Chief Yellow Robe. Above left is the buffalo, a much revered creature of the Sioux. Below it is a Sioux painted buffalo robe featuring a standard sunburst design.

very far away or the white man would kidnap them.

Chano remembered warriors coming back and telling exciting tales of their battles with the white men who promised to stay away from the Lakota-oyate lands but who were always forgetting their promises.

When Chano was about fifteen years old, his dreams of glory in an Indian world vanished. General R. H. Pratt came to the headmen of the tribe and asked them to send one of their children east to a school called Carlisle. He told them that life would change rapidly for them. The buffalo were being killed off and reservations were being formed. He explained that the leaders should know about the new world so different from the Indian way of living.

Against his will my father was given to General Pratt to go away to Carlisle. I have pictures of my father taken when he first arrived at the school with skin clothing, moccasins, and long hair. Then pictures when his clothing had been taken away and he was given the uniform of the school to wear. His hair was cut short. For a long time he thought his mother had died. He had been the first taken to the barber to have his hair cut. Among the Sioux it is a sign of mourning to do so. He thought the other boys were mourning her too, as they had their hair cut.

The children were not allowed to speak their own language, only English, and many weeks had passed by before my father learned that his mother was still alive.

The teachers were very kind to him, but until he learned the language and understood them, he did not trust them. He was a good student. He took part in all the athletics and played on the football team. During the summers he worked on the farms. He also attended the Moody Institute summer school at Northfield, Massachusetts.

Before he left Carlisle, Chauncey Yellow Robe, which was now Canowicakte's name, was chosen to represent the North American Indians at the Congress of Nations at the opening of the World's Columbian Exposition in Chicago.

Canowicakte graduated with honors with the class of 1895. Shortly thereafter he entered government service and spent the greater part of his life at various Indian schools. He was for many

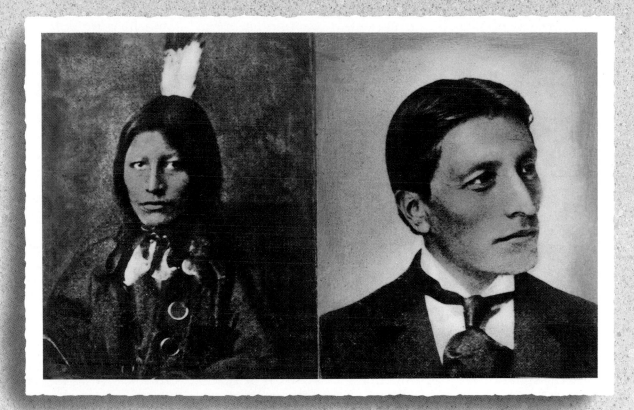

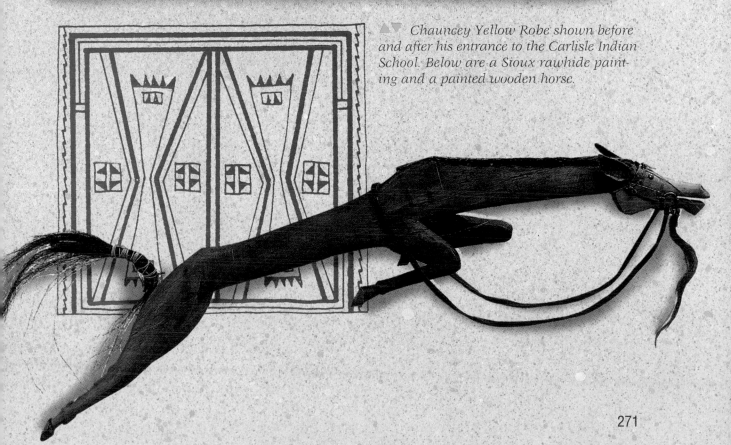

▲▼ *Chauncey Yellow Robe shown before and after his entrance to the Carlisle Indian School. Below are a Sioux rawhide painting and a painted wooden horse.*

years at the large nonreservation boarding school at Rapid City, South Dakota.

At Rapid City my father met my mother. They fell in love and were married and continued living and working there. My father was disappointed that he did not have a son but soon reconciled himself to his three daughters.

We were very lucky to have parents who taught us about our cultural background and who tried as the Lakotas had for generations to tell us the stories they had heard in their youth. After they were dead, I found several of the stories written out in my mother's and father's handwriting.

My father became very well known for his activities, first with The Society of American Indians. He was much sought after by many organizations as a speaker and soon became known as a "bridge between two cultures."

He spoke out many times critically, and in such a way that he was considered a spokesman for the Sioux.

My father presided at the ceremonies at Deadwood, South Dakota, when the Sioux inducted President Calvin Coolidge into the tribe.

Despite his distaste for the way in which the American Indian was depicted in movies he was persuaded to play a leading role in *The Silent Enemy,* written and produced by Douglas Burden, a trustee of the American Museum of Natural History. This was the first movie produced with an all-Indian cast and no professional actors. It was the story of the Ojibways' struggle against their silent enemy, hunger.

During this time he was also running for Congress in his home state of South Dakota.

He did the talking prologue for the picture *The Silent Enemy;* since the prologue was made in New York City studios, it was last to be filmed. During that time he caught a cold that became pneumonia. He died at the Rockefeller Institute Hospital after a brief illness.

Shortly after my father's death President Coolidge, usually a man of few words, wrote a wonderful tribute to him. In part he said, "He represented a trained and intelligent contact between two different races. He was a born leader who realized that the destiny of the Indian is indissolubly bound up with the destiny of our country. His loyalty to his tribe and his people made him a most patriotic American."

TONWEYA AND THE EAGLES

Everyone was excited. It was the Month of Grass Appearing, and the whole camp was busy getting ready to move over the plains to a new home. They would be close to more game and they looked forward to the move. Everyone that is except Chano. He loved this camping spot and already felt lonely for the distant hills.

Tahcawin had packed the parfleche cases with clothing and food and strapped them to a travois made of two trailing poles with a skin net stretched between them. Another travois lay on the ground ready for the new tipi.

Chano was very happy when Tasinagi suggested the three of them ride up to their favorite hills for the last time.

As the three of them rode along, Tasinagi called Chano's attention to the two large birds circling overhead. They were Waŋbli, the eagle. Chano knew they were sacred to his people and that they must never be killed.

He looked at the eagle feather in his father's hair, a sign of bravery, and wondered why it was that the Lakotas as well as many other Indians held Waŋbli, the eagle, in

such great respect. Someday he would ask his father about this.

The two eagles they were watching did not seem afraid of the three travelers. They flew nearer and nearer, swooping down in ever narrowing circles. They seemed to be trying to attract the attention of the travelers.

Suddenly Chano called out, "Look, Ate! The feathers on their wings are tipped with red. I never knew that Waŋbli had red feathers!"

"Are you sure of this, my son?" Tasinagi asked.

"Yes, Father. Both birds had tips of bright red on their wings."

"Tahcawin," said Tasinagi, "our son has been favored by the sight of the sacred birds of Tonweya. Few have seen them and it is a sign of good for him."

"What do you mean, Ate?" asked Chano. "What are the sacred birds of Tonweya?"

"They are the eagles who saved Tonweya's life many, many snows ago. Tonweya was a great chief and a great medicine man."

Chano immediately begged his father to tell him the story. Tasinagi motioned for Chano to ride by his side and began:

"It was the summer when the big ball of fire fell from the sky. A band of Lakotas were camping just about where we are now. Among them was a young man whose name was Tonweya. He was not only good to look upon, but he was a great runner and hunter. He was very brave in the face of danger. Everyone said that someday he would be a chief. Brave and good chiefs are always needed in every tribe.

"One day Tonweya went out hunting. He found a small herd of buffalo grazing near the hills and picking out a young fat cow sent an arrow straight into her heart. While he was skinning the buffalo, he noticed a large eagle circling above him. Watching her flight he saw that she settled on a ledge

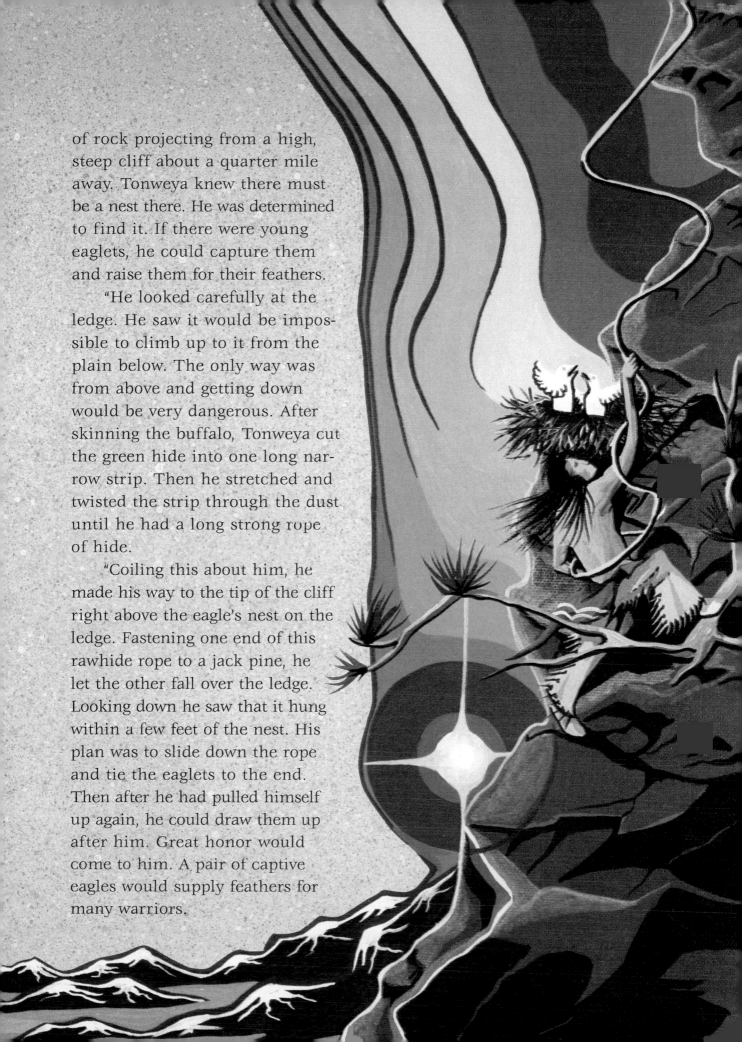

of rock projecting from a high, steep cliff about a quarter mile away. Tonweya knew there must be a nest there. He was determined to find it. If there were young eaglets, he could capture them and raise them for their feathers.

"He looked carefully at the ledge. He saw it would be impossible to climb up to it from the plain below. The only way was from above and getting down would be very dangerous. After skinning the buffalo, Tonweya cut the green hide into one long narrow strip. Then he stretched and twisted the strip through the dust until he had a long strong rope of hide.

"Coiling this about him, he made his way to the tip of the cliff right above the eagle's nest on the ledge. Fastening one end of this rawhide rope to a jack pine, he let the other fall over the ledge. Looking down he saw that it hung within a few feet of the nest. His plan was to slide down the rope and tie the eaglets to the end. Then after he had pulled himself up again, he could draw them up after him. Great honor would come to him. A pair of captive eagles would supply feathers for many warriors.

"Tonweya carefully lowered himself over the edge of the cliff and soon stood on the ledge. There were two beautiful young eaglets in the nest, full feathered, though not yet able to fly. He tied them to his rope and prepared to climb up. But just as he placed his weight on the rope, to his great surprise it fell down beside him. The green hide had been slipping at the knot where he had tied it to the tree; when he pulled on it to go up again, the knot came loose and down came the rope.

"Tonweya realized immediately that he was trapped. Only Wakan-tanka, the Great Mystery, could save him from a slow death by starvation and thirst. He looked below him. There was a sheer drop of many hundreds of feet with not even the slightest projection by which he might climb down. When he tried to climb up, he could find neither handhold nor foothold. Waŋbli had chosen well the place for a nest.

"Despite his brave heart terror gripped Tonweya. He stood looking off in the direction he knew his people to be. He cried out, 'Ma hiyopo! Ma hiyopo! Help me!' but only the echo of his own voice answered.

"As the sun was setting, the mother eagle returned to her nest. She screamed in rage when she saw a man with her eaglets. Round and round she flew. Now and then she would charge with lightning speed toward Tonweya and the young birds. The two eaglets flapped their wings wildly and called out to her. Finally in despair the mother eagle made one more swoop toward her nest, and then screaming defiantly, flew off and disappeared. Night fell and the stars came out. Tonweya was alone on the ledge with the two little birds.

"When the sun came up, Tonweya was very tired. He had not slept during the night. The ledge was so narrow, he was afraid he might roll off if he fell asleep. The sun rose high in the heavens and then started its descent into the west. Soon it would be night. Tonweya looked forward with dread to the lonely vigil he must again keep. He was very hungry and so terribly thirsty.

"The second day Tonweya noticed a small spruce growing in a cleft of the rocks some four feet above him. He tied a piece of his rope to this tree and he fastened the other end around his waist. That way even if he stumbled, he would not fall off the ledge. More important still, he could chance some sleep, which he needed badly.

"The third day passed as the others had; heat, hunger, unquenchable thirst. The hope that some of his people might come in search of him was gone. Even if they came, they would never think of looking for him on the cliffs. The mother of the eaglets did not return. Tonweya's presence had frightened her away.

"By this time the two eaglets, seeing that Tonweya had no intention of hurting them, had made friends with him. They allowed Tonweya to touch them at will. Tonweya could see that they were as hungry as he was, so taking out his knife he cut small pieces from the rawhide rope and fed them. This act of kindness removed the last vestige of fear they might have had. They played all about him. They allowed him to hold them aloft. They flapped their wings bravely as he lifted them toward the sun. As he felt the upward pull of their wings, there came to him an idea. Since he had no wings of his own, why could he not make use of the wings of his eagle brothers? He raised his arms toward the sky and called upon Wakan-tanka for wisdom.

"The night of the third day, the one on which he had fed the eaglets for the first time, was raw and chill. When Tonweya stretched out for what little sleep he could get, he shivered with the cold. As if understanding his need, the two little eaglets left their nest and coming over to where he lay nestled their warm, fluffy bodies close beside him. In a few moments Tonweya was asleep.

"While he was asleep, he dreamed. In his dream Wakan-tanka spoke to him. He told him to be brave, the two eaglets would save him. Tonweya awoke suddenly. The eagles were still beside him. As they felt him move, they nestled even closer to him. He placed his arms around them. He knew that his time to die had not yet come. He would once more see his people. He was no longer afraid.

"For days thereafter Tonweya fed the rawhide rope to his eagle friends. Luckily it was a long rope, for it was, of course, almost a whole buffalo hide. But while the eaglets thrived on it and grew larger and stronger each day, Tonweya grew thinner and weaker. It rained one day and water gathered in the hollows of the rocks on the ledge. Still he was very hungry and thirsty. He tried to think only of caring for the eaglets.

"Each day Tonweya would hold them up by their legs and let them try their wings. Each day the pull on his arms grew stronger. Soon it was so powerful it almost lifted him from his feet. He knew the time was coming for him to put his idea into action. He decided he must do it quickly, for weak as he was he would be unable to do it after a few more days.

"The last of the rawhide was gone, the last bit of water on the ledge was drunk. Tonweya was so weak, he could hardly

stand. With an effort he dragged
himself upright and called his
eagle brothers to him. Standing on
the edge of the ledge he called to
Wakan-tanka for help. He grasped
the eaglets' legs in each hand and
closing his eyes he jumped.

"For a moment he felt himself
falling, falling. Then he felt the
pull on his arms. Opening his eyes
he saw that the two eagles were
flying easily. They seemed to be
supporting his weight with little
effort. In a moment they had
reached the ground. Tonweya lay
there too exhausted, too weak to
move. The eagles remained by his
side guarding him.

"After resting awhile Tonweya
slowly made his way to a little
stream nearby. He drank deeply
of its cool water. A few berries
were growing on the bushes
there. He ate them ravenously.
Strengthened by even this little
food and water, he started off in
the direction of the camp. His
progress was slow, for he was
compelled to rest many times.
Always the eaglets remained by
his side guarding him.

"On the way he passed the
spot where he had killed the buffalo. The coyotes and vultures had
left nothing but bones. However

his bow and arrows were just where he had left them. He managed to kill a rabbit upon which he and his eagle friends feasted. Late in the afternoon he reached the camp, only to find that his people had moved on. It was late. He was very tired so he decided to stay there that night. He soon fell asleep, the two eagles pressing close beside him all night.

"The sun was high in the sky when Tonweya awoke. The long sleep had given him back much strength. After once more giving thanks to Wakan-tanka for his safety he set out after his people. For two days he followed their trail. He lived on the roots and berries he found along the way and what little game he could shoot. He shared everything with his eagle brothers, who followed him. Sometimes they flew overhead, sometimes they walked behind him, and now and then they rested on his shoulders.

"Well along in the afternoon of the second day he caught up with the band. At first they were frightened when they saw him. Then they welcomed him with joy.

"They were astonished at his story. The two eagles who never left Tonweya amazed them. They were glad that they had always been kind to Waŋbli and had never killed them.

"The time came when the eagles were able to hunt food for themselves and though everyone expected them to fly away, they did not. True, they would leave with the dawn on hunting forays, but when the evening drew near, they would fly back fearlessly and enter Tonweya's tipi, where they passed the night. Everyone marveled at the sight.

"But eagles, like men, should be free. Tonweya, who by now understood their language, told them they could go. They were to enjoy the life the Great Mystery, Wakan-tanka, had planned for them. At first they refused. But when Tonweya said if he ever needed their help he would call for them, they consented.

"The tribe gave a great feast in their honor. In gratitude for all they had done Tonweya painted the tips of their wings a bright red to denote courage and bravery. He took them up on a high mountain. He held them once more toward the sky and bidding them good-bye released them. Spreading their wings they soared away. Tonweya watched them until they disappeared in the eye of the sun.

"Many snows have passed and Tonweya has long been dead. But now and then the eagles with the red-tipped wings are still seen. There are always two of them and they never show any fear of people. Some say they are the original sacred eagles of Tonweya, for the Waŋbli lives for many snows. Some think they are the children of the sacred ones. It is said whoever sees the red-tipped wings of the eagles is sure of their protection as long as he is fearless and brave. And only the fearless and brave may wear the eagle feather tipped with red."

When Tasinagi finished the story, he looked to see if the red-winged eagles were still following them. They were there. He knew then that his son Chano was one of those to be blessed by great good in his life.

A
SONG
OF
GREATNESS

When I hear the old men
Telling of heroes,
Telling of great deeds
Of ancient days,
When I hear them telling,
Then I think within me
I too am one of these.

When I hear the people
Praising great ones,
Then I know that I too
Shall be esteemed,
I too when my time comes
Shall do mightily.

*a Chippewa Indian song
transcribed by Mary Austin*

Unit 4

THE

BEST BAD

THING

**by Yoshiko Uchida
illustrated by
Kinuko Y. Craft**

*When Rinko's mother asks her to spend the last
month of her vacation helping the recently widowed Mrs. Hata, Rinko
is sure that her summer will be ruined. People say that Mrs. Hata is
a little eccentric, and Rinko believes them. Furthermore, Rinko has
never been away from home, and she does not want to travel
to East Oakland to harvest cucumbers in Mrs. Hata's fields. Rinko cannot
convince her parents to let her stay home, but they do agree to let
her come back after two weeks if she is still uncomfortable at Mrs. Hata's.*

*When she arrives in East Oakland, Rinko has
to adjust to living in an old, shabby house with Mrs. Hata and her two
sons, Zenny and Abu. Rinko soon makes friends with the boys, and
one day they dare her to hitch a ride on one of the freight trains that run
alongside the Hatas' house. Even though Mrs. Hata has forbidden
them to ride the trains, Rinko and the boys do it, and Rinko badly sprains
her ankle in jumping off a freight. A mysterious old man who lives near
the Hatas fixes her ankle, and although her foot feels better, Rinko can't
shake the feeling that more bad things will follow.*

I knew turning my ankle was a bad omen. Mama always says bad things happen in threes, so I knew I probably had two more coming. Or maybe, I thought, coming to East Oakland was the first bad thing and I was already on my second one.

Sometimes when two bad things happen, Mama will purposely break something she doesn't care about and say, "There! That's the third bad thing. Now we're finished."

I wished I could get my two more bad things over with fast, but I certainly couldn't break any of Auntie Hata's dishes. She didn't have that many to spare.

What really made me feel so awful about the whole thing was that Auntie Hata didn't get mad when I told her what I'd done. What she said was, "Ah, well, Rinko, I guess you're still only a child after all."

And she put cold compresses on my ankle and kept me off my feet, which made me feel worse than if she'd gotten mad and scolded me for being so stupid. Mama might just as well have sent Joji, I thought, for all the help I was to Auntie Hata.

As soon as my ankle was better, I tried to make up for everything and be a more responsible person. I was still limping, but I could help Auntie Hata hang out her wash, which she scrubbed in a big metal tub heated on the wood stove. And I ironed her sheets and pillow-cases so she'd have nice smooth sheets to sleep on. I could see why she usually didn't bother and why her clothes looked wrinkled. Ironing wasn't easy when you had to heat a big heavy iron on the wood stove.

I also swept out the whole house, which wasn't hard since there were no rugs, and I used damp tea leaves to keep down the dust. It didn't matter what day I cleaned, because Auntie Hata didn't have a special day for it like Mama, who wants it done on Saturdays.

Auntie Hata seemed to do things when the spirit moved her, and that was fine with me.

One morning I got up even before the first train to help with breakfast. Actually, what I wanted to do was ask Auntie Hata about the old man before Zenny and Abu came down.

I saw she already had a pot of rice bubbling on the stove and was poking at the fire, talking to it so it would burn brighter.

"Shall I help make the soup?" I asked.

"That would be nice," Auntie Hata said into the fire. "I'll go out and get some fresh cucumbers."

And before I could even say, "old man," she was out the back door and gone.

The next thing I knew, she was calling to me.

"Rinko, Rinko! Hurry! Come quick!"

I was sure something awful had happened, like maybe she'd come across a snake out in the fields. I grabbed a knife and ran out, ready to stab the snake if I had to. But Auntie Hata was just standing there, smiling and pointing.

"Look, Rinko, it's been raining spiders."

Sure enough, there were tiny spiders and wispy webs all over the fields and the morning dew was caught in them like tiny crystal beads. It was the prettiest thing.

"Will the spiders eat the cucumbers?" I asked.

"Not likely. They'll probably all be blown off somewhere by the wind and be gone by tomorrow." Auntie Hata bent down for a closer look at the shimmery webs and said, "What a shame."

I knew exactly what she meant. I think it's awful that spiders work so hard spinning beautiful lacy webs—so neat and perfect—only to have them destroyed in a second by the wind or some giant human being.

Auntie Hata picked her cucumbers carefully so she wouldn't destroy any of the webs. And I guess that's when I began to like her, because that's exactly what I would have done. That is also when I smelled something burning.

"It's the rice!" I yelled.

When Auntie Hata and I got back to the house, the kitchen was filled with smoke, and Zenny and Abu were standing there yelling, "Fire! Fire! The stove's on fire!"

"It's only the rice," I hollered, and I flapped a dish towel to get rid of the smoke, while Auntie Hata grabbed the pot from the stove.

By the time we sat down to have our soup and some of the rice we saved from the top of the pot, I'd given up trying to have a private conversation with Auntie Hata. I just blurted out my question in front of Zenny and Abu.

"What's wrong with the old man, anyway?" I asked. "He's so strange and unfriendly." And I told what he'd said about not mentioning him to Mrs. Sugar or our minister.

Auntie Hata stopped eating and looked at me thoughtfully. Then she said, "He's had some hard times." As though that would explain everything.

"Like what?"

I could tell Auntie Hata was thinking carefully what to say, like Papa when he rubs his mustache.

"It's not always easy to make a life for yourself in a strange land," she said. "Sometimes . . . often, you're afraid, and you close yourself off and shut people out."

I could understand that. I've felt that way myself lots of times even if I'm *not* in a strange land. But I wondered why the old man should be afraid of me or my friends?

"Aw, the old man ain't afraid of nothing," Zenny said.

"He sure ain't," Abu agreed.

But Auntie Hata didn't seem to hear them. "We all get scared sometimes," she said. "And lonely too. Oh, yes. Lonely lots of times."

"Well, you don't have to be lonely while I'm here," I reminded her.

Auntie Hata smiled, crinkling her eyes into two small crescent moons. "That's right, Rinko."

She reached over to pat my shoulder and then got up to clear the table, and I still didn't know a thing about the old man.

The second bad thing happened when I'd almost forgotten about the first one. It was a lot worse than my sprained ankle, and it didn't happen to me.

It happened just as we were going to take more cucumbers to the factory. We had loaded up the truck and were ready to leave when an old beat-up truck came rattling along, and I heard a sound like the honking of a tired goose.

I knew what it was when I saw the canvas flapping over the sides of the truck and a scale dangling in the back. It looked just like the truck of a Japanese peddler who comes to our house once a week on Thursday afternoons.

His truck is filled with crates of carrots and string beans, taro root and long white radish, ginger and burdock root, and gallon tins of bean curd squares floating in water. There are also hundred-pound sacks of white rice and barrels of soy sauce and tubs of yellow pickled radish. Everything in the truck smells awful and wonderful at the same time and makes my mouth water.

A smiling, skinny Japanese man jumped out of this truck and Auntie Hata called to him. "You're exactly the person I wanted to see, Mr. Kogi. I'm all out of bean curd cakes, and I need a sack of rice."

She hurried into the house to get a pan for the bean curd cakes, and that was when I heard the freight train coming.

Zenny and Abu took a quick look at each other and yelled, "We'll be right back."

I knew exactly what they were up to. "You'd better
not!" I said. "You'd better come back right now."

But they completely ignored me, and I couldn't go
after them because the peddler was talking to me. He
twisted the cover off a small jar of pink grease and
poked it under my nose.

"Here, smell," he said. "It's hair pomade made by
my missus. It comes in three different scents."

I took a sniff and said, "Strawberry," as if I was
taking a smelling test.

"That's right," he said. "Want to try some?"

He was smiling and waiting, and I could see the gold
fillings in his front teeth. I didn't want to hurt his feelings,
but I certainly didn't want to put that pink grease on my
hair and go around smelling like strawberries. Auntie
Hata came back just in time to rescue me.

"Oh, is that more of your hair pomade?" she asked, and she took a big dab with her finger, bent over, and smeared it all over her shoes.

"It's much better than shoe polish," she said, laughing, "and I have the best smelling shoes in East Oakland."

The peddler laughed too. I guess he didn't really care whether Auntie Hata used his pomade on her head or her feet.

She didn't have enough money to pay for the rice, but the peddler heaved the big sack on his shoulder and carried it into the kitchen for her.

"Pay me next time," he said, and he rattled off in his noisy truck.

Auntie Hata looked around for Zenny and Abu. "Now where did those two rascals go?"

"I know," I said. "I'll go get them." And I left Auntie Hata cranking up the truck's motor.

I ran out the front gate and headed toward the slight rise, just before the freight train started down the slope. The train rolled by as I got there, and just as I thought, Zenny and Abu were hitching a ride. Abu was on the front ladder of one car and Zenny on the back.

"Get off!" I yelled. "We're leaving."

"OK," Zenny hollered back.

"Right now!" I shouted.

So Zenny jumped, landed on his feet and ran hard
until he got his balance.

Abu turned to wave at me.

"Get off! Get off!" I yelled.

But he didn't. He was looking back at me instead of
where he should jump. And when he finally did jump,
he fell to the ground and rolled backwards toward the
wheels of the train.

"Watch out!" Zenny hollered.

"Stop!" I screamed at the train. But it kept right on
going, and I thought I saw a wheel roll over Abu's arm
before he could roll away.

I heard somebody screaming like crazy but didn't
know it was me. Abu had rolled away from the tracks,
but his right arm was twisted, as if it didn't belong to his
body, and there was blood and grease and dirt all over it.
His glasses lay smashed on the ground beside him.

I was still screaming when I got to him, and Zenny yelled, "Stop screaming, Rinko."

But I saw Abu all crumpled up on the ground, and I couldn't stop.

"Abu's dead!" I screamed. "Abu's dead! Abu's dead!"

Auntie Hata must've heard me, because all of a sudden she was next to me and Zenny. She cried out when she saw Abu and knelt down beside him.

"Abu Chan, Abu Chan. *Doshita? Doshita?* What happened?" she murmured over and over. She felt his head and touched his cheek and tried to check his pulse.

"I'm sorry, Ma. I'm sorry," Zenny sobbed. Tears were streaming down his face.

I was crying too and still screaming, "Abu's dead!"

He was so still, with no color in his face. His eyes were closed and his arm was twisted and horrible looking.

"Stop screaming, Rinko," Auntie Hata said to me in a firm voice. "Abu is going to be all right, but we've got to get him to a hospital quickly."

She took a handkerchief from her pocket and tied it around Abu's arm to stop the bleeding. Then she picked him up carefully and carried him to the truck. Zenny and I trailed after her, sobbing and crying. She told us to get in the truck first, and then she lifted Abu onto our laps.

I could see she didn't want to let go of him, but she had to drive, so she put Abu's head and shoulders on my lap and stretched his legs over Zenny's. I was surprised how heavy he was. I could feel my heart pounding all over my body and I felt awful about all the mean things I'd said to Abu. I didn't know if he could hear me, but I talked to him.

"It's OK, Abu. You're going to be OK. You'll see." I felt as though he'd stay alive as long as he could hear me talking to him. So I talked all the way to the hospital. And Zenny kept patting his legs.

I don't know how Auntie Hata got to Highland Hospital so fast. I guess she knew the way because she'd taken Mr. Hata there to see the doctor, even though he hated the place.

As soon as we got there, the doctors rushed Abu into the emergency room, and Auntie Hata and Zenny and I waited in the corridor outside.

I guess I feel about hospitals the way Mr. Hata did—that once you're stuck in one, you're going to come out in a wooden box. I kept wishing we could hurry up and get Abu out of that awful place. Well, after a while the doctor came and told us they were taking Abu to surgery.

We all jumped up from the bench, and I yelled, "Surgery! You mean you're going to cut off his arm?"

"Oh, please, no!" Auntie Hata cried.

But the doctor told us not to worry, that they'd take good care of Abu, and that we should just sit down and wait.

I guess we must've sat there in that crowded hallway for a couple of hours, with nobody paying any attention to us. I felt as though an egg beater was churning up my stomach and everything else all together. And I guess Auntie Hata felt the same way, because she kept twisting a handkerchief in her hands until it was almost in shreds. Every once in a while she would send Zenny to go ask somebody about Abu.

"What's happening to my brother?" he'd ask anybody in a white uniform.

And whoever he talked to would just say something like, "Everything's OK, sonny. Don't worry. Go sit down till your doctor comes to talk to you."

So we sat and waited and waited and waited, and by then I felt all ground up like the sesame seeds in Mama's mortar. When I went to look at a clock, it was almost six o'clock.

Finally a doctor came out and called, "Mrs. Hata?"

Auntie Hata shot up from the bench as if she'd exploded from a cannon. She had a hard time finding the right words to ask the doctor what she wanted to know. "My boy, he's OK? He's OK? Please?"

"Your boy has lost a lot of blood but we gave him a transfusion," the doctor said slowly. "There's been some nerve damage, and he may not regain full use of his right arm. But he's holding his own. You can go see him now in Ward C."

Auntie Hata was trying hard to understand, but she wasn't sure. "Abu's OK?" she asked me over and over. "He's OK?"

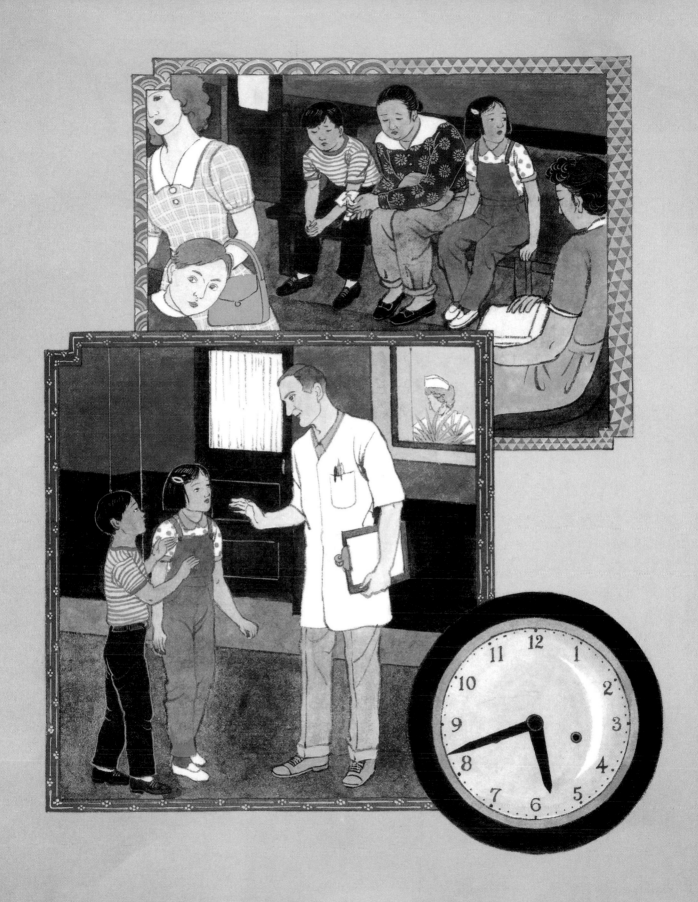

I wasn't sure myself. All I could say was, "I think so, Auntie Hata."

We found our way to Ward C, and there was Abu in a big room filled with a lot of sick people. He was in a corner bed and he looked small and helpless with his arm bandaged clear up to his shoulder. He was asleep and couldn't talk to us, but Auntie Hata wouldn't leave him.

"You know the way to the old man's Eagle Cafe?" she asked Zenny.

"I can find it."

"Well, you and Rinko walk there and tell him what happened. Wait until he gets off work. Then take the streetcar home with him."

She took two nickels from her coin purse and gave one to each of us for carfare. She said she wanted to be there when Abu woke up and didn't know when she'd get home.

"Rinko, can you make some supper for the two of you?"

I nodded. We could always have cucumbers with soy sauce and pour hot tea over the rice left over from breakfast. I didn't want to leave Auntie Hata there by herself, but she didn't look scared or frightened anymore. She was calm and strong, the way the old man had been the day he chased off the bully at the railroad tracks.

"Go on now," she said, and she nudged us toward the door. There certainly wasn't anything vague about Auntie Hata then. She took charge as though she knew exactly what to do.

I guess Zenny and I must've walked about thirty blocks to The Eagle Cafe. My knees ached and one big toe throbbed, but I was too worried about Abu to think about myself. I felt it was my fault that Abu was lying in the hospital half dead. If only I'd stopped him before he rode that freight, I thought.

I knew Zenny was feeling as bad as I was, because he didn't say one word all the way to Seventh Street. We just plodded along like two strangers, each of us bundled up in our own gloomy thoughts.

When we finally got to The Eagle Cafe, we found the old man frying some potatoes at the grill. He was wearing a white apron and chef's hat, and he was so surprised to see us, he just froze with the egg turner clutched in his hand.

"Zenny! Rinko! What are you doing here?"

That was when Zenny and I both started talking, and I felt as though I was drowning in all the words that came tumbling out of my mouth. Between the two of us, we told the old man everything that had happened.

"And Abu? How is he now?" the old man asked when we finally stopped.

"The doctor said he had nerve damage," I said. "He's lost a lot of blood. Maybe . . . maybe he's going to die." I began to cry again.

For a minute the old man didn't know what to do with us. Then he went to talk to a bald-headed white man in a rumpled gray sweater who was sitting at the cash register. He called him Mr. Sabatini, and I guess he was the owner of the cafe. When the old man came back, he told us to sit down at the counter and he'd make us something to eat.

"I get off soon," he said, "and by the time you finish eating, I'll be ready to go home with you."

Then the old man was making toast, breaking eggs on the grill, and frying two ham steaks and some potatoes. It was like the time I'd seen him painting the samurai on his kite. His hands were steady and sure and knew exactly what to do without the old man's even having to think about it. I never saw anybody cook so fast. And suddenly everything was there in front of me, hot and sizzling, on a thick white plate, and it smelled so wonderful I nearly fainted.

Zenny and I pitched in and ate as though we hadn't seen any food for three weeks. It was strange eating breakfast for supper, but I'd been eating lunch for breakfast every day at Auntie Hata's, and it didn't seem to make any difference to my stomach. I sopped up all the runny egg yolk with my toast and ate every bit of the ham and potatoes.

The old man kept an eye on us while he served some other customers, and for dessert he gave each of us a piece of apple pie. He also poured a little coffee into our milk, and I had two glasses.

When it was time to go, the old man tried to pay Mr. Sabatini, but he wouldn't take his money.

"Forget it, Manki," he said. "It's on the house." I thought he'd called him monkey.

"He called you Manki," Zenny said as soon as we were outside. "That ain't your name, is it?"

The old man shook his head. "Maybe someday he will take the trouble to call me by my proper name, Mankichi," he said, and he strode so fast toward the corner to catch the streetcar, Zenny and I had to run to keep up.

The streetcar rattled and poked along until it finally reached the end of the line, and then we still had about a mile to walk to get home.

It was really spooky walking along that dark road with only the empty fields stretching out around us. I was dying to hold a friendly hand, but nobody offered me one, so I hugged myself real hard instead. I also kept watching for spirits in case there were any hovering around in the weeds.

I guess Zenny knew what I was doing because he said, "They ain't there tonight."

In a way that made me feel worse, because then I wondered if maybe the spirits were at the hospital waiting to take Abu to the spirit world. I thought maybe Abu's papa was there that minute, trying to take Abu with him.

"No!" I yelled into the dark fields. "You can't take him."

Zenny gave me a funny look, but I guess he was used to having his mama pop out with strange remarks. The old man turned to look at me too, but he didn't say anything either.

The old man came home with us, and we all sat in the kitchen waiting for Auntie Hata. The old man asked Zenny about his kite, and I was beginning to feel left out again when Auntie Hata finally came home. I took one look at her face and knew something terrible had happened.

"What is it, Mrs. Hata?" the old man asked. "Is it Abu?"

"No, no, Abu is all right. He's asleep and the doctor made me leave. But it's gone!"

"What is, Ma?"

"The truck. Our truck's gone!"

"The truck? The truck's gone?" I asked like an echo.

The old man made Auntie Hata sit down and told her to calm herself. "Are you sure you just didn't forget where you parked it?"

"No, no. I left it right by the entrance."

"That's right," I said remembering. We'd pulled up at the emergency entrance and piled out without giving the truck another thought.

"And you left the keys in it?" Zenny asked.

Auntie Hata nodded sadly. "The keys, the cucumbers, the truck . . . somebody's taken them all."

"Maybe somebody parked it for you," I said hopefully.

"I walked around that hospital three times looking for it," Auntie Hata said, shaking her head. "It's gone. Somebody's stolen our truck!"

There it was, I thought, feeling terrible. That was the third bad thing to happen. My ankle, Abu's accident, and now the truck. Things seemed to be going from bad to worse ever since I arrived, and I began to feel like a jinx on Auntie Hata's life.

"I'll call Papa. He'll think of something." I started to get up and then remembered there was no phone in the house and that I'd have to wait until the next day to call from the hospital.

"I'll speak to the cop who comes to The Eagle for coffee every morning," the old man said. "Maybe he can help you find your truck."

But nothing we said could cheer her up. "I can't earn a living without the truck," Auntie Hata said miserably.

She let out a low moan, as though all the energy was drifting out of her body, like air going out of a balloon.

"We're finished, old man," she said slowly. "I think we're finished."

As soon as I called Mama and Papa the next day, they rushed over to the hospital. And they brought Reverend Mitaka with them. He is a bachelor, who Tami's mother is dying to find a wife for, and he is so shy, he never looks up from his notes when he preaches. He also has bad eyes and wears such thick glasses he looks a little like an owl.

I wished Mama hadn't brought him, but I guess she thought he could comfort Auntie Hata. Or maybe she thought Abu would get better if he prayed over him. I was sincerely hoping he wouldn't, but Reverend Mitaka prayed all right. He put his hand on Abu's forehead, and we stood around his bed as if we were having a prayer meeting.

I was so embarrassed because everybody in the ward was staring at us. I kept my eyes open all the time, watching to see if Abu would open his, but he didn't. Zenny had his eyes open too and was making circles on the floor with his left toe.

When I was feeling like I wanted to sink right into the floor, Reverend Mitaka finally stopped, and Auntie Hata took him and Mama and Papa aside to tell them about Abu's arm.

Zenny and I tried to get Abu to open his eyes.

"Hey, Abu, it's me," Zenny said, bending close to his ear. "You OK?"

Abu's eyelids flickered and he managed a small smile.

"Yeah," he said in a thin voice. He sounded as though he was inside a tunnel. "Next time I'll jump better."

"Next time nothing," I said, sounding like his mother. "You'd better stick to flying kites."

The minute I said that I could have choked myself for being so stupid. How was Abu going to fly a kite if he couldn't use his right hand?

"Listen, Abu," I said, changing the subject as fast as I could. "You don't have to pay me that million billion dollars you still owe me. OK?"

That made Abu grin a little bit. "OK. Shake," he said, and he stuck the fingers of his left hand out from under the covers. They felt hot and weak, and Abu couldn't even give my hand a squeeze.

I couldn't stand seeing him look so pathetic. "Listen, I'll bring your turtle, Herbert, to see you next time. OK?" I said, and I left in a hurry to go see what Mama and Papa were talking about. They were discussing Auntie Hata's truck.

"Let me look around," Papa said. "Maybe I can find another old truck and fix it up for you."

But Auntie Hata just shook her head. "What's the use?" she said. "Summer's almost over and the cucumbers will soon be gone. Then what will I do? I can't do

gardening the way Mr. Hata used to. No, I don't need another truck. All I want is for Abu to get well."

"He will, Mrs. Hata," Mama said. "He will."

When it was time to leave, Mama took me aside. "Well, Rinko," she said. "Your two weeks are about up. Do you want to come home with us or will you stay until the end of the month?"

I was surprised she should even ask, but I guess she did it to make me realize what I'd already decided. I hadn't even thought about going home early.

"I can't leave," I said to Mama. "Auntie Hata *really* needs me now."

Mama put her arm around me and gave me a hard squeeze. "Good," she said. "I hoped you'd say that."

Papa checked with me too. "You're sure you're all right?" he asked. "You're sure you want to stay?"

"Sure, Papa," I said. "I've got some unfinished business in East Oakland."

Papa looked puzzled, but I couldn't tell him I had to stay to find out what was bothering the old man. And I didn't admit the real reason I wanted to stay, which was that I'd grown to like Auntie Hata. In fact, I liked her a lot.

MEET
YOSHIKO UCHIDA

Yoshiko Uchida wrote her first stories when she was only ten years old, using brown wrapping paper that she made into booklets. She also kept a journal. Because she grew up during the Great Depression of the 1930s, she learned to save things, like her books and journals. It's lucky that she did, because the memories she recorded helped her create the award-winning books she has written as an adult.

All of Uchida's books are about Japanese or Japanese-American characters. *The Best Bad Thing* is the second book in her trilogy about Rinko, a girl growing up in the hard times of the 1930s. Although these books don't describe Uchida's own life exactly, she says that a lot of herself is in Rinko.

Some of Uchida's memories of growing up are more pleasant than others. She spent the first twenty years of her life in pleasant neighborhoods in northern California. But in 1941, the Japanese attacked Pearl Harbor, and her life changed dramatically. Panicked about the possibility of more attacks and spies, the American government rounded up Japanese Americans who lived on the West Coast. Uchida wrote about her family's experiences in *Journey to Topaz* and later in the award-winning *Journey Home,* which continues the family's story after World War II.

Today, when Uchida talks to students about the camps, she always asks why they think she wrote about these experiences. "'You wrote about them so it won't happen again,' they say." But she also feels that her books have a larger message. "I hope my readers can be caring human beings who don't think in terms of labels—foreigners or Asians or whatever—but think of people as human beings. If that comes across, then I've accomplished my purpose."

my friend

my friend is
like bark
rounding a tree

he warms
like sun
on a winter day

he cools
like water
in the hot noon

his voice
is ready
as a spring bird

he is
my friend
and I
am his

Emily Hearn

Dear Mr.

Henshaw

by Beverly Cleary
illustrated by R. J. Shay

Leigh Botts wants to be a famous author someday. He's been corresponding with his favorite author, Boyd Henshaw, who suggests that he keep a diary. Through his diary, Leigh learns a lot about himself and about the many changes going on in his life. Leigh's in a new school in a new town. He isn't finding it easy to make friends, and on top of that, someone keeps stealing things from his lunchbag. One day he rigs up a burglar alarm for a lunchbox, and it really works!

Leigh's parents are divorced, and he really misses his father, who drives a truck cross-country and is on the road most of the time. When he calls his father unexpectedly one day, he is about to take another boy and his mother out for pizza. Leigh worries that his father might remarry.

He also has other things on his mind. There's a Young Writers' contest at his school, and the prize will be lunch with a "Famous Author." Leigh is hoping to win.

Tuesday, March 20

Yesterday Miss Neely, the librarian, asked if I had written anything for the Young Writers' Yearbook, because all writing had to be turned in by tomorrow. When I told her I hadn't, she said I still had twenty-four hours and why didn't I get busy? So I did, because I really would like to meet a Famous Author. My story about the ten-foot wax man went into the wastebasket. Next I tried to start a story called *The Great Lunchbox Mystery,* but I couldn't seem to turn my lunchbox experience into a story because I don't know who the thief (thieves) was (were), and I don't want to know.

Finally I dashed off a description of the time I rode with my father when he was trucking the load of grapes down Highway 152 through Pacheco Pass to a winery. I put in things like the signs that said STEEP GRADE, TRUCKS USE LOW GEAR and how Dad down-shifted and how skillful he was handling a long, heavy load on the curves. I put in about the hawks on the telephone wires and about that high peak where Black Bart's lookout used to watch for travelers coming through the pass so he could signal to Black Bart to rob them, and how the leaves on the trees along the stream at the bottom of the pass were turning yellow and how good tons of grapes smelled in the sun. I left out the part about the waitresses and the video games. Then I copied the whole thing over in case neatness counts and gave it to Miss Neely.

Saturday, March 24

Mom said I had to invite Barry over to our house for supper because I have been going to his house after school so often. We had been working on a burglar alarm for his room which we finally got to work with some help from a library book.

I wasn't sure Barry would like to come to our house which is so small compared to his, but he accepted when I invited him.

Mom cooked a casserole full of good things like ground beef, chilies, tortillas, tomatoes and cheese. Barry said he really liked eating at our house because he got tired of eating with a bunch of little sisters waving spoons and drumsticks. That made me happy. It helps to have a friend.

Barry says his burglar alarm still works. The trouble is, his little sisters think it's fun to open his door to set it off. Then they giggle and hide. This was driving his mother crazy, so he finally had to disconnect it. We all laughed about this. Barry and I felt good about making something that worked even if he can't use it.

Beep! Beep! Beep! Beep!

WARNING! BURGLAR ALARM

...my friend, Barry.

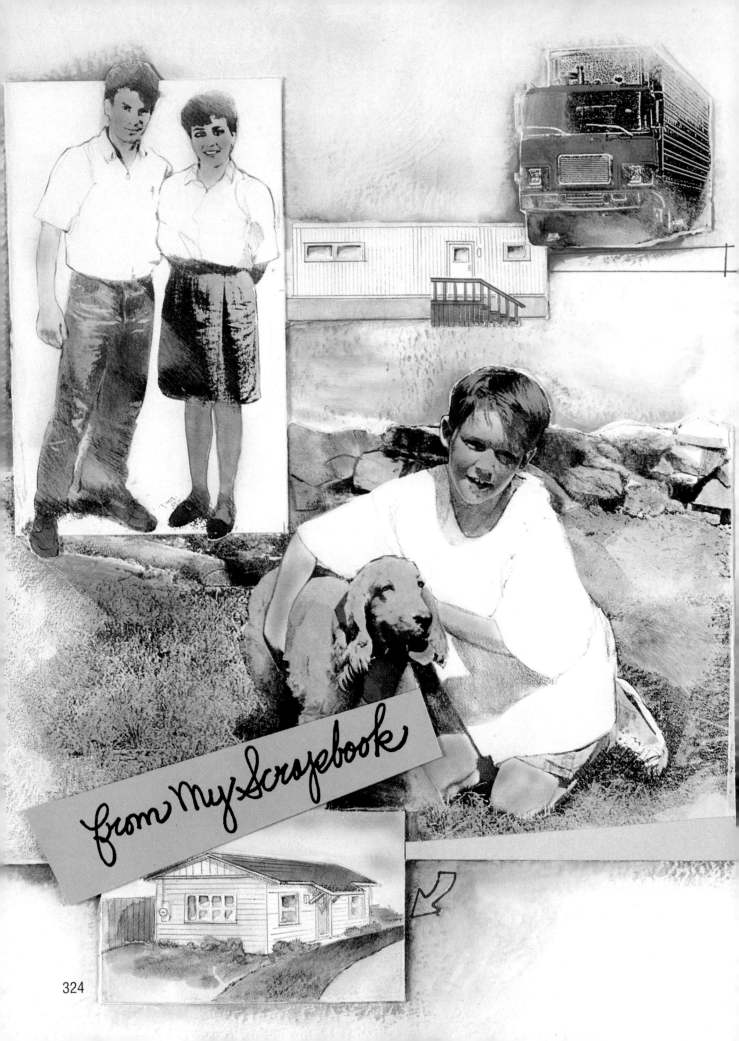

from My Scrapbook

Barry saw the sign on my door that said KEEP OUT MOM THAT MEANS YOU. He asked if my Mom really stays out of my room. I said, "Sure, if I keep things picked up." Mom is not a snoop.

Barry said he wished he could have a room nobody ever went into. I was glad Barry didn't ask to use the bathroom. Maybe I'll start scrubbing off the mildew after all.

Sunday, March 25

I keep thinking about Dad and how lonely he sounded and wondering what happened to the pizza boy. I don't like to think about Dad being lonesome, but I don't like to think about the pizza boy cheering him up either.

Tonight at supper (beans and franks) I got up my courage to ask Mom if she thought Dad would get married again. She thought awhile and then said, "I don't see how he could afford to. He has big payments to make on the truck, and the price of diesel oil goes up all the time, and when people can't afford to build houses or buy cars, he won't be hauling lumber or cars."

I thought this over. I know that a license for a truck like his costs over a thousand dollars a year. "But he always sends my support payments," I said, "even if he is late sometimes."

"Yes, he does that," agreed my mother. "Your father isn't a bad man by any means."

Suddenly I was mad and disgusted with the whole thing. "Then why don't you two get married again?" I guess I wasn't very nice about the way I said it.

Mom looked me straight in the eye. "Because your father will never grow up," she said. I knew that was all she would ever say about it.

Tomorrow they give out the Young Writers' Yearbook! Maybe I will be lucky and get to go have lunch with the Famous Author.

Today wasn't the greatest day of my life. When our class went to the library, I saw a stack of Yearbooks and could hardly wait for Miss Neely to hand them out. When I finally got mine and opened it to the first page, there was a monster story, and I saw I hadn't won first prize. I kept turning. I didn't win second prize which went to a poem, and I didn't win third or fourth prize, either. Then I turned another page and saw Honorable Mention and under it:

A DAY ON DAD'S RIG
by
Leigh M. Botts

There was my title with my name under it in print, even if it was mimeographed print. I can't say I wasn't disappointed because I hadn't won a prize, I was. I was really disappointed about not getting to meet the mysterious Famous Author, but I liked seeing my name in print.

Some kids were mad because they didn't win or even get something printed. They said they wouldn't ever try to write again which I think is pretty dumb. I have heard that real authors sometimes have their books turned down. I figure you win some, you lose some.

Then Miss Neely announced that the Famous Author the winners would get to have lunch with was Angela Badger. The girls were more excited than the boys because Angela Badger writes mostly about girls with problems like big feet or pimples or something. I would still like to meet her because she is, as they say, a real live author, and I've never met a real live author. I am glad Mr. Henshaw isn't the author because then I would *really* be disappointed that I didn't get to meet him.

Friday, March 30

Today turned out to be exciting. In the middle of second period Miss Neely called me out of class and asked if I would like to go have lunch with Angela Badger. I said, "Sure, how come?"

Miss Neely explained that the teachers discovered that the winning poem had been copied out of a book and wasn't original so the girl who submitted it would not be allowed to go and would I like to go in her place? Would I!

Miss Neely telephoned Mom at work for permission and I gave my lunch to Barry because my lunches are better than his. The other winners were all dressed up, but I didn't care. I have noticed that authors like Mr. Henshaw usually wear old plaid shirts in the pictures on the back of their books. My shirt is just as old as his, so I knew it was OK.

Miss Neely drove us in her own car to the Holiday Inn, where some other librarians and their winners were waiting in the lobby. Then Angela Badger arrived with Mr. Badger, and we were all led into the dining room which was pretty crowded. One of the librarians who was a sort of Super Librarian told the winners to sit at a long table with a sign that said Reserved. Angela Badger sat in the middle and some of the girls pushed to sit beside her. I sat across from her. Super Librarian explained that we could choose our lunch from the salad bar. Then all the librarians went off and sat at a table with Mr. Badger.

There I was face to face with a real live author who seemed like a nice lady, plump with wild hair, and I couldn't think of a thing to say because I hadn't read her books. Some girls told her how much they loved her books, but some of the boys and girls were too shy to say anything. Nothing seemed to happen until Mrs. Badger said, "Why don't we all go help ourselves to lunch at the salad bar?"

What a mess! Some people didn't understand about salad bars, but Mrs. Badger led the way and we helped ourselves to lettuce and bean salad and potato salad and all the usual stuff they lay out on salad bars. A few of the younger kids were too short to reach anything but the bowls on the first rows. They weren't doing too well until Mrs. Badger helped them out. Getting lunch took a long time, longer than in a school cafeteria, and when we carried our plates back to our table, people at other tables ducked and dodged as if they expected us to dump our lunches on their heads. All one boy had on his plate was a piece of lettuce and a slice of tomato because he thought he was going to get to go back for roast beef and fried chicken. We had to straighten him out and explain that all we got was salad. He turned red and went back for more salad.

"A Day On Dad's Rig"

by

Leigh M. Botts

I was still trying to think of something interesting to say to Mrs. Badger while I chased garbanzo beans around my plate with a fork. A couple of girls did all the talking, telling Mrs. Badger how they wanted to write books exactly like hers. The other librarians were busy talking and laughing with Mr. Badger who seemed to be a lot of fun.

Mrs. Badger tried to get some of the shy people to say something without much luck, and I still couldn't think of anything to say to a lady who wrote books about girls with big feet or pimples. Finally Mrs. Badger looked straight at me and asked, "What did you write for the Yearbook?"

I felt myself turn red and answered, "Just something about a ride on a truck."

"Oh!" said Mrs. Badger. "So you're the author of *A Day on Dad's Rig!*"

Everyone was quiet. None of us had known the real live author would have read what we had written, but she had and she remembered my title.

HONORABLE MENTION
Young writer's yearbook
This is to certify that

Leigh M. Botts

completed with honors a written story about a personal experience
and is to be congratulated for an assignment well done.

_____ _____
Teacher   *Angela Badger*
                   Author

"I just got honorable mention," I said, but I was thinking, She called me an author. *A real live author called me an author.*

"What difference does that make?" asked Mrs. Badger. "Judges never agree. I happened to like *A Day on Dad's Rig* because it was written by a boy who wrote honestly about something he knew and had strong feelings about. You made me feel what it was like to ride down a steep grade with tons of grapes behind me."

"But I couldn't make it into a story," I said, feeling a whole lot braver.

"Who cares?" said Mrs. Badger with a wave of her hand. She's the kind of person who wears rings on her forefingers. "What do you expect? The ability to write stories comes later, when you have lived longer and have more understanding. *A Day on Dad's Rig* was splendid work for a boy your age. You wrote like *you,* and you did not try to imitate someone else. This is one mark of a good writer. Keep it up."

I noticed a couple of girls who had been saying they wanted to write books exactly like Angela Badger exchange embarrassed looks.

"Gee, thanks," was all I could say. The waitress began to plunk down dishes of ice cream. Everyone got over being shy and began to ask Mrs. Badger if she wrote in pencil or on the typewriter and did she ever have books rejected and were her characters real people and did she ever have pimples when she was a girl like the girl in her book and what did it feel like to be a famous author?

I didn't think answers to those questions were very important, but I did have one question I wanted to ask which I finally managed to get in at the last minute when Mrs. Badger was autographing some books people had brought.

"Mrs. Badger," I said, "did you ever meet Boyd Henshaw?"

"Why, yes," she said, scribbling away in someone's book. "I once met him at a meeting of librarians where we were on the same program."

"What's he like?" I asked over the head of a girl crowding up with her book.

"He's a very nice young man with a wicked twinkle in his eye," she answered. I think I have known that since the time he answered my questions when Miss Martinez made us write to an author.

On the ride home everybody was chattering about Mrs. Badger this, and Mrs. Badger that. I didn't want to talk. I just wanted to think. A real live author had called *me* an author. A real live author had told me to keep it up. Mom was proud of me when I told her.

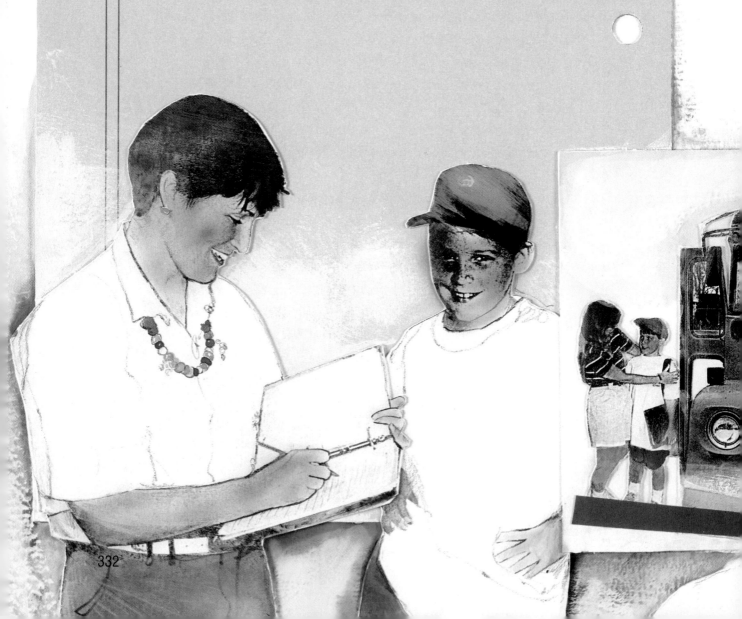

Meet Beverly Cleary

In 1982, Beverly Cleary received several letters from boys who had read her books. "Please," they suggested, "write a book about a boy whose parents are divorced." As she thought about this, she began to get ideas. She overheard a remark about a father who forgot to call his son as promised. She learned about a student who had rigged up a burglar alarm for his lunchbox. These bits and pieces went into the book. Cleary says, "*Dear Mr. Henshaw* was a most satisfying book to write. It seemed almost to write itself."

Surprisingly, Cleary was a poor reader when she began school. By the third grade, however, she had learned to read and to love books. In fact, her school librarian suggested that Cleary write children's books when she grew up. Cleary liked the idea but didn't write her first book until many years later. When she and her husband moved into a new house, they found several packages of blank paper in a closet. Her husband gave her a pencil sharpener, and she began to write. Her first book, *Henry Huggins,* was an instant success, as was its sequel, *Henry and Beezus*. Cleary has won many awards for her writing, including two Newbery Honor Awards for her books about a girl named Ramona and a Newbery Medal for *Dear Mr. Henshaw.*

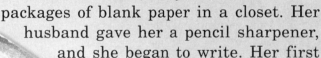

Calvin and Hobbes

by Watterson

I NEED HELP ON MY HOMEWORK. WHAT'S A PRONOUN?

A NOUN THAT LOST ITS AMATEUR STATUS.

MAYBE I CAN GET A POINT FOR ORIGINALITY.

WITH GREAT EFFORT, CALVIN THE HUMAN INSECT ADVANCES THE PAPER IN THE TYPEWRITER.

HIS ONLY HOPE FOR PROPER MEDICAL TREATMENT LIES IN HIS ABILITY TO WRITE A LEGIBLE MESSAGE TO HIS FAMILY!

HE CRAWLS TO EACH KEY AND JUMPS!

WHO WROTE "HELP I'M A BUG" ON MY LETTER TO GRANDMA?

EVIDENTLY SOME BUG. HOW STRANGE.

HI, HOBBES. ARE YOU READING THAT BOOK I GAVE YOU?

YES. IT'S VERY GOOD.

YOU LIKE IT?

SURE. I THINK IT'S...

WAIT A MINUTE.

WOULD YOU MIND WRITING IT IN TWO PAGES FOR ME BY TOMORROW MORNING?

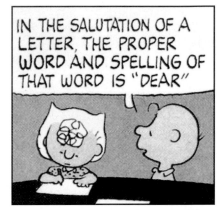

Who

am I?

The trees ask me,
And the sky,
And the sea asks me
    Who am I?

The grass asks me,
And the sand,
And the rocks ask me
    Who I am.

The wind tells me
At nightfall,
And the rain tells me
    Someone small.

    Someone small
    Someone small
    But a piece
        of
          it
        all.

by Felice Holman

Three

We were just three,
Two loons and me.
They swam and fished,
I watched and wished,
That I, like them, might dive and play
In icy waters all the day.
I watched and wished. I could not reach
Where they were, till I tried their speech,
And something in me helped, so I
Could give their trembling sort of cry.
One loon looked up and answered me.
He understood that we were three.

Elizabeth Coatsworth

Ben and Me

An Astonishing Life of Benjamin Franklin
❦ As written by his Good Mouse AMOS
Discovered, Edited & Illustrated by ❦❦❦

ROBERT LAWSON

FOREWORD

The manuscript which forms this book was sent me recently by an architect friend. While altering an old Philadelphia house, workmen uncovered a small chamber beneath a bedroom hearthstone. This tiny room, for such it appeared to be, was about eighteen inches square. It contained various small articles of furniture, all of the Colonial Period. In one of these, a secretary desk, was found a manuscript book, the leaves of which, about the size of postage stamps, were covered with minute writing.

With the aid of a powerful reading-glass my friend managed to decipher the story which follows.

Scarce able to believe that such a remarkable document could be other than some ancient hoax, he sent it to various authorities for their opinions.

Scientists of the Brownsonian Institute have assured him that their analyses of the paper and ink prove them definitely to be of Early American manufacture, and that the writing was most certainly done with a quill pen of that period.

More startling still was the report from officials of the National Museum of Natural History, stating that, incredible as it might seem, there could be no possible doubt that the handwriting was that of—a mouse!

So without attempting any explanation, with only a few minor corrections of spelling and grammar, and the addition of some drawings, I give you Amos' story in his own words.

I am aware that his account of Franklin's career differs in many respects from the accounts of later historians. This I cannot explain but it seems reasonable to believe that statements made by one who lived on terms of such intimacy with this great man should be more trustworthy than those written by later scholars.

ROBERT LAWSON
Rabbit Hill
May, 1939

341

I, AMOS

Since the recent death of my lamented friend and patron Ben Franklin, many so-called historians have attempted to write accounts of his life and his achievements. Most of these are wrong in so many respects that I feel the time has now come for me to take pen in paw and set things right.

All of these ill-informed scribblers seem astonished at Ben's great fund of information, at his brilliant decisions, at his seeming knowledge of all that went on about him.

Had they asked me, I could have told them. It was ME.

For many years I was his closest friend and adviser and, if I do say it, was in great part responsible for his success and fame.

Not that I wish to claim too much: I simply hope to see justice done, credit given where credit is due, and that's to me—mostly.

Ben was undoubtedly a splendid fellow, a great man, a patriot and all that; but he *was* undeniably stupid at times, and had it not been for me—well, here's the true story, and you can judge for yourself.

$\mathcal{I}$ was the oldest of twenty-six children. My parents, in naming us, went right through the alphabet. I, being first, was **A**mos, the others went along through **B**athsheba, **C**laude, **D**aniel—and so forth down to the babies: **X**enophon, **Y**sobel, and **Z**enas.

We lived in the vestry of Old Christ Church on Second Street, in Philadelphia—behind the paneling. With that number of mouths to feed we were, naturally, not a very prosperous family. In fact we were really quite poor as poor as church-mice.

But it was not until the Hard Winter of 1745 that things really became desperate. That was a winter long to be remembered for its severity, and night after night my poor father would come in tired and wet with his little sack practically empty.

We were driven to eating prayer-books, and when those gave out we took to the Minister's sermons. That was, for me, the final straw. The prayer-books were tough, but those sermons!

Being the oldest, it seemed fitting that I should go out into the world and make my own way. Perhaps I could in some way help the others. At least, it left one less to be provided for.

So, saying farewell to all of them—my mother and father and all the children from Bathsheba to Zenas—I set forth on the coldest, windiest night of a cold and windy winter.

Little did I dream, at that moment, of all the strange people and experiences I should encounter before ever I returned to that little vestry home! All I thought of were my cold paws, my empty stomach—and those sermons.

$\mathcal{I}$ have never known
how far I traveled that night, for,
what with the cold and hunger, I
must have become slightly deliri-
ous. The first thing I remember
clearly was being in a kitchen and
smelling CHEESE! It didn't take
long to find it; it was only a bit of
rind and fairly dry, but how I ate!

Refreshed by this, my first real
meal in many a day, I began to explore the house. It was painfully
bare; clean, but bare. Very little
furniture, and that all hard and
shiny; no soft things, or dusty corners where a chap could curl up

and have a good warm nap. It was
cold too, almost as cold as outdoors.

Upstairs were two rooms. One
was dark, and from it came the
sound of snoring; the other had a
light, and the sound of sneezing. I
chose the sneezy one.

In a large chair close to the
fireplace sat a short, thick, round-
faced man, trying to write by the

light of a candle. Every few moments he would sneeze, and his square-rimmed glasses would fly off. Reaching for these he would drop his pen; by the time he found that and got settled to write, the candle would flicker from the draught; when that calmed down, the sneezing would start again, and so it went. He was not accomplishing much in the way of writing.

Of course I recognized him. Everyone in Philadelphia knew the great Doctor Benjamin Franklin, scientist, inventor, printer, editor, author, soldier, statesman and philosopher.

He didn't look great or famous that night, though, he just looked cold—and a bit silly.

He was wrapped in a sort of dressing-gown, with a dirty fur collar; and on his head was perched an odd-looking fur cap.

The cap interested me, for I was still chilled to the bone—and this room was just as bleak as the rest of the house. It was a rather disreputable-looking affair, that cap; but in one side of it I had spied a hole—just about my size.

Up the back of the chair I went, and under cover of the next fit of sneezes, in I slid. What a cozy place *that* was! Plenty of room to move about a bit; just enough air; such soft fur, and such warmth!

"Here," said I to myself, "is my home. No more cold streets, or cellars, or vestries. HERE I stay."

At the moment, of course, I never realized how true this was to prove. All I realized was that I was warm, well fed and—oh, so sleepy!

And so to bed.

WE INVENT THE FRANKLIN STOVE

I slept late the next morning. When I woke my fur-cap home was hanging on the bedpost, and I in it.

Dr. Franklin was again crouched over the fire attempting to write, between fits of sneezing and glasses-hunting. The fire, what there was of it, was smoking, and the room was as cold as ever.

"Not wishing to be critical—" I said. "But, perhaps, a bit of wood on that smoky ember that you seem to consider a fire might—"

"WASTE NOT, WANT NOT," said he, severe, and went on writing.

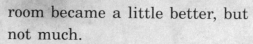

"Well, just suppose," I said, "just suppose you spend two or three weeks in bed with pewmonia—would that be a waste or—"

"It would be," said he, putting on a log; "whatever your name might be."

"Amos," said I. . . . "And then there'd be doctors' bills—"

"BILLS!" said he, shuddering, and put on two more logs, quick. The fire blazed up then, and the room became a little better, but not much.

"Dr. Franklin," I said, "that fireplace is all wrong."

"You might call me Ben—just plain Ben," said he. . . . "What's wrong with it?"

"Well, for one thing, most of the heat goes up the chimney. And for another, you can't get *around* it. Now, outside our church there used to be a Hot-chestnut Man. Sometimes, when business was rushing, he'd drop a chestnut. Pop was always on the look-out, and almost before it touched the ground he'd have it in his sack—and down to the vestry with it. There he'd put it in the middle of the floor—and we'd all gather round for the warmth.

"Twenty-eight of us it would heat, and the room as well. It was all because it was OUT IN THE OPEN, not stuck in a hole in the wall like that fireplace."

"Amos," he interrupts, excited, "there's an idea there! But we couldn't move the fire out into the middle of the room."

"We could if there were something to put it in, iron or something."

"But the smoke?" he objected.

"PIPE," said I, and curled up for another nap.

I didn't get it, though. Ben rushed off downstairs, came back with a great armful of junk, dumped it on the floor and was off for more. No one could have slept, not even a dormouse. After a few trips he had a big pile of things there. There were scraps of iron, tin and wire. There were a couple of old warming-pans, an iron oven, three flatirons, six pot-lids, a wire birdcage and an anvil. There were saws, hammers, pincers, files, drills, nails, screws, bolts, bricks, sand, and an old broken sword.

He drew out a sort of plan and went to work. With the clatter he made there was no chance of a nap, so I helped all I could, picking up the nuts and screws and tools that he dropped—and his glasses.

Ben was a fair terror for work, once he was interested. It was almost noon before he stopped for a bit of rest. We looked over what had been done and it didn't look so bad—considering.

It was shaped much like a small fireplace set up on legs, with two iron doors on the front and a smoke pipe running from the back to the fireplace. He had taken the andirons out of the fireplace and boarded that up so we wouldn't lose any heat up the chimney.

Ben walked around looking at it, proud as could be, but worried.

"The floor," he says. "It's the floor that troubles me, Amos. With those short legs and that thin iron bottom, the heat—"

"Down on the docks," said I, "we used to hear the ship-rats telling how the sailors build their cooking fires on board ship. A layer of sand right on the deck, bricks on top of that, and—"

"Amos," he shouts, "you've got it!" and rushed for the bricks and sand. He put a layer of sand in the bottom of the affair, the bricks on top of that, and then set the andirons in.

It looked pretty promising.

"Eureka!" he exclaims, stepping back to admire it—and tripping over the saw. "Straighten things up a bit, Amos, while I run and get some logs."

"*Don't* try to run," I said. "And by the way, do you come through the pantry on the way up?"

"Why?" he asked.

"In some ways, Ben," I said, "you're fairly bright, but in others you're just plain dull. The joy of creating may be meat and drink to you; but as for me, a bit of cheese—"

He was gone before I finished, but when he came back with the logs he did have a fine slab of cheese, a loaf of rye bread, and a good big tankard of ale.

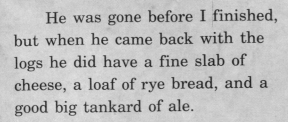

We put in some kindling and logs and lit her up. She drew fine, and Ben was so proud and excited that I had to be rather sharp with him before he would settle down to food. Even then he was up every minute, to admire it from a new angle.

Before we'd finished even one sandwich, the room had warmed up like a summer afternoon.

"Amos," says he, "we've done it!"

"Thanks for the WE," I said. "I'll remember it."

Robert Lawson

*R*obert Lawson was trying to decide how to write a book about Ben Franklin. His wife happened to see a picture of Franklin and commented that Franklin's fur hat looked like "a rat's nest." That gave Lawson the idea to write *Ben and Me*, about a mouse who lived in Franklin's fur cap. Lawson named the character Amos, because the name sounds like "a mouse."

Ben and Me was the first book Lawson wrote, although he had already illustrated several others, including the children's classic *Ferdinand*, which is about a gentle bull. Lawson went on to write many other books on a wide range of subjects. In the process, he became the first person to win both a Caldecott Medal (for *They Were Strong and Good*) and a Newbery Medal (for *Rabbit Hill*).

Lawson illustrated his first book in 1930, and he died in 1957. During those twenty-seven years, he wrote and illustrated dozens of books. Many of them have become classics and are still popular today, including *Mr. Revere and I*, a book about Paul Revere told from the point of view of his horse.

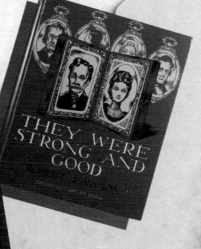

CURIOUS BEN

What made Ben Franklin, with only two years of schooling, a leading scientist of the 18th century? The answer: curiosity. "Why does it do that?" Ben would ask. "How does that work?"

When he noticed that gypsum (a chalklike substance occurring naturally in rocks) spread on a field made grass grow greener, he suggested farmers try putting it on their crops. As a result, he's credited with introducing the notion of artificial fertilizer. And Franklin was one of the first to realize that lead poisoning was the cause of a disease that commonly destroyed the health of printers, painters, and plumbers.

When Ben decided to find out why it took so much longer to sail from England to America than the other way around, he talked to whaling captains from Nantucket. They told him about what we now call the Gulf Stream, a rapid current that runs through the Atlantic. Franklin then set out to chart this current. On his many transatlantic crossings, he carefully recorded the water temperature several times a day, discovering that, "a stranger

Franklin is credited with inventing this odometer. When fixed to his carriage, it accurately measured road miles.

may know when he is in the Gulf Stream by the warmth of the water, which is much greater than that of the water on each side of it."

Ben Franklin investigating electrical attraction and repulsion.

352

Warming an entire room with a fireplace, Ben realized, was "next to impossible." His solution: the Pennsylvania fireplace, an open iron box with air chambers on each side. The box fit into a fireplace and allowed heat to radiate more efficiently into a room. A modified version of this, called the Franklin stove, was devised by a scientist friend of Franklin's and can be found in many homes today.

This generator, which produced static electricity, was made to Ben's specifications.

The Franklin Wannabee

The Real Franklin

Check It Out!
Franklin proved that darker cloth absorbed more heat than lighter cloth by an ingenious experiment performed on a sunny winter day. How do you think he did it? (answer below)

(answer) He laid squares of different colored cloth on the snow-covered ground. The darker the cloth, the faster the snow beneath it melted.

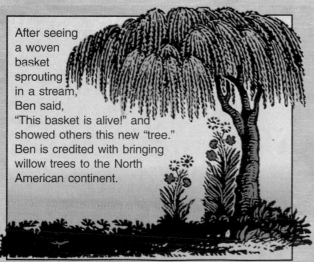

After seeing a woven basket sprouting in a stream, Ben said, "This basket is alive!" and showed others this new "tree." Ben is credited with bringing willow trees to the North American continent.

Franklin claimed to have developed a smokeless candle and invented a candle made from whale oil. It burned brighter and lasted longer than ordinary candles and, he maintained, it left no grease spots when it dripped.

353

DON'T TRY THIS!

Franklin is probably most famous for his kite experiment. As the story goes, he and his son raised a silk kite on a long cord into a sky filled with black clouds. A metal rod was bound to the kite, and an iron key was attached to the end of the cord. Franklin and his son tied a silk string to the end of the cord, where the key was, and held on to that.

As storm clouds approached, the metal rod drew electricity (what Franklin called "electric fire") from them. When rain wet the kite and the cord, electricity was freely conducted (water is a good conductor of electricity) from the rod to the key. Franklin touched the key with his knuckle and received an electrical shock. This proved his theory that lightning was really electricity.

Franklin was willing to risk a shock to test for electricity, but he also knew enough about this form of electricity to end the experiment before lightning struck. Franklin warned anyone attempting his experiment to stand at a window or in a doorway, keeping the silk cord dry and away from the doorframe or windowframe. If the silk became wet, a lightning strike could be fatal.

EXPERIMENTS WITH ELECTRICITY

If you've ever rubbed a balloon with a piece of wool, like a wool scarf or sweater, and stuck it to a wall, you've seen static electricity in action. Here's what happens. A material can have either a positive or negative electrical charge. When you rub a balloon with wool, negative charges are rubbed off the wool onto the balloon. The positive charges on the surface of the wall are attracted to the extra negative charges on the balloon and the two stick together. Here are some more things you can do with static electricity. These all work best in cool, dry places.

1. Rub a plastic comb with a piece of wool to charge it with static electricity.

2. See if the comb will pull a Ping-Pong ball along a flat surface.

3. Mix some salt and pepper grains in a dish. See if the comb will pull the pepper grains out of the mixture.

4. See if the comb will make your hair stand on end.

5. See if you can make a small stream of water from a faucet bend with the comb.

6. Put some unflavored powdered gelatin in a flat dish. Rub a balloon with a piece of wool. Touch the charged balloon to the gelatin. Then raise the balloon slightly. Watch gelatin icicles appear.

Several people successfully tried Ben's experiment—in France, England, Russia, and Belgium. However, Professor Georg Wilhelm Richmann was not so lucky. He was electrocuted in 1753.

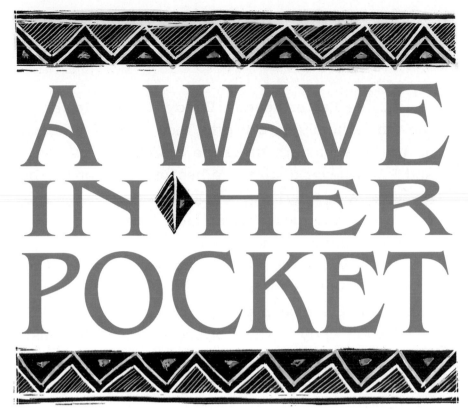

A WAVE IN HER POCKET

by Lynn Joseph • illustrated by Brian Pinkney

Almost all families in Trinidad have a tantie. A tantie is usually a grandaunt who helps to take care of all the grandnephews and grandnieces. She often gives advice to mothers on raising children even if she herself has no children. On family outings she entertains the children by gathering them all together and telling them stories. Sometimes she tells stories to teach them a lesson. Sometimes she tells stories to scare them or make them laugh. But the main thing about a tantie's stories is that she always has one ready, because any time is story time.

Many of the stories that tanties tell originate in the countries of West Africa. Others begin right in Trinidad. And some tanties make up stories that no one else has ever told before.

Here is one of my tantie's best stories, remembered forever.

357

One Easter holiday, Daddy decided to take the whole family on a trip to Toco. Toco is a beach on the northeastern tip of the island. My cousins and I had never gone there because it's not the best place for a sea bath.

"Too many rocks," said Uncle Rupert.

"And clumpy sand," said Auntie Hazel.

"And waves too big to jump over," added Mama.

Still, Daddy wanted us to go because Toco is one of the prettiest places to see.

We left early in the morning. The sun had just started lighting up the tops of the coconut trees. They looked like giant candles. Daddy packed up our car with Mama in the front seat, and me, Susan, and Cedric in the back.

Aunts and uncles and other cousins packed up their cars too. When everyone was ready, we drove off down the narrow pitch road, one behind the other like a trail of goats.

At first, Cedric, Susan, and I had plenty room in the backseat. But then Daddy pulled up in front of Tantie's home. The five other cars parked behind Daddy, filling up Tantie's empty street. Tantie sat waiting on her bright red porch.

"Where Tantie go sit?" asked Susan.

Nobody answered. We knew Tantie would pick the car *she* wanted to ride in. We watched as she climbed down her front steps slow slow. She was carrying a basket bigger than two of me. And she was heading for our car.

"Well, is now de backseat go get crowded," said Cedric.

"Shush," Mama said, as Daddy got out and helped Tantie in. She squeezed in between me and Cedric and placed her basket smack-dab on her lap.

We could barely see each other over the big basket. I hoped Tantie would open it up and share out some black cake or plums. But Tantie sat there like she was at the movies, her two eyes staring straight ahead, as Daddy drove down the street.

"What wrong with Tantie?" Cedric whispered behind her head.

I shrugged.

Susan said, "Tantie, why you don't tell us a story?"

But for the first time ever, Tantie shook her head. "No stories today, dear."

Mama and Daddy were singing aloud to old calypso playing on the radio so I guess they didn't notice that Tantie was acting strange and looking sad. I decided to cheer her up, and Susan and Cedric must have had the same idea.

Susan said, "Look, Tantie," and pointed to a boy walking at the side of the road with five baby goats following him. But Tantie didn't even look.

Then Cedric said, "Tantie, I think I go win de marble-pitching contest at school." But Tantie didn't even say, "Good luck."

Then I said, "Tantie, you lived in Toco when you were little. It have plenty fun things to do there?" Tantie acted like she didn't hear a word I said.

Suddenly, Daddy rounded a bend in the road. We started driving down into a beautiful valley. The sea sprang up all around. It was sparkling like a blue Carnival costume. The waves were smacking the rocks with big kisses and then ducking back into the sea. The trees were green and spread out wide like fans. Even the rocks looked different here. They jutted out from the land like big, brown fishermen waiting to catch fish.

It seemed like all this prettiness woke Tantie up. She stopped sitting still and started looking around. She looked out Susan's window and smiled at the trees and the sky. She looked out the front window and smiled at the next hill coming up. Then she looked out my window where the blue sea was shining in the sunlight, and her smile disappeared clean off her face.

"Tantie, what's wrong?" I asked.

Tantie just stared and stared at the sea. Then the strangest thing happened. A tear rolled down her face. It was just me who saw. I didn't know what to do. I put my head on Tantie's shoulder and squeezed her hand real tight.

Daddy drove up and down one hill after another. Each valley was prettier than the one before. I didn't look at Tantie anymore but I could feel her staring out my window.

Finally, we reached Toco. The first thing I saw as Daddy parked the car was a huge turtle walking on the sand. His head was out of his shell and he was looking all around. When he saw us, though, he stuck his head quick quick back in his shell and sat on the beach like a rock. Tantie saw this and laughed. I laughed too, 'cause I was happy to see Tantie not sad anymore. Cedric and Susan and Mama and Daddy started laughing also. When everybody else arrived they thought we were a bunch of crazies because we were sitting on the beach laughing at a rock.

After a while Mama and Daddy and Auntie Hazel and the rest of the family gathered the picnic baskets and climbed over the rocks to find a good place to eat. I decided to

stay by the turtle to see if he'd stick his head back out. Tantie stayed too.

She sat down next to the turtle. "Hello!" she shouted, and bent her face close. I was sitting on the other side of the turtle. He was so big it looked like Tantie and I were at a table for two.

"Tell him hello," said Tantie.

"Hello, Mr. Turtle," I shouted and patted him on his hard old shell.

Then Tantie said, "He remind me of a story. Want to hear?"

I was so glad that Tantie had changed her mind about not telling any stories today that I couldn't answer. I just nodded my head and Tantie began her tale.

"A long time ago, a young girl lived by a deep blue sea like this one. She had brown skin like de rocks, long braids like de seaweed, and everyone said her eyes were like de midnight wave.

"This girl loved de sea and de sea animals more than anything else. She loved de seashells, and de starfish, de snails, and de sand dollars. She even loved de yellow sand crabs that no one else liked. Her favorite, however, was de big old turtles. She called them her grandfathers.

"These turtles came out only at night. During de day they hid themselves by de rocks so no one could see them. But de girl figured out a way. She climbed on top a tall, smooth rock that overhung de rocks where de turtles hid and she dropped small fish below. Then she waited on her rock and watched as turtle heads popped out to snap up de fish. Each day de girl took them fish to eat and after a while de grandfather turtles began waiting for her.

"As de girl grew older she began to love something even more than her grandfather turtles. Actually, it was someone. His name was Godfrey and he was a young fisherman. Every morning de girl stood on de beach and watched Godfrey set out in his little pirogue. And every afternoon she waited for him to pull in his nets.

"In her mind she said, 'Hello, Godfrey.' And in her mind he answered, 'Hello Delphine.' But she never said it out loud."

"Tantie," I interrupted excitedly. "Isn't Delphine your name too?"

"Yes, chile, it is," said Tantie. Then she went on.

"After Godfrey put his fish into big baskets and sold them to de village women, he tied up his pirogue and walked home. When he passed Delphine he smiled, and his face glowed like de sun.

"Delphine knew there was no one else like him. And she also knew that just like de waves would always come one after de other, she and Godfrey would be together forever."

"Tantie," I interrupted again. "This not de kind of story you usually tell."

Tantie nodded her head. "I guess 'cause this not really a made-up one, chile."

"Whatcha mean, Tantie? It for true?"

Tantie only smiled and put her finger to her lips to shush me. Then she went on.

"One morning around this same time of year when de villagers were planning a big Easter celebration, Delphine watched Godfrey set out in his pirogue. But this time she felt a darkness deep down inside herself. She stepped up to him and, for the first time ever, touched his hand.

"'Don't go,' she said in her mind. She looked in his eyes and saw de sea. And his smile was better than de sun. But she couldn't say her words out loud. She stepped back and let him go."

"How come she couldn't talk?" I asked, forgetting all about Tantie's shush finger. "Was she scared that Godfrey wouldn't listen to her?"

Tantie smiled slowly. "Yes, I think that's why. Anyway, let me tell de rest of de story.

"That afternoon Delphine waited and waited for Godfrey to come back. She climbed on top her high rock and shaded her eyes from de sun. She looked and looked, but she couldn't see anything but waves.

"De next afternoon Delphine climbed on top her rock again. She waited and waited. She even forgot to feed de turtles. But Godfrey still didn't come. Every day she climbed de rock and looked at de sea for Godfrey. But only de waves looked back at her. Then one day as she stood on her rock, Delphine thought she heard de waves singing a song.

"I'll marry my love, the deep blue sea,
And carry him in my pocket.
I'll marry my love
And carry my love,
A wonderful wave in my pocket."

"Tantie, what that song mean? How can you carry a wave in your pocket?" I asked.

"That's what Delphine wondered, too," said Tantie. "She thought it was a song from Godfrey but she didn't know what it meant."

"Well, did she ever figure it out?" I asked, looking at the big waves splashing onto the sand.

"No," said Tantie sadly. "She never figured it out. After a while she stopped climbing de rock. And she moved far away to a town with plenty people, and streets instead of sand, and cars instead of pirogues. But especially no waves to sing that song to her."

Tantie looked out over the sea.

"Tantie," I said softly. "Are you de same Delphine in de story?"

Even though I had guessed it, I was surprised when she nodded her head. Poor Tantie. I listened to the waves hitting the sand until it sounded as if they were singing Tantie's song.

"Tantie, I think I know what that song means," I said slowly.

Tantie looked up at me with a funny expression on her face. Like she had forgotten I was there. "Okay, Amber, tell me what it means," she answered. I could see her eyes were still far away.

"Well," I said. "De song says 'I'll marry my love, the deep blue sea, and carry him in my pocket.' And you said that you loved de sea *and* you loved Godfrey. Well, when Godfrey never came back from de sea, he was part of de sea. So, 'my love, the deep blue sea' means him, Godfrey." I patted the turtle on his hard shell and hoped Tantie was understanding me.

"Marrying someone means that person will always be right next to you, and carrying something in your pocket means de same thing. So, when de song said to marry your love and carry him in your pocket, it meant to keep Godfrey close to you always. Like in your heart, I guess." I glanced over at Tantie. "And it's a happy song, not a sad one, because it called Godfrey a wonderful wave in your pocket. So de sea was singing a song from Godfrey

to you saying to never forget him and to keep him close always."

Well, when I finish that long speech, Tantie's face was shining bright bright.

"Amber," she said. "You alone done figure it out." And she got up and gave me a big hug. I was so happy that I forgot sometimes I'm a little bit afraid of her and I hugged her back hard. Then she grabbed my hand. "Come on," she said. "Let's you and me go dip our arms in de water and give Godfrey de sea a hug. Then we go find your mama and them so we can eat!"

And that's just what me and Tantie did.

◆ MEET ◆ LYNN JOSEPH ◆ AND ◆ BRIAN PINKNEY

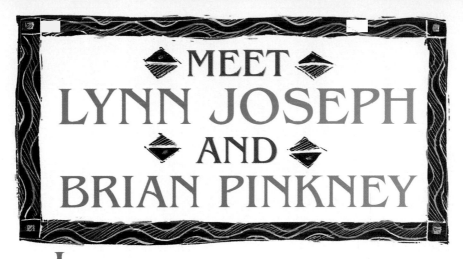

Lynn Joseph was born in Trinidad, a Caribbean island nation. While still a child, she moved to the United States with her family but returned every summer to visit Trinidad. As a result, her childhood was filled with the music, food, and culture of that island.

Joseph, like many authors, weaves memories and details from her childhood into her writing. Joseph's family often went to Toco Beach, where "A Wave in Her Pocket" takes place. Joseph remembers hearing about people who rode the huge leatherback turtles there. "It was dangerous and rough, and I remember being told that sometimes the turtles took people too far out, and they drowned."

Joseph is also the author of a book of poetry titled *A Coconut Kind of Day: Island Poems.*

Brian Pinkney is the son of the artist Jerry Pinkney (who illustrated *The Talking Eggs*). Although he grew up watching his talented father work, he developed his own technique while in art school—the scratchboard technique used in the pictures in this story. In addition to children's books, Pinkney has done illustrations for newspapers and magazines.

Secret Talk

by Eve Merriam

I have a friend
and sometimes we meet
and greet each other
without a word.

We walk through a field
and stalk a bird
and chew a blade of
pungent grass.

We let time pass
for a golden hour
while we twirl a flower
of Queen Anne's lace

or find a lion's face
shaped in a cloud
that's drifting, sifting
across the sky.

There's no need to say,
"It's been a fine day"
when we say goodbye:
when we say goodbye
we just wave a hand
and we understand.

Unit 5

TAKE
the HIGH
ROAD

GRANDMA ESSIE'S COVERED WAGON

by **DAVID WILLIAMS** • *illustrated by* **WIKTOR SADOWSKI**

I was born in a log cabin near Duenweg, Missouri, almost ninety years ago. There were six kids in our family—Stella, Opal, Kenneth, me, Jack, and Violet—and we lived in two little rooms. Papa worked as a hired hand, which didn't pay enough for us to buy nice things. But we didn't know any different and were happy—we had no idea Papa dreamed of something more.

P apa saved his money, then decided to go west and farm wheat. "There's lots of rich land in Kansas," he said, and soon we were all dreaming. Papa bought a frame wagon that farmers had used to haul crops. He bent wooden stays from one side to the other, nailed them down to form hoops, and stretched a white canvas over. As he worked, we watched our covered wagon rise, a magic ship that could take us anywhere.

Inside, Papa built shelves and Mama put in a little monkey stove. We loaded the wagon with all our clothes and blankets, and Kenneth hooked four mules to the front. Our calf, Molly, who was so gentle we kids used her for a pony, was tied to the back along with the milk cow. At last we were off to see the world.

Mama had made quilts, rugs, and comforts for everyone to sit on, and she rode with Violet on her lap. Opal, who was pregnant and got sick some of the time, sat between her husband, Arthur, and Stella. Kenneth rode up front with Papa. Jack and I rode wherever we felt like. Sometimes when we were restless, we'd even jump out and trot behind the wagon. We'd throw dirt clods at each other or ride Molly. There were lots of wild things outside—wolves, coyotes, foxes—but if they scared us, we'd just jump back inside and be safe.

We traveled through Kansas on dust and rock roads that went on forever. Sometimes we'd pass little farms and Mama'd buy eggs. She'd make pancakes in the morning out of scratch and brew Papa's coffee in a blue granite percolator. In the evenings we'd eat lots and lots of potatoes.

There were nights we never made it to a town and had to sleep on the earth. Mama would pull out every quilt, and we'd light a campfire. Stella would play the mandolin and sing songs like "From Jerusalem to Jericho" and "When the Roll Is Called Up Yonder, I'll Be There." We'd all join her on the chorus, then fall asleep together under the stars.

We went clear to western Kansas like that, to a little farm with an orchard and a red two-story house. Jack and I loved standing in the stairwell and yelling our names. We'd try to see who could be the loudest, our voices echoing back. Then we'd run every which way, our new home so big we thought it was a castle! We had beds to sleep on, and real cotton sheets. Mama sewed curtains out of old dresses. We scrubbed the walls and woodwork with rags, and soon the place looked good.

ost of the land was prairie. It rolled on forever, like the back of some huge animal that might get up and run. The wind would whip out of nowhere, and sometimes Jack and I would grab the thick cushions off the sofa, take them outside, and hold them against our bellies. When the wind blew, we'd let go. The cushions would hold to us like magic!

It was hard for Papa to get the new place going. But wealthy wheat farmers *did* live in Kansas, and one little rich boy liked me.

He invited me to his house for dinner one time, where there were all these cantaloupes and watermelons, but I was too bashful to taste any of them.

We had a horse named Major, who wouldn't get started once he'd stopped. One game was to pretend we were in the Big Top, then walk under Major or sit on his back. All the time, he'd just stand there, covered with the wild prairie flowers we'd decorated him with, nothing able to make him budge.

One day I was upstairs looking out our window, and there was the funniest sight I'd ever seen—a big black cloud winding up. I ran downstairs to Papa, who'd just come in from the fields.

"Take a look at this, Papa!" I cried. "There's something in the sky!"

At first he thought I was seeing things, but then he hollered, "It's a tornado!" and rushed us all to the cellar. The air was thick as a stampede. We huddled in the dark together, underground,

our hands over our ears. Violet wouldn't stop crying.

A big river ran between our house and town. The tornado
followed it, so we were saved.

We went barefoot through summer and fall and had to walk
to school that way. Stella had always wanted a pair of white
dress shoes, but Papa said no, we couldn't afford them. We sat
with the other barefoot kids in the back of our one-room schoolhouse, the rich kids and their shoes up front.

Somehow, a front-row girl and I became friends. She had red hair and could really jump rope. She wore beautiful shiny black shoes, but I got to where I barely noticed them. We'd sing "Every Time I Go to Town Boys Start Kicking My Dog Around" and run through the playground, laughing.

Christmas Eve Papa went out and chopped down a small tree with bare branches. Mama had cut pictures out of the Sears-and-Roebuck catalog, and we hung them all over till the tree looked alive. She'd made rag dolls with button eyes and long yarn braids for us girls, and Papa had carved Kenneth a toy horse and made Jack a wagon. After all our popcorn was popped and eaten, all our cranberries strung, we sang "Away in a Manger" with Stella.

Then Christmas day, Opal had her baby! We tiptoed upstairs to peek at our first nephew, as big as a hand, healthy and screaming. Arthur was so happy about being a father he asked Stella to play her mandolin in the kitchen, then he danced.

Papa raised wheat, hay, and corn, but the second year in
Kansas came a drought. Fields turned to dust. Plants wouldn't
grow. Our horses went hungry, and the river ran dry. Jack and I
could walk across it from mud bank to mud bank, seeing the dead
fish and rounded river rocks. We'd pick those rocks up and hurl
them just as far as we could, asking ourselves what happened.

Papa lost all his money, and we had to sell the farm. I said

good-bye to my ducks. Our hound dogs, Papa gave to some
neighbors. We auctioned off our horses, cows, and furniture,
keeping only what would fit into the wagon, then we loaded it
up and were gone.

Stella played "Diamonds in the Rough" as we bumped down
the dusty road. There was just the sound of her fingers plucking
strings and the sight of our own farm floating away.

We headed south, down to Oklahoma. Mama's folks lived near Oologah in a log cabin that reminded us of our home in Missouri. They were part Indian, Grandpa with his coal-black hair and mustache. He wore a felt hat with a big brim and played the fiddle, always wanting us kids to stay put and be his audience.

"You sit there," he'd say, "I want you to listen to this fiddle." But all *we* wanted was to go to the creek and swim.

Grandma'd tell us animal stories every night, smoking a clay pipe that we loved to light. Grandpa'd give us a stick to put in the coals, then we'd get the tip of it on fire and touch it to the

tobacco while Grandma puffed.

There was a big garden behind their cabin, and a kitchen
that wasn't fastened on, and always plenty to eat. We camped at
their place all summer and never wanted to leave.

But Papa heard about the oil fields in Big Heart, Oklahoma,
and once more we loaded up the wagon. I tried to give Grandma
the doll Mama'd made me. "I want Mary to have a real home like
yours," I said, but Grandma thought Mary might need me, that I
should take her.

Grandma and Grandpa waved to us from their porch as we
left. Grandpa held his fiddle in one hand and Grandma cried.

Big Heart was a boom town. I'd never seen so many people or heard so much noise. The land was flat as a pancake, but the oil derricks that rose up every fifty feet made it look like a metal forest. Buildings were being put up left and right—banks, restaurants, saloons—and the streets were mud. There weren't any houses to live in. Papa set a tent up in a shantytown where other oil workers' families lived, and we parked the covered wagon. We sold our mules. Papa, Kenneth, and Arthur got jobs in the oil fields and were gone sunup to sundown, and always came home exhausted.

Stella began working for the Salvation Army to help raise money for the orphanage. As she played her mandolin and sang, oilmen would drop big silver dollars onto the drum. She sang in the streets all winter, then fell in love with the Salvation Army captain and planned to get married. But one day she took sick: just started coughing and couldn't stop. The doctor said she'd gotten ill from "exposure," being outside too long in the cold.

We prayed for her. We told her stories. We held her hand. Nothing would make her better.

One cold day in March, Stella died. Papa walked downtown and bought her a pair of white dress shoes, like she'd always wanted, to be buried in. But he wouldn't go to the funeral. He sat in the tent by himself while Mama and the rest of us went out past the oil derricks to the cemetery. The preacher said a few words, then we sang. And for a moment we all swore we heard Stella singing with us.

ama thought I could get a job waiting tables, to help the family out. I was scared to try, but one day I walked into the Black Gold Restaurant and asked if they needed any help.

"How old are you?" this big woman asked.

"Fourteen," I lied.

"Well, let's see if you can work," she said, and soon I was carrying trays of food with my hands shaking the whole time and bringing home tips.

After a year in Big Heart we had saved enough to go. We bought two new mules and loaded the covered wagon for the last time. "We're heading back to Missouri," Papa said, and we moved to Seneca, on the Missouri-Oklahoma border. Opal and Arthur rented a house, and Papa bought a farm. It wasn't as nice as our place in Kansas, but we were so glad to have a home. Where the floors had cracks, Mama laid out rugs she'd made. She even wallpapered with newspapers to cover the spaces between the walls' wooden slats. And we went to bed nights feeling good.

There was a huge strawberry patch out back, so we went into business. When the berries ripened, we picked and boxed them, twenty-four to a crate, to be shipped out on the train. I made friends with a neighbor girl who worked for us, and sometimes before we started to fill a new quart we'd each write our name and address on the bottom. That way whoever bought the strawberries would know who we were.

One day Mama called me into the house. "A letter's come to you from New York City," she said. It was from a boy who'd gotten one of the strawberry quarts with my name inside. He said he wanted to marry me, but Mama wouldn't let me go.

Papa broke up the old covered wagon and sawed it to pieces. He made things from the wood—a table and chairs, a bookcase, a porch swing like the one we're sitting on.

I stayed in Seneca until I grew up and met your grandpa, an iron ore miner from Diamond. He was handsome. One day we went to Joplin and got married. Then we bought this house almost seventy years ago—here where I had my babies. My babies grew up, left home, and had their babies. But I never moved away.

AUTHOR'S NOTE

As far back as I can remember, I've been listening to Grandma Essie's stories. Every summer my parents would take us kids "back home" to Missouri to sit on her porch swing and hear about things far different from what we knew. Grandma's father had once boarded Frank and Jesse James. She knew Wyatt Earp's cousin. And then there was the wonderful story of the covered wagon.

The stories Grandma Essie told from her childhood had a huge effect on me as a young boy, and in the fall of 1988 when Grandma came to visit, at the age of eighty-seven, I talked to her about capturing one in a book. Grandma was excited by the idea. All the details of her early days traveling in the covered wagon flooded back, and over the course of a week we went over them, meticulously re-creating each of the scenes. Here, then, is her story, in mostly her words, that I've helped shape and arrange.

The above photograph is of the family's Kansas farm. Twelve-year-old Essie is standing barefoot at the far right. To her left are sister Opal and her baby; sister Violet; brothers Kenneth and Jack; sister Stella; an unknown hired hand; Grandma Essie's Mama; and finally Papa. Grandma remembers when the picture was taken—everyone was working in the fields when a traveling photographer happened by.

Grandma Essie has lived from the covered wagon days to the days when people fly to the moon. When you listen to her, I hope you can see the stern Midwestern landscape, feel the rowdy Kansas wind, and hear Grandma Essie's own voice as I hear it, wiser and stronger for having lived this life, but with an echo of the young girl who has never completely gone away.

Meet
DAVID WILLIAMS

David Williams loves music. He began singing when he was two. When he was 12, Williams started playing guitar. He also loves travel. Every summer his family drove from Illinois to Missouri to visit Grandma Essie. When he grew up, Williams traveled the country playing music for audiences.

Eventually, Williams became a teacher. One day he and some fourth graders decided to write a song about the environment. Williams went on to write more songs for children on his own. His album *Oh, the Animals* won an award from the American Library Association.

If you enjoyed *Grandma Essie's Covered Wagon*, you might also enjoy David Williams's music and his book *Walking to the Creek*.

WALKING
TO THE
CREEK

by David Williams
Illustrated by Thomas B. Allen

Stopping by Woods on a Snowy Evening

Whose woods these are I think I know.
His house is in the village though;
He will not see me stopping here
To watch his woods fill up with snow.

My little horse must think it queer
To stop without a farmhouse near
Between the woods and frozen lake
The darkest evening of the year.

He gives his harness bells a shake
To ask if there is some mistake.
The only other sound's the sweep
Of easy wind and downy flake.

The woods are lovely, dark and deep,
But I have promises to keep,
And miles to go before I sleep.
And miles to go before I sleep.

Robert Frost

Meet
Delia Ray

Delia Ray knows first-hand the hardships of the Yukon. To research her book *Gold! The Klondike Adventure*, she traveled to White Horse, a small city in the heart of gold-rush country. There, she had planned to study historical photographs and papers in the local museum. But the museum was closed! Next, she got snowed in. "It helped me get a picture of what it must have been like for the early goldseekers," she says. Eventually, though, she spent a week in the government archives, poring over letters, Mounted Police records, and other documents dating back to 1897.

At the University of Washington in Seattle, Ray discovered a treasure-trove of photographs and accounts by people who had joined in the Klondike gold rush. "I began to think anybody who ever came back to Seattle wrote a book about the Klondike experience," she jokes.

"I loved looking at the old Klondike photos," recalls Ray. "Some were taken in people's cabins, . . . usually by photographers who knew the people involved. The book really began with the photos."

KLONDIKE

Fever

by Delia Ray

George Washington Carmack

Skookum Jim

Tagish Charley

The city of Seattle was usually still asleep at daybreak on weekend mornings, but this Saturday large crowds of people rushed to the downtown waterfront at dawn. They shouted excitedly to one another, pointed across the water, and craned their necks to see. The *Portland* was coming! With its smokestack puffing and whistle blowing, the steamship chugged its way toward shore. On board was the most precious cargo ever to enter the Seattle harbor—sixty-eight miners from the Klondike and more than two tons of gold.

It was two days earlier when the first of the gold ships had arrived in San Francisco, California. The steamer *Excelsior* had sailed into port, bringing its load of gold and the news that an even richer treasure ship was on its way to Seattle. Finally, the *Portland* appeared in Seattle on July 17, 1897—almost one year after George Washington Carmack and his close friends Tagish Charley and Skookum Jim made their discovery on Bonanza Creek.

To the impatient spectators on the dock, the *Portland* seemed to move in slow motion. "Show us the gold!" yelled the onlookers, and several miners on board lifted their heavy sacks for all to see. A thrill swept through the crowd, as each person imagined the glittering gold dust and nuggets inside the bags.

The big ship carefully pulled alongside the wharf and the gangplank was lowered.

When the first miner stepped into full view, the people stared in amazement. He heaved a buckskin bag to his shoulder and steadied the load. His face was lean and weather-beaten, lined with the strain of hard work and long Yukon winters. Behind him two men staggered down the ramp, each grasping the end of a sagging blanket. One after another they came, carrying old leather suitcases, pine boxes, and pickle jars—anything that would hold the heavy piles of gold. The commotion on the docks grew with each miner that appeared. "Hurray for the Klondike!" the people cried.

As the ragged and bearded men set foot on shore, they squinted into the crowd, searching for familiar faces. Instead of old friends and relatives,

The passengers of the Portland *arrived in Seattle with over two tons of gold and fantastic stories of the rich Klondike. Several of the miners in this photograph rest their sacks of gold on their shoulders.*

Newspaper headlines reflected the excitement created by the arrival of the Portland.

they were greeted by throngs of reporters eager for the story of the Golden North. Most of the miners tried to escape the newsmen with their persistent questions and headed for the best restaurant they could find. They ordered huge feasts with fresh fruit and vegetables, for many had been living on a diet of beans and flapjacks for months.

One of the reporters' favorite front page subjects was Clarence Berry, who had stepped off the *Portland* with $130,000 in gold nuggets. With his magnificent strength and honest ways, the broad-shouldered miner instantly became Seattle's hero. Berry had set out from California to find his fortune three years earlier, leaving behind his childhood sweetheart and a bankrupt fruit farm. When he reached Alaska, Berry joined forty other anxious goldseekers bound for the Yukon. The long winter journey over the mountains was harsh, and many in the group gave up in despair. More turned back when a fierce storm whipped up, destroying all of their supplies, but Berry pressed on. Of the forty goldseekers who began

the trip, only he and two other men reached their final destination.

As the newspapers reported, Berry was not discouraged when he did not strike gold during his first year in the Klondike. He returned to California only long enough to marry his sweetheart, Ethyl Bush. Then back to the Yukon he went, with his new wife wrapped in a fur robe and bearskin hood.

Berry was working as a bartender in the saloon at the town of Forty Mile when George Carmack entered with his shotgun shell full of gold dust. Berry threw down his apron and joined the stampede to the Klondike goldfields. Before long he had hired twenty-five workmen to help harvest the riches from his claim on Eldorado Creek. The gold lay thick, so thick that Mrs. Berry—as *The Seattle Times* reported—could walk through the diggings and pick up nuggets "as easily as a hen picks up grains of corn in a barnyard." In one season she gathered more than $10,000 in nuggets during her occasional strolls through the claim.

Clarence Berry plays a fiddle with some friends in the Klondike, while a dog holds his hat.

407

After the solitude of a rustic cabin in the North, the Berrys were not prepared for the swarms of reporters and followers that trailed them into restaurants and surrounded them on the street. The couple fled to San Francisco, but the crowds were just as curious there. The callers lined up outside the Berrys' room at the Grand Hotel, until finally Mr. Berry allowed them to enter. Inside Room 111 was a glittering exhibition of gold. The visitors marveled over nuggets as big as chicken eggs and glass bottles full of gold dust, each labeled with the worth it contained.

In Seattle the excitement had reached a state of frenzy. The streets were packed with people

A group of businessmen proudly display one and one-half tons of gold at the Alaska Commercial Company office in the Klondike. At today's prices, this amount would be worth well over ten million dollars.

who rushed downtown to celebrate the news from the North. Large groups gathered at banks and shop windows, where stacks of gold bricks and piles of shining nuggets were on display. One could not walk down the street without hearing the word *Klondike* spoken in a dozen different conversations.

The reason for this wild excitement was simple: The Klondike gold ships arrived during a time of terrible poverty for the United States. Thousands of businesses were closing, and millions of people had lost their jobs. It was not unusual to see a man die of hunger in the streets or a family pushed out of its home because of unpaid bills. This period of hardship, known as an economic depression, had lasted for several years and it seemed that it would never end.

The arrival of the *Portland* and the *Excelsior* was like a dream come true for the poverty-stricken nation. Penniless men read with delight each new tale of wealth in the daily papers. They read about William Stanley, who left Seattle as a poor bookshop owner and returned a millionaire. Now Stanley's wife could quit her job as a laundry-woman and order a whole new wardrobe of fancy clothes. They read about Tom Lippy, a former athletic instructor. He and his wife brought back $60,000 in gold—a fortune in 1897, when a full meal could be purchased for 25 cents. Everywhere, people were certain they could make a trip to the Yukon and strike it rich, just as William Stanley and Tom Lippy had.

The Klondike gold rush was on. "THE POPULATION IS PREPARING TO MOVE TO THE KLONDIKE" shouted the newspaper headlines.

Eager to reach Dawson, the Klondike "City of Gold," many goldseekers hastily built sailboats such as the Yukon Flyer.

"EVERY MAN SEEMS TO HAVE CAUGHT THE KLONDIKE FEVER." Within hours after the gold ships had sailed into harbor, many men and women were quitting their jobs and preparing to head north. Seattle streetcar workers abandoned their trolleys on the track. Nuns left their churches, and a quarter of the police force resigned. Even the mayor announced his resignation and promptly bought a steamboat for carrying passengers to the Klondike.

Firemen, store clerks, school teachers, lawyers, and doctors—workers from Seattle to San Francisco decided to trade their regular paychecks for picks and shovels. But the West Coast of the United States was not the only region to be turned upside down by the Yukon discoveries. "Klondike fever" had spread to cities and towns throughout the country—and throughout the world. In New York, 2,000 people tried to buy tickets for the Klondike before the news of the gold strikes was one day old. Soon, groups of fortune hunters from Australia, Scotland, England, France, Italy, and other countries were also making their way toward the Yukon.

Many people could not afford to buy the steamship ticket or the supplies needed to travel northward. However, there were other ways for a poor, but determined, man to join the gold rush. Often a more wealthy acquaintance, who could not make the trip himself, was willing to provide a "grubstake"—the money needed to buy provisions for the journey. In return, the Klondiker had to promise that he would pay his debt with a share of whatever gold he found.

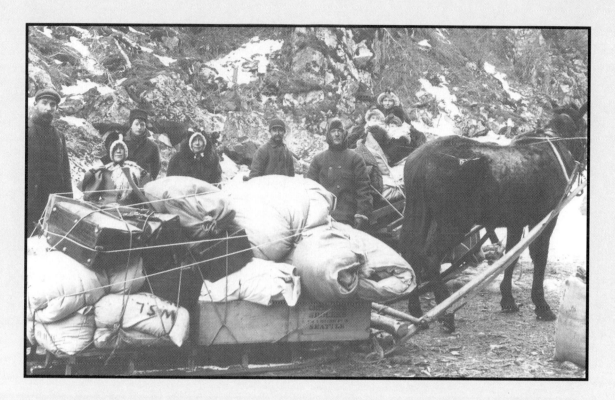

The hardware stores and grocery counters were booming with business. In Seattle, San Francisco, and other West Coast port cities, gold-seekers jammed store aisles. Never had shopping lists been so carefully prepared. Each Klondiker wanted to face the Arctic winds and long journey ahead with the warmest clothes and most nourishing food that money could buy.

By the winter of 1897, Canadian government officials had passed a law forbidding anyone from entering the goldfields without enough supplies to last an entire year. Once a prospector had spent $500 to buy a year's worth of goods for the Klondike, his load weighed about 2,000 pounds. Many newspapers and guidebooks printed checklists of the exact items needed for a proper outfit, as the miners called their store of provisions.

Not only hardened miners and strong men followed the dangerous Klondike trails. As this photograph shows, entire families—even grandmothers and small children—joined the rush over White Pass.

These were just some of the supplies that the future prospectors took along:

flour (150 pounds)	1 frying pan
bacon (150 pounds)	1 coffee pot
beans (100 pounds)	11 bars of soap
dried apples (25 pounds)	1 tin of matches
dried peaches (25 pounds)	1 box of candles
dried apricots (25 pounds)	1 medicine chest
rice (25 pounds)	1 pick
butter (25 pounds)	1 shovel
granulated sugar (100 pounds)	1 ax
coffee (15 pounds)	1 gold pan
tea (10 pounds)	1 handsaw
salt (10 pounds)	1 hatchet
pepper (1 pound)	6 towels
vinegar (1 gallon)	1 sheet-iron stove
1 tent	nails (16 pounds)

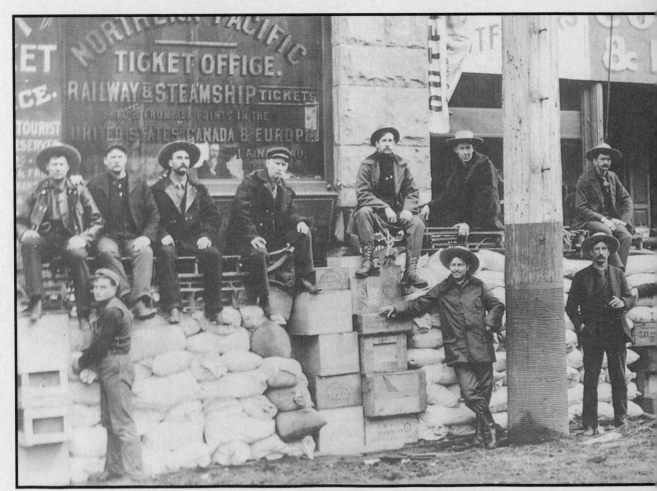

As the Klondikers waited for their hour of departure, they proudly sauntered up and down the streets in their new iron-toed boots and plaid flannel shirts. By now they were used to the scenes of confusion around them. The sidewalks were piled ten feet high with sacks of flour and crates of mining equipment ready to be sold to the next wave of stampeders. Long lines of people formed outside steamship offices, where the tickets were quickly sold out and clerks turned away hundreds of disappointed goldseekers. Dogs of every breed—huskies, Labradors, Saint Bernards, and golden retrievers—ran barking through the streets with their owners chasing after them. Dogs had suddenly become very valuable possessions, for many

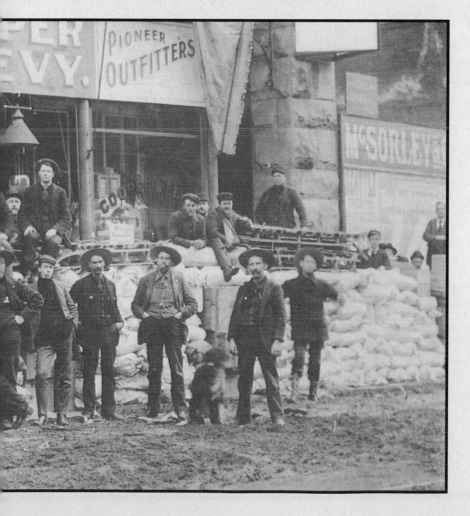

In Seattle many merchants made fortunes selling equipment to gold-seekers. Here, a group of future miners, ready to set out for the Klondike, stand in front of a wall of flour sacks and mining supplies.

Many businesses profited from the world's fascination with the Klondike. Eager fortune hunters paid the Yukon Mining School for lessons in driving dog teams, panning for gold, and using sluiceboxes.

would be trained to haul sleds full of supplies over the Klondike snow.

The stampeders often paused to watch street salesmen show off the newest products designed for those traveling north. There were Klondike medicine chests, Klondike blankets, and Klondike electric gold pans. There were portable Klondike houses, which the peddlers told their customers were "as light as air," even with the double bed and special Yukon stove that folded up inside. Dried food was sold in large quantities to future miners who wanted to save weight and space in their backpacks. Although most of the food was colorless and tasted bad, the miners bought everything from dried onions and turnips to evaporated rhubarb and potatoes.

Many dishonest merchants made money during the gold rush by selling worthless products or taking advantage of the innocent goldseekers. One Klondiker, Arthur Dietz, stopped on the street to watch a salesman pour some yellow powder from a sack and make a plate of scrambled eggs. Dietz was so impressed that he bought 100 pounds of the evaporated eggs for him and his traveling companions. It was not until the group was well on its way to the Klondike that Dietz opened the sacks. He realized that the yellow powder inside was really not eggs at all. The

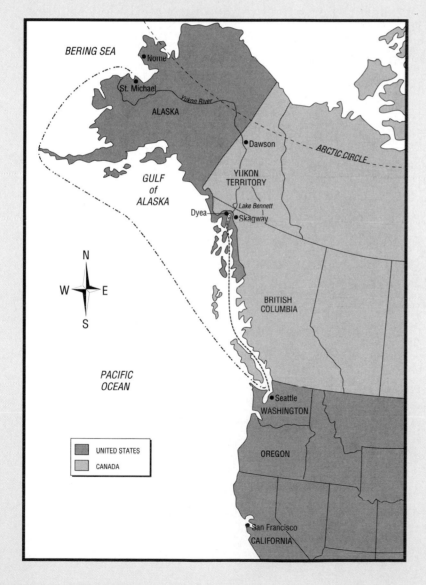

This map shows the two most popular routes to the Klondike—the Inside Passage, which led goldseekers through Dyea or Skagway, and the All-Water Route through St. Michael and up the Yukon River to Dawson. While Seattle was the world's busiest Klondike port, stampeders also set out for Dawson from other major harbors along the West Coast.

deceitful salesman had switched sacks and sold him 100 pounds of corn meal.

Like Arthur Dietz, thousands of goldseekers would face many unexpected difficulties on the Klondike trail. Most of the fortune hunters rushed to buy their tickets without truly knowing where their journey would lead them or what obstacles lay ahead. They read guidebooks about the Klondike, but even these were often inaccurate and misleading. Several books told readers that the Klondike was located in Alaska, when actually the region lay just across the Canadian border. Other travel guides incorrectly led readers to believe that the trails to the Klondike were like winding country lanes.

Many people also had unrealistic ideas of what their lives would be like once they reached the Klondike. One man set out for the Yukon as if he were taking a pleasant northern vacation. His outfit included thirty-two pairs of moccasins, one case of pipes, two Irish setters, a puppy, and a badminton set. Another man, who worked as a dance instructor, had hopes that he could give dancing lessons to the miners and Indians of the North, while digging nuggets during his spare time in the summer. A woman from Ireland planned to move her entire family to the Yukon, where she imagined her sons and daughters would attend school in the daytime and dig gold in the early mornings and late evenings. None of these Klondikers expected the harsh Arctic climate or understood that, to make any money, gold digging had to be a full-time job.

No one had more impractical ideas of how to become wealthy in the Klondike than the

businessmen, scientists, and inventors of the day. The newspapers were full of advertisements for strange new inventions that were "guaranteed" to make gold mining easier and pockets fuller. A business called the Trans-Alaskan Gopher Company promised to train gophers to claw through the icy gravel and uncover nuggets of gold.

Another scheme was the "Klondike Bicycle." Its inventor, Jacob Coxey, told reporters that his special bike could carry 500 pounds of supplies all the way to the Yukon. With its unfolding sidewheels, handlebar attachments, and rawhide-bound frame, the unsuccessful Klondike Bicycle was a comical looking vehicle. Certainly, if Jacob Coxey had ever seen the Yukon's steep mountains

In the early days of the gold rush, many newcomers arrived in Dawson expecting to find a wealthy town with tidy shops and clean streets. Instead, they found confusion and rivers of mud.

417

As steam from the ship's boilers fills the air, passengers look down on hundreds of friends, relatives, and spectators who jam the docks, waiting to see the Humboldt *leave for the Klondike.*

and dense forests, he never would have invented such an odd contraption.

As the summer of 1897 passed, a new ship left for the Klondike almost every day. The gold-seekers boarded the most unusual assortment of boats ever assembled. Coal ships, yachts, schooners, barges, and old fishing boats—any vessel that could float became a gold ship. Many boats that had long ago been declared unsafe were quickly brought in from the shipyards. Even with the hasty repairs that were made, many Klondike boats were referred to as "floating coffins."

Despite warnings, the excited stampeders did not seem to care whether their boats were seaworthy or not. The gold-crazed people pushed up the ramps, filling every available space on board. Passengers stood elbow-to-elbow. Over the ships' railings, several tearful faces appeared. Many goldseekers would not see their families again for months and months. But as the crowd below cried, "Three cheers for the Klondike!" and the ship whistles blasted a farewell, most of the passengers forgot their sadness.

Their Klondike adventure had finally begun.

As stampeders confidently set out on untraveled routes to the Klondike, a transformation took place in the North. On their way to Dawson, many stampeders discovered fertile ground for farming. Others stumbled upon creeks showing traces of gold. Men and women cut their journeys short and stayed to develop the land. As if a hidden door had been flung open, the mystery surrounding Alaska and northwest Canada disappeared. Suddenly, the North was a frontier for opportunity.

Few mining fortunes were made in the Klondike. In the early days comforts were rare and hardships were common. Yet, most of those who took part in this strange mass movement northward continued to share one special thought until they died: they would not have missed the Klondike adventure for anything in the world.

Thousands of men and women returned to their normal lives after the Klondike gold rush, but their outlook on the world had changed profoundly. The stampede taught those who reached Dawson that they could survive hardships and make a home in a desolate land—achievements that had seemed impossible only a few months before.

Martha Baker Wilson

Martha Baker Wilson went searching for gold in the Yukon with her husband, Charles (abbreviated "Chas."), and her brother Fred. They did not find any gold. However, the family was successful in selling the fish they caught. In her diary, Martha often notes that there was nothing to do but work and play cards. She, her family, and a small circle of friends found some relief from the boredom at holiday time.

Tues. 20 (Clear) (1 Above)

We have not done anything this week. Mr. Berg came in and had a game of cards. We almost saw the sun. The clouds were bright and golden. I was so pleased with the scene that I could easily persuade myself that I did see the sun.

Wed. Dec. 21, 1898 (Clear) (13 Above)

Chas. brought a big load of wood this eve. We have a christmas gift. a box of candy—from Miss Hollingsworth. for all three of us She will take dinner with us Sunday. and then we will eat our candy. Beef is getting cheaper. we may come to the conclusion that we can afford to eat a little. I do hope so.

Thursday. 22 (Snow) (9 Below)

Fred brought an apple to me. it was fine. I could eat a whole box of apples if I had them. Fred is going to try to trade some fish or rather sell some. and then we will get beef for the money. Biz. is not as good as it was a year ago. and may never be as good as it was or has been. I do not think that I will go out with the boys.

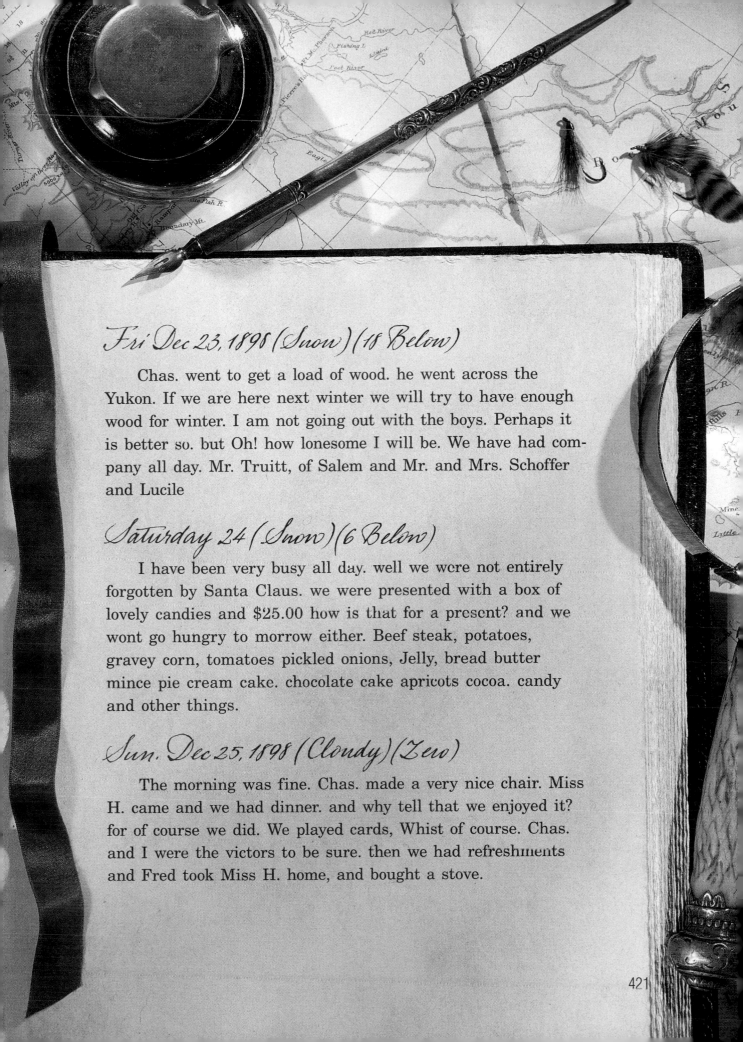

Fri Dec 23, 1898 (Snow) (18 Below)

Chas. went to get a load of wood. he went across the Yukon. If we are here next winter we will try to have enough wood for winter. I am not going out with the boys. Perhaps it is better so. but Oh! how lonesome I will be. We have had company all day. Mr. Truitt, of Salem and Mr. and Mrs. Schoffer and Lucile

Saturday 24 (Snow) (6 Below)

I have been very busy all day. well we were not entirely forgotten by Santa Claus. we were presented with a box of lovely candies and $25.00 how is that for a present? and we wont go hungry to morrow either. Beef steak, potatoes, gravey corn, tomatoes pickled onions, Jelly, bread butter mince pie cream cake. chocolate cake apricots cocoa. candy and other things.

Sun. Dec 25, 1898 (Cloudy) (Zero)

The morning was fine. Chas. made a very nice chair. Miss H. came and we had dinner. and why tell that we enjoyed it? for of course we did. We played cards, Whist of course. Chas. and I were the victors to be sure. then we had refreshments and Fred took Miss H. home, and bought a stove.

421

LIKE A MEMORY

A train goes by in the evening,
distant and old.
It crosses the fields,
like a memory.

Who saw the smoke rise,
round and slow?
Who heard the whistle,
calling all the town?

(Two or three white houses
along a path,
a fence of aralias
and two almond trees.)

A train goes by in the evening,
distant and old.

On the platform, silent,
a passenger
watches the smoke fade away
like a memory.

COMO UN RECUERDO

Pasa un tren en la tarde,
lejano y viejo.
Va atravesando el campo,
como un recuerdo.

¿Quién vio crecer el humo,
redondo y lento?
¿Quién escuchó el silbato,
llamando al pueblo?

(Dos o tres casas blancas
junto a un sendero,
una cerca de aralias
y dos almendros.)

Pasa un tren en la tarde,
lejano y viejo.

En el andén, callado,
un pasajero
mira borrarse el humo,
como un recuerdo.

Emilio de Armas

New Mexico, *painted by Thomas Hart Benton, 1926.*

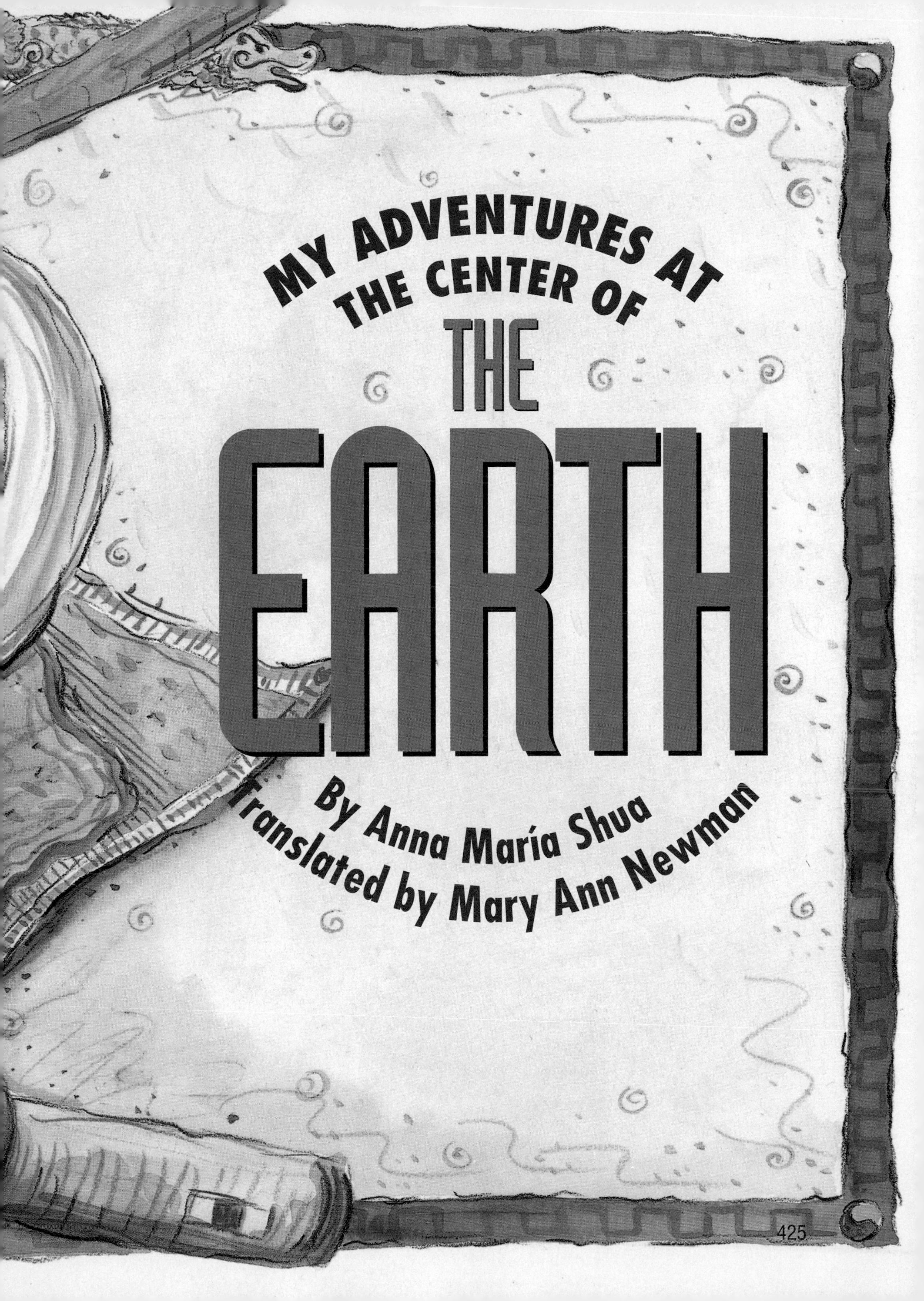

MY ADVENTURES AT THE CENTER OF

THE

EARTH

By Anna María Shua

Translated by Mary Ann Newman

When I was a little girl, people didn't travel as much as they do now. Most airplanes had propellers. The first super-sonic airplanes were just beginning to fly. We called them "jet planes," and they were really something special. If you don't believe me, ask your dad. Since taking a plane was practically an adventure and traveling by ship took a long time, people stayed home a lot more.

¡Explore China!

Once I noticed this, I had a great idea for making some money. I needed money to take a trip to the Amazon. I had to buy tents, sleeping bags, mosquito netting and canoes. I would also have to pay a guide to lead the way and hire other people to follow behind with the baggage.

It was a very simple idea. I would just dig a tunnel so deep that by crossing through the center of the earth, I would reach China, which is exactly on the other side. People could travel to China through my tunnel on foot. I planned to charge admission to anyone who wanted to make the trip, except my family and my best friend at school. It was a sure thing!

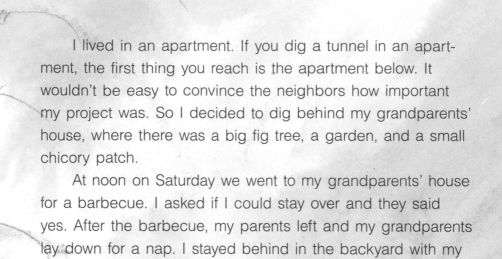

I lived in an apartment. If you dig a tunnel in an apartment, the first thing you reach is the apartment below. It wouldn't be easy to convince the neighbors how important my project was. So I decided to dig behind my grandparents' house, where there was a big fig tree, a garden, and a small chicory patch.

At noon on Saturday we went to my grandparents' house for a barbecue. I asked if I could stay over and they said yes. After the barbecue, my parents left and my grandparents lay down for a nap. I stayed behind in the backyard with my pail and shovel, ready to get started.

Since there was no plastic in those days, most toys were made of wood and beach toys were made of metal. My big

and sturdy shovel was made of tin. I had bought it with the money the tooth fairy left for me after my first tooth fell out. If you don't believe me, just ask my mother. Under my sweater I had wrapped a good length of string around my waist. String always comes in handy.

I began digging under the fig tree. At first the earth was soft and black. It came up easily with my shovel. I was careful not to hurt the roots of the tree. Soon I dug past the layer where the earthworms live. The ground started getting harder and dryer. I had a lot of practice digging, though, because I had just come back from a week at the beach. I scraped out steps in the walls of the tunnel. That was so I could climb back out when I wanted to.

At a certain point, I ran into my first problem. There was no more soil. Now I had to dig into rock. My tin shovel couldn't do that. Then I remembered that there is one stone that's harder than any other, a stone that can even cut steel—the diamond. And my grandmother had a diamond in her wedding ring.

When I came up to look for my grandmother's ring, the fig tree was missing. It was hidden under the mountain of earth and debris I had dug out of the hole.

I tiptoed into my grandparents' bedroom and borrowed the ring, which was on the night table. Along the way I picked up my grandfather's flashlight because it was getting dark in the hole. Passing through the kitchen I saw a dozen bananas in a bag of groceries. I took them, too, thinking I might get hungry. I wasn't worried about getting thirsty, because I was sure that there would be subterranean rivers or lakes. And if you don't believe me, just think how they get water in the country with pumps to bring it up from below.

My grandmother's diamond ring cut right through the rock, so I kept on digging my underground road to China. The problem was, the closer I got to the center of the earth, the hotter it became. Only then did I realize that I had forgotten one important detail: below the earth's crust there is only molten rock, the kind that erupts from volcanoes in the form of lava and fire.

Things looked bad. My project was on the edge of disaster. First of all, I could melt to death long before I reached China. Second of all, I would never be able to charge admission to go through such a dangerous place. And, finally, if I made a volcano appear in my grandparents' backyard, they would never let me sleep over again.

I was very thirsty. My throat
was dry. My tongue stuck to the roof
of my mouth. Where were the subterranean rivers? I hardly had enough
strength to go on splitting rock. I wasn't sure
I'd have enough strength to climb out of the hole.
Just as I was losing hope, the rock I hit with the
diamond sounded hollow. A piece of it gave way.
Through the hole I could see a gigantic cave. I turned off
the flashlight. The space was lighted with the glow of strange
violet-colored stones in the floor and walls of the cave. (One
of them is still sitting on my bookcase.)

I was really relieved to see that the cave (which was so big that I couldn't tell where it ended) held a huge subterranean lake. I tied the end of my string to a rocky ledge. Using the string, I let myself down to the cave floor. There I sank up to my waist in the high, thick, pink moss that blanketed the rocks. If you come to my house some day, I'll show you a handful of dry moss. I keep it between the pages of a book as a souvenir.

There were clusters of giant mushrooms spread out in little forests many meters high. I ran over to the lake. The cold, clear water quenched my thirst.

Suddenly I saw the head of a reptile at the end of a long, thin neck, peeking out from one of the mushroom forests. The animal moved towards me. An enormous body with legs like tree trunks fol- lowed behind.

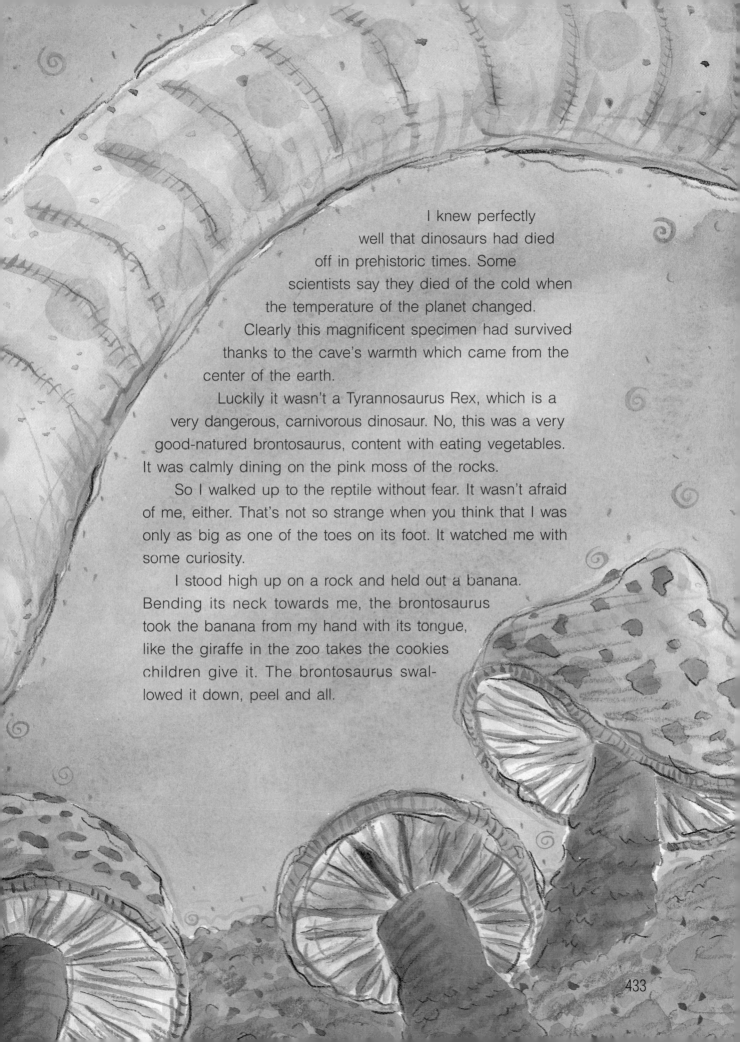

I knew perfectly well that dinosaurs had died off in prehistoric times. Some scientists say they died of the cold when the temperature of the planet changed.

Clearly this magnificent specimen had survived thanks to the cave's warmth which came from the center of the earth.

Luckily it wasn't a Tyrannosaurus Rex, which is a very dangerous, carnivorous dinosaur. No, this was a very good-natured brontosaurus, content with eating vegetables. It was calmly dining on the pink moss of the rocks.

So I walked up to the reptile without fear. It wasn't afraid of me, either. That's not so strange when you think that I was only as big as one of the toes on its foot. It watched me with some curiosity.

I stood high up on a rock and held out a banana. Bending its neck towards me, the brontosaurus took the banana from my hand with its tongue, like the giraffe in the zoo takes the cookies children give it. The brontosaurus swallowed it down, peel and all.

433

I was very happy. Even if I didn't finish my tunnel to China, another fine business opportunity had presented itself. I could sell tickets to the neighborhood children for a ride around the block on the brontosaurus's back. To do this I had to find a way to bring the animal all the way up to my grandparents' backyard.

I was very strong—so strong I could even beat the boys at arm wrestling. Even so, I knew that all the power of my muscles was not enough to lift a three-thousand-ton dinosaur. Besides, the dinosaur would never fit through the narrow tunnel that had led me down to the cave.

First of all, I decided I would somehow have to tie the dinosaur up with my string. The animal had begun to trust me and soon followed behind, eating the bananas I left in his path. That was how I led him over to some rocks from which I climbed up onto his back. I came down the other

side (slipping over his scaly skin as if it were a slide). Then I went under his belly and climbed up again. In this way I wrapped a couple of lengths of string around his huge body. I tied the string with many knots.

Next I climbed up to the roof of the cave. Then began the tiring job of widening the tunnel as I made my way toward the opening. For the time being, I didn't try to lift the dinosaur; I had another plan. Widening the tunnel was a tremendous, exhausting task that completely wore down the diamond in the ring. And if you don't believe me, ask my dear grandmother, who never quite forgave me.

Finally I reached the surface. There I had to break apart all the patio tiles to make room for the brontosaurus. Meanwhile, Bronti was calmly grazing in the cave, because I had carefully kept feeding out string as I made my way up. (I did it the way a good fisherman keeps letting out line to a fish so it'll think it's getting away with the worm). I was afraid that any sudden tug would frighten him before the time came to pull him up.

My grandparents' backyard was totally destroyed. I had turned it into a mountain on the edge of a cliff. A little worried,

I went out into the street. Making a loop with the end of the string I was holding, I waited for a truck to go by.

I needed a truck almost as heavy as Bronti. At last one came by that looked big and strong enough. I skillfully tossed the string and lassoed the cab of the truck. The driver was surprised to find himself suddenly slowed down by the animal's weight. He tried to speed up by racing the motor. The truck was long out of sight when my brontosaurus emerged from the tunnel.

Bronti seemed delighted to make the acquaintance of the sky, the sun, and the backyard of my grandparents' house. With his help I put all the stones, dirt, and rubble back in the hole. The fig tree hadn't been hurt at all. Everything was as before, except for the broken tiles. Those I had to stick back together with Glue-All, the best kind of glue there was when I was a little girl.

When my grandparents woke up from their nap, they were amazed to see my brontosaurus, who was eating the chicory in their garden. And though I had great success giving dinosaur rides to the neighborhood kids, all the money I made went to buy a new ring for my grandmother and new tiles for the patio—not to mention what it cost to feed Bronti. He ate about a ton of grass a day.

Bronti lived for many years in my grand-parents' backyard. He had a bad habit of eating all the figs. Grandmother complained because she couldn't use them anymore to make her favorite jam. Other than that, he was a very sweet and good-hearted animal. When he died of old age, I gave his bones to the Museum of Natural History. And if you don't believe me, go there any day and in the dinosaur hall you'll see the skeleton of my beloved friend, the brontosaurus.

Of course, I still had to solve one problem: how to get the money I needed for my big trip to the Amazon jungle.

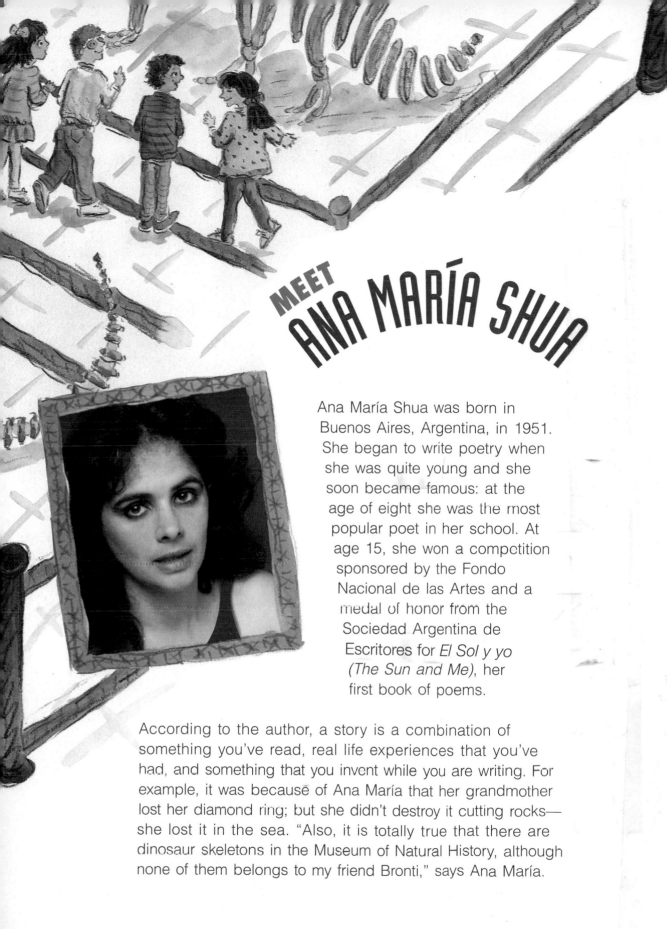

MEET ANA MARÍA SHUA

Ana María Shua was born in Buenos Aires, Argentina, in 1951. She began to write poetry when she was quite young and she soon became famous: at the age of eight she was the most popular poet in her school. At age 15, she won a competition sponsored by the Fondo Nacional de las Artes and a medal of honor from the Sociedad Argentina de Escritores for *El Sol y yo (The Sun and Me)*, her first book of poems.

According to the author, a story is a combination of something you've read, real life experiences that you've had, and something that you invent while you are writing. For example, it was because of Ana María that her grandmother lost her diamond ring; but she didn't destroy it cutting rocks—she lost it in the sea. "Also, it is totally true that there are dinosaur skeletons in the Museum of Natural History, although none of them belongs to my friend Bronti," says Ana María.

441

Wouldn't

You?

If I
Could go
As high
And low
As the wind
As the wind
As the wind
Can blow—

I'd go!

John Ciardi

443

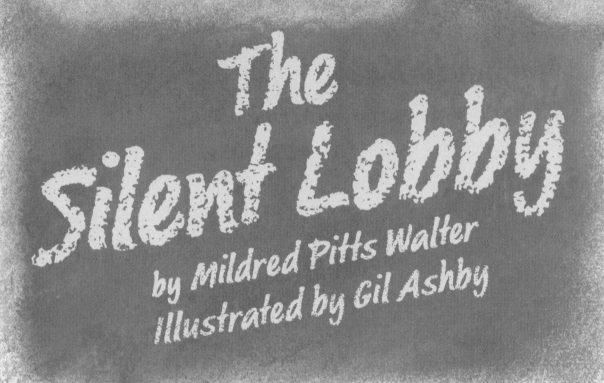

The Silent Lobby

by Mildred Pitts Walter
Illustrated by Gil Ashby

The old bus chugged along the Mississippi highway toward Washington, D.C. I shivered from icy winds and from excitement and fear. Excitement about going to Washington and fear that the old bus would stall again on the dark, lonely, icy road and we'd never make it.

Oh, just to sleep. The chug-chug-chugging of the old motor was not smooth enough to make soothing sounds, and I could not forget the words Mama and Papa had said just before me and Papa left to pick up twenty other people who filled the bus.

"It's too dangerous," Mama had said. "They just might bomb that bus."

"They could bomb this house for that matter," Papa said.

"I know," Mama went on. "That's why I don't want you to go. Why can't you just forget about this voting business and let us live in peace?"

"There can be no peace without freedom," Papa said.

"And you think someone is going to give you freedom?" Mama asked with heat in her voice. "Instead of going to Washington, you should be getting a gun to protect us."

"There are ways to win a struggle without bombs and guns. I'm going to Washington and Craig is going with me."

"Craig is too young."

"He's eleven. That's old enough to know what this is all about," Papa insisted.

I knew. It had all started two years ago, in 1963. Papa was getting ready to go into town to register to vote. Just as he was leaving, Mr. Clem, Papa's boss, came and warned Papa that he should not try to register.

"I intend to register," Papa said.

"If you do, I'll have to fire you." Mr. Clem drove away in a cloud of dust.

"You ought not go," Mama said, alarmed. "You know that people have been arrested and beaten for going down there."

"I'm going," Papa insisted.

"Let me go with you, Papa." I was scared, too, and wanted to be with him if he needed help.

"No, you stay and look after your mama and the house till I get back."

Day turned to night, and Papa had not returned. Mama paced the floor. Was Papa in jail? Had he been beaten?

We waited, afraid. Finally, I said, "Mama, I'll go find him."

"Oh, no!" she cried. Her fear scared me more, and I felt angry because I couldn't do anything.

At last we heard Papa's footsteps. The look on his face let us know right away that something was mighty wrong.

"What happened, Sylvester?" Mama asked.

"I paid the poll tax, passed the literacy test, but I didn't interpret the state constitution the way they wanted. So they wouldn't register me."

Feeling a sense of sad relief, I said, "Now you won't lose your job."

"Oh, but I will. I tried to register."

Even losing his job didn't stop Papa from wanting to vote. One day he heard about Mrs. Fannie Lou Hamer and the Mississippi Freedom Democratic Party. The Freedom Party registered people without charging a poll tax, without a literacy test, and without people having to tell what the Mississippi Constitution was about.

On election day in 1964, Papa proudly voted for Mrs. Hamer, Mrs. Victoria Grey, and Mrs. Annie Devine to represent the people of the Second Congressional District of Mississippi. Eighty-three thousand other black men and women voted that day, too. Great victory celebrations were held in homes and churches. But the Governor of Mississippi, Paul B. Johnson, declared all of those eighty-three thousand votes of black people illegal. He gave certificates of election to three white men—William Colmer, John Williams, and a Mr. Whittier—to represent the mostly black Second Congressional District.

Members of the Freedom Party were like Papa—they didn't give up. They got busy when the governor threw out their votes. Lawyers from all over the country came to help. People signed affidavits saying that when they tried to register they lost their jobs, they were beaten, and their homes were burned and churches bombed. More than ten thousand people signed petitions to the governor asking him to count their votes. There was never a word from the governor.

My mind returned to the sound of the old bus slowly grinding along. Suddenly the bus stopped. Not again! We'd never make it now. Papa got out in the cold wind and icy drizzling rain and raised the hood. While he worked, we sang and clapped our hands to keep warm. I could hear Sister Phyllis praying with all her might for our safety. After a while we were moving along again.

I must have finally fallen asleep, for a policeman's voice woke me. "You can't stop here near the Capitol," he shouted.

"Our bus won't go," Papa said.

"If you made it from Mississippi all the way to D.C., you'll make it from here," the policeman barked.

At first the loud voice frightened me. Then, wide awake, sensing the policeman's impatience, I wondered why Papa didn't let him know that we would go as soon as the motor started. But Papa, knowing that old bus, said nothing. He stepped on the starter. The old motor growled and died. Again the policeman shouted, "I said get out of here."

"We'll have to push it," Papa said.

Everyone got off the bus and pushed. Passersby stopped and stared. Finally we were safe on a side street, away from the Capitol with a crowd gathered around us.

"You mean they came all the way from Mississippi in that?" someone in the crowd asked.

Suddenly the old bus looked shabby. I lowered my head and became aware of my clothes: my faded coat too small; my cotton pants too thin. With a feeling of shame, I wished those people would go away.

"What brings you all to the District?" a man called to us.

"We've come to see about seating the people we voted for and elected," Papa answered. "Down home they say our votes don't count, and up here they've gone ahead and seated men who don't represent us. We've come to talk about that."

"So you've come to lobby," a woman shouted. The crowd laughed.

Why were they laughing? I knew that to lobby meant to try to get someone to decide for or against something. Yes, that was

why we had come. I wished I could have said to those people who stood gawking at us that the suffering that brought us here was surely nothing to laugh about.

The laughter from the crowd quieted when another woman shouted, "You're too late to lobby. The House of Representatives will vote on that issue this morning."

Too late. That's what had worried me when the old bus kept breaking down. Had we come so far in this cold for nothing? Was it really too late to talk to members of the House of Representatives to persuade them to seat our representatives elected by the Freedom Party, *not* the ones chosen by the governor?

Just then rain began to fall. The crowd quickly left, and we climbed onto our bus. Papa and the others started to talk. What would we do now? Finally, Papa said, "We can't turn back now. We've done too much and come too far."

After more talk we all agreed that we must try to do what we had come to do. Icy rain pelted us as we rushed against cold wind back to the Capitol.

A doorman stopped us on the steps. "May I have your passes?"

"We don't have any," Papa replied.

"Sorry, you have to have passes for seats in the gallery." The doorman blocked the way.

"We're cold in this rain. Let us in," Sister Phyllis cried.

"Maybe we should just go on back home," someone suggested.

"Yes. We can't talk to the legislators now, anyway," another woman said impatiently.

"No," Papa said. "We must stay if we do no more than let them see that we have come all this way."

"But we're getting soaking wet. We can't stand out here much longer," another protested.

"Can't you just let us in out of this cold?" Papa pleaded with the doorman.

"Not without passes." The doorman still blocked the way. Then he said, "There's a tunnel underneath this building. You can go there to get out of the rain."

We crowded into the tunnel and lined up along the sides. My chilled body and hands came to life pressed against the warm walls. Then footsteps and voices echoed through the tunnel. Police. This tunnel . . . a trap! Would they do something to us for trying to get in without passes? I wanted to cry out to Papa, but I could not speak.

The footsteps came closer. Then many people began to walk by. When they came upon us, they suddenly stopped talking. Only the sound of their feet echoed in the tunnel. Where had they come from? What did they do? "Who are they, Papa?" I whispered.

"Congressmen and women." Papa spoke so softly, I hardly heard him, even in the silence.

They wore warm coats, some trimmed with fur. Their shoes gleamed. Some of them frowned at us. Others glared. Some sighed quickly as they walked by. Others looked at us, then turned their eyes to their shoes. I could tell by a sudden lift of the head and a certain look that some were surprised and scared. And there were a few whose friendly smiles seemed to say, Right on!

I glanced at Papa. How poor he and our friends looked beside those well-dressed people. Their clothes were damp, threadbare, and wrinkled; their shoes were worn and mud stained. But they all stood straight and tall.

My heart pounded. I wanted to call out to those men and women, "Count my papa's vote! Let my people help make laws, too." But I didn't dare speak in that silence.

Could they hear my heart beating? Did they know what was on my mind? "Lord," I prayed, "let them hear us in this silence."

Then two congressmen stopped in front of Papa. I was frightened until I saw smiles on their faces.

"I'm Congressman Ryan from New York," one of them said. Then he introduced a black man: "This is Congressman Hawkins from California."

"I'm Sylvester Saunders. We are here from Mississippi," Papa said.

"We expected you much earlier," Congressman Ryan said.

"Our old bus and bad weather delayed us," Papa explained.

"That's unfortunate. You could've helped us a lot. We worked late into the night lobbying to get votes on your side. But maybe I should say on *our* side." Mr. Ryan smiled.

"And we didn't do very well," Congressman Hawkins said.

"We'll be lucky if we get fifty votes on our side today," Congressman Ryan informed us. "Maybe you would like to come in and see us at work."

"We don't have passes," I said, surprised at my voice.

"We'll see about getting all of you in," Congressman Hawkins promised.

452

A little later, as we found seats in the gallery, Congressman Gerald Ford from the state of Michigan was speaking. He did not want Mrs. Hamer and other fairly elected members of the Freedom Party seated in the House. He asked his fellow congressmen to stick to the rule of letting only those with credentials from their states be seated in Congress. The new civil rights act would, in time, undo wrongs done to black Americans. But for now, Congress should let the men chosen by Governor Johnson keep their seats and get on with other business.

Then Congressman Ryan rose to speak. How could Congress stick to rules that denied blacks their right to vote in the state of Mississippi? The rule of letting only those with credentials from a segregated state have seats in the House could not *justly* apply here.

I looked down on those men and few women and wondered if they were listening. Did they know about the petitions? I remembered what Congressman Ryan had said: "We'll be lucky if we get fifty. . . ." Only 50 out of 435 elected to the House.

Finally the time came for Congress to vote. Those who wanted to seat Mrs. Hamer and members of the Freedom Democratic Party were to say, yes. Those who didn't want to seat Mrs. Hamer were to say, no.

At every yes vote I could hardly keep from clapping my hands and shouting, "Yea! Yea!" But I kept quiet, counting: thirty, then forty, forty-eight . . . only two more. We would lose badly.

Then something strange happened. Congressmen and congresswomen kept saying "Yes. Yes. Yes." On and on, "Yes." My heart pounded. Could we win? I sat on my hands to keep from clapping. I looked at Papa and the others who had come with us. They all sat on the edge of their seats. They looked as if they could hardly keep from shouting out, too, as more yes votes rang from the floor.

When the voting was over, 148 votes had been cast in our favor. What had happened? Why had so many changed their minds?

Later, Papa introduced me to Congressman Hawkins. The congressman asked me, "How did you all know that some of us walk through that tunnel from our offices?"

"We didn't know," I answered. "We were sent there out of the rain."

"That's strange," the congressman said. "Your standing there silently made a difference in the vote. Even though we lost this time, some of them now know that we'll keep on lobbying until we win."

I felt proud. Papa had been right when he said to Mama, "There are ways to win a struggle without bombs and guns." We had lobbied in silence and we had been *heard*.

President Lyndon B. Johnson shakes hands with Dr. Martin Luther King, Jr., after signing the Omnibus Civil Rights Act on June 29, 1964.

Note: *This story is a fictional account of one demonstration by African Americans during the decade of the 1960s. Many nonviolent demonstrations were held for voting rights, for jobs, and for freedom to use restaurants, libraries, schools, and public restrooms. This one took place on January 4, 1965.*

On June 29, 1964, President Lyndon Baines Johnson signed the Omnibus Civil Rights Act banning discrimination in voting, jobs, public facilities, and in housing. On August 6, 1965, President Johnson signed the Voting Rights Act, which guarantees the right to vote without penalties or poll taxes.

Meet Mildred Pitts Walter

Mildred Pitts Walter had never thought of writing books. Then she met a book salesperson. She told him that there were not enough stories about African American children. He suggested that Walter try writing one. She did, and his company published her first book, *Lillie of Watts.*

Writing "The Silent Lobby" was important to Walter. She herself was deeply involved in the civil rights movement. During the 1950s and 1960s, Walter worked hard for equal rights in Los Angeles, California, her home. She struggled to make sure that people of every color could live wherever they wanted.

Many of Mildred Pitts Walter's characters show the same courage she did. "My characters must make choices," Walter observed, "and once they have made those choices, they have to work them through. That's what life is—making a series of choices—and people who cannot choose for themselves don't grow."

Tired of Giving In

One quiet woman refuses to give up her seat on a city bus—and changes America forever.

On the evening of December 1, 1955, when Rosa Parks refused to give up her seat on a bus to a white man, she wasn't trying to be a hero. She was just tired— tired of giving in.

Ever since her girlhood in Alabama, Rosa had resented the way African Americans were treated. Nearly a hundred years after Addy's time,* people in the South were still *segregated*, or separated, by color. Blacks and whites had different schools, different restaurants—even different bathrooms. Things were supposed to be "separate

African Americans were not allowed into this waiting room.

*Addy is a character in the book *Happy Birthday, Addy* by Connie Porter, which takes place in the 1860s.

Rosa rides in front for the first time in her life.

On that December night, the driver asked the people in Rosa's row to get up so a white man could sit down. Everyone got up—except Rosa. The police arrested her and took her to jail.

Leaders in the black community saw Rosa's arrest as a chance to fight segregation. Lawyers took Rosa's case all the way to the Supreme Court, the highest court in America. Meanwhile, black people in Montgomery *boycotted*, or refused to ride, city buses for a whole year. They organized car pools or walked instead.

Because of the boycott, Rosa lost her job. She got phone calls from people who said she should be killed. But Rosa believed in her cause. Finally, on December 20, 1956, the Supreme Court ordered an end to segregation on the Montgomery city buses.

but equal"—but the truth was, black people got the worst of everything.

Rosa especially disliked having to ride segregated buses to and from her job in downtown Montgomery. Whites got to sit in the front of the bus, but blacks had to sit in back. If the front was full, bus drivers made black people give their seats to white people, even though they'd paid the same bus fare.

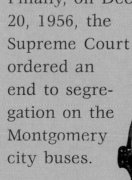

Rosa Parks became a symbol for African-American rights.

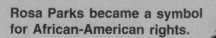

Puddle, © 1952 by M. C. Escher/Cordon Art, Baarn, Holland

The Old Walking Song

by J. R. R. TOLKIEN

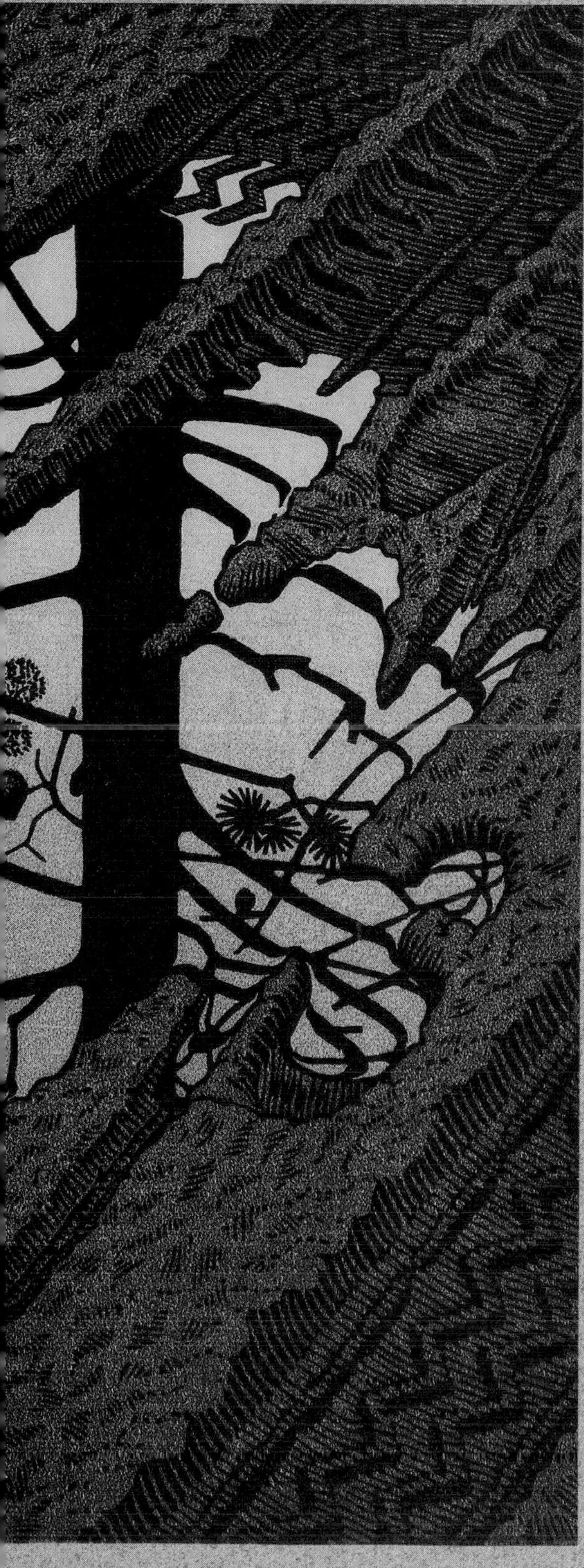

The Road goes ever on and on

Down from the door where it began.

Now far ahead the Road has gone,

And I must follow, if I can,

Pursuing it with eager feet,

Until it joins some larger way

Where many paths and errands meet.

And whither then? I cannot say.

Unit 6

ZOOM IN!

HOW to THiNK

ANSWERING QUESTIONS BY

LiKe a ScieNtiSt

THE SCIENTIFIC METHOD

by Stephen P. Kramer

illustrated by Kim Behm

"Whump, whump" went the tires of Pete's bike. The sounds were so close together they seemed like one noise.

"Hey!" screamed Pete. He pointed to the side of the road. "Look out! Get over!"

Jim could barely see the outline of Pete's arm in the darkness, but he swerved to the left. He coasted along the shoulder of the road until he caught up with Pete. Pete had stopped and was looking back.

"What's wrong?" asked Jim.

Pete shook his head. "A snake! A huge snake . . . I rode over it! On the side of the road! I didn't see it until too late . . . I couldn't even turn."

"Probably just an old inner tube," said Jim. "Come on, let's go."

"Was not," replied Pete, shaking his head again. "Want to go back and see?"

Jim hesitated for a moment. "All right," he answered. "I'm not scared."

Pete unhooked the flashlight from the frame of his bike. The boys laid their bicycles in the weeds beside the road and slowly walked back. The flashlight made a faint yellow spot on the pavement.

Pete shone the flashlight far ahead. "Up there," he said. "That's where I rode over it."

Jim looked around. "I don't see anything."

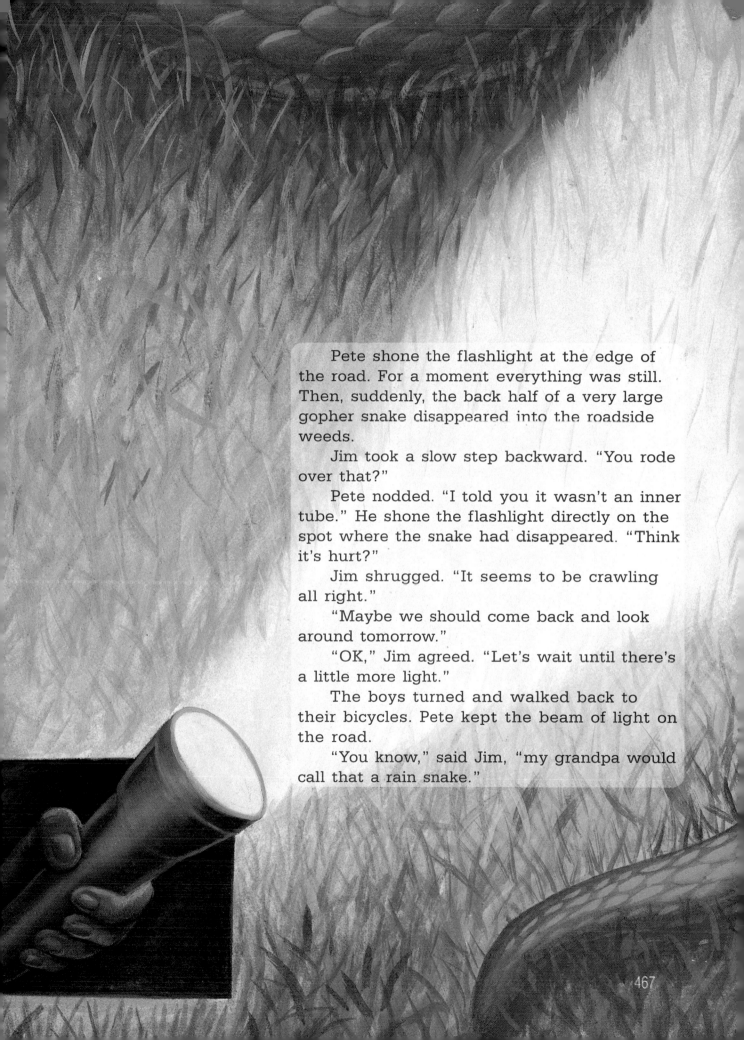

Pete shone the flashlight at the edge of the road. For a moment everything was still. Then, suddenly, the back half of a very large gopher snake disappeared into the roadside weeds.

Jim took a slow step backward. "You rode over that?"

Pete nodded. "I told you it wasn't an inner tube." He shone the flashlight directly on the spot where the snake had disappeared. "Think it's hurt?"

Jim shrugged. "It seems to be crawling all right."

"Maybe we should come back and look around tomorrow."

"OK," Jim agreed. "Let's wait until there's a little more light."

The boys turned and walked back to their bicycles. Pete kept the beam of light on the road.

"You know," said Jim, "my grandpa would call that a rain snake."

"What?" asked Pete.

"A rain snake. He'd say you could make it rain for sure with a snake like that."

"How?"

"Well," said Jim, "my grandpa grew up way back in the hills. When he was a boy, the farmers would sometimes use a dead snake to make it rain. They'd find a large tree with a strong low branch and throw the snake over the branch. A big snake like that would bring rain for sure."

Pete leaned over and picked up his bike. "You believe that?"

"Naw," answered Jim quickly. Then he scratched his head and looked back down the road. "But, well, I never tried it. I don't know. My grandpa says they did it a lot. Maybe it'd work for some people, sometimes. . . ."

What do *you* think? Can throwing a dead snake over a tree branch bring rain?

Every day you answer questions—dozens or even hundreds of them. What should I wear today? What assignments do I need for school? Can I eat an extra piece of toast and still get to the bus on time? What should I do tonight?

Some questions you answer correctly. Others you don't. Some questions are important. You spend lots of time thinking about them. Other questions aren't important. You guess at the answer or just choose an answer automatically.

How Do You Answer Questions?

You think about many things when you try to answer a question. You try to remember things you know that might help you. You look for new information about the question. Sometimes you try to guess how someone else would answer the question. Other times you might pick an answer because of what you would *like* the answer to be.

Sometimes these things help you find a correct answer. Other times they lead you to a wrong answer.

Here are three stories. Each story has a question. Each story tells about something that could happen to you, and each story will show a different way of answering a question.

AVALANCHE!

INFORMATION

You're sitting on your bed one afternoon reading a book about a mountain climber. Things are getting very exciting (an avalanche has just started) when your little brother Ralphie walks into the room. He strolls past your bed and looks out the window.

"Hey," he says, "someone's in Mr. Murphy's backyard."

Your teeth start to grind. You've lost your place but you try not to show it. A long time ago you learned that sometimes the best way to get along with Ralphie is to ignore him.

"Hey," says Ralphie, "they're going into the Murphys' house."

You frown and roll over, wondering when Ralphie is going to go away.

"Hey," says Ralphie, "they're coming out of the Murphys' house. They're carrying something that's all covered up. They're stealing something from the Murphys!"

You sit up straight. The Murphys? Someone is stealing something from the Murphys?

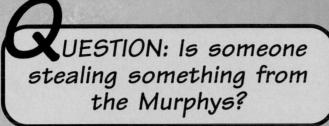

QUESTION: Is someone stealing something from the Murphys?

Then, out the window you see a truck. It is parked in front of the Murphys' house. Painted in large blue letters on the side of the truck are the words "Jake's TV Repair."

You shake your head.

"Go on," you tell Ralphie. "Take off."

"They're stealing something from the Murphys' house," says Ralphie. "The bad man just went back inside."

"It's not a bad man," you explain. "Someone's just picking up the TV. Can't you see that truck out there?"

"They're not taking the TV," Ralphie insists.

"Get out!" you shout.

"No!" says Ralphie.

"I said get out!" you scream, throwing a pillow at Ralphie.

So Ralphie finally leaves, walking out of the room very slowly.

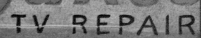

471

RRRING!

That night at dinner the telephone rings. Your father answers it. When he returns to the table, he says, "The Murphys just got home. While they were gone this afternoon, someone broke into their house and stole some money. The burglars also took some silverware and Mr. Murphy's violin.

"Most of our neighbors were gone this afternoon. The Johnsons didn't see anything because they were watching a repairman fix their TV all afternoon. Did any of you see anything?"

Ralphie sits up straight and begins nodding.

What happened? The question was: Is someone stealing something from the Murphys? You and Ralphie both made observations. Ralphie's observations told him the answer was yes. Your observations told you the answer was no. Why did you and Ralphie end up with different answers to the same question?

You answered the question incorrectly because of the way you used an observation. You saw a TV repair truck through the front window. Your observation was a good one. You noticed what kind of truck was on your street and where it was parked. The problem was how you used your observation. You thought the truck was giving you information about who was in the Murphys' house. Actually, Ralphie was giving you better information.

Information must be used carefully. Having information does not always mean you will answer a question correctly. If the information is not true or is not used in the right way, it can lead to a wrong answer.

It's Wednesday morning, just before lunch. Your teacher arranged for someone from the zoo to come and show your class some animals. You have seen an iguana, a mongoose, and a large snake. Now the zookeeper reaches into a wooden box and pulls out a fishbowl. He sets the bowl on a low table at the front of the room. Three small gray fish swim back and forth.

"Who knows the name of these fish?" asks the zookeeper.

Everyone is quiet. You stare at the fish for a moment. Of course you know what they are. They're guppies! They look just like the fish in your sister's aquarium. You've spent hours watching guppies.

Quickly, you raise your hand, but you're sitting in the last row and the zookeeper doesn't see you.

You wave your hand back and forth. The girl next to you ducks.

"These are gastromorphs," says the zookeeper. "They live in slow, muddy streams in Africa. They are very danger-ous. They will eat almost anything that moves."

Quickly, you pull your hand down and look around. "Whew," you think. "That could have been embarrass-ing." Then you lean forward and squint at those fish again.

"We always keep a strong screen over this fishbowl when we visit schools. If anyone were to stick a hand in the water, well, these little fish would immediately attack and begin taking bites out of it."

GASTRO

This time the question seems easy. The fish look a lot like guppies. They swim like guppies. They're even the size and color of guppies. But would you stick your hand in the bowl? Of course not! The zookeeper just told you they are gastromorphs. Zookeepers know their animals, right? So the fish must be gastromorphs. Maybe.

Here's what really happened. The zookeeper who was supposed to visit your class got sick. The zoo sent over the person who normally takes care of birds. The zookeeper who came to your class knew a lot about birds, but not much about fish.

His first stop that morning was at the mammal house to pick up the mongoose. Then he went to the reptile house to get the iguana and the snake. He took all three animals with him into the fish house.

It was dark in the fish house. All the fish were arranged alphabetically in separate aquariums. The guppies were in the aquarium next to the gastromorphs. The zookeeper picked up a net, walked over to the gastromorphs, and leaned over the aquarium to dip some out. Just then the snake began to crawl out of its bag, so the zookeeper reached down to push it back in. When he stood up straight again he had three fish in his net. He dumped them into the fishbowl and hurried to your school. What he didn't know was that he had accidentally dipped the net into the wrong tank. He had netted three guppies instead of three gastromorphs.

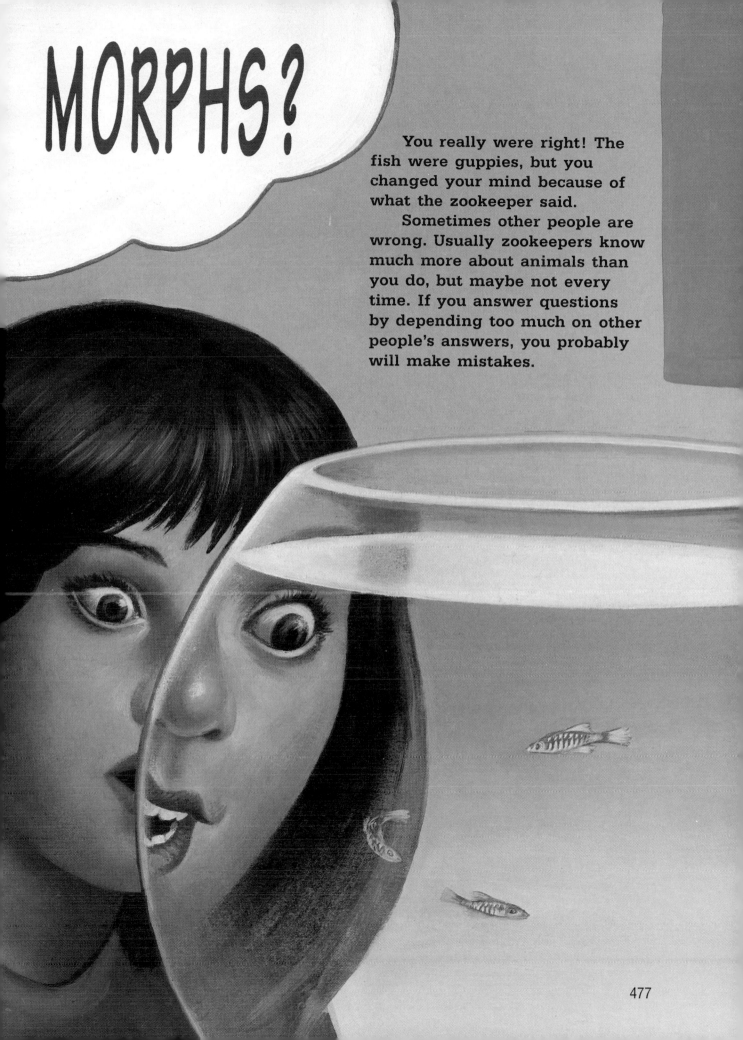

MORPHS?

You really were right! The fish were guppies, but you changed your mind because of what the zookeeper said.

Sometimes other people are wrong. Usually zookeepers know much more about animals than you do, but maybe not every time. If you answer questions by depending too much on other people's answers, you probably will make mistakes.

Because We Want To

Sometimes we know how we would like a question to be answered. We choose an answer to a question because it's the answer we like. Let's look at another story.

It's Friday afternoon, and the last bell of the day has just rung. You gather up your books and start toward the door of your classroom. As you step into the hallway your teacher calls out, "Don't forget to finish your math assignment. It's due Monday morning." You look down and check to be sure you have your math book.

The weekend passes quickly. On Friday night you go to a basketball game. On Saturday your family goes to the beach. Finally, on Sunday evening you clear a spot on the kitchen table and start to work on your assignment.

Just then the telephone rings. You hurry to answer it.

"Hi," says Pat. "What are you doing?"

"Math," you answer.

"Hey," says Pat, "I've got a better idea. There's a good movie downtown. My dad gave me some money. Let's go."

"I can't," you answer. "I haven't even started this assignment yet."

"It's a great movie," says Pat. "Everyone says so."

"Look, report cards are coming out next week. I need a good grade on this paper."

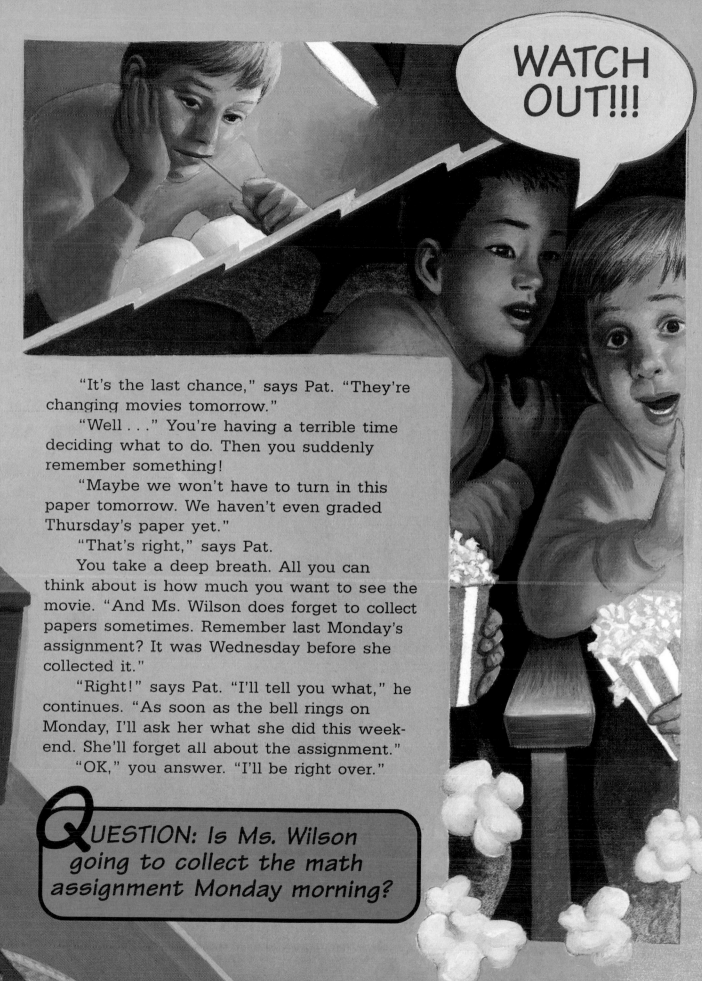

WATCH OUT!!!

"It's the last chance," says Pat. "They're changing movies tomorrow."

"Well . . ." You're having a terrible time deciding what to do. Then you suddenly remember something!

"Maybe we won't have to turn in this paper tomorrow. We haven't even graded Thursday's paper yet."

"That's right," says Pat.

You take a deep breath. All you can think about is how much you want to see the movie. "And Ms. Wilson does forget to collect papers sometimes. Remember last Monday's assignment? It was Wednesday before she collected it."

"Right!" says Pat. "I'll tell you what," he continues. "As soon as the bell rings on Monday, I'll ask her what she did this week-end. She'll forget all about the assignment."

"OK," you answer. "I'll be right over."

QUESTION: Is Ms. Wilson going to collect the math assignment Monday morning?

479

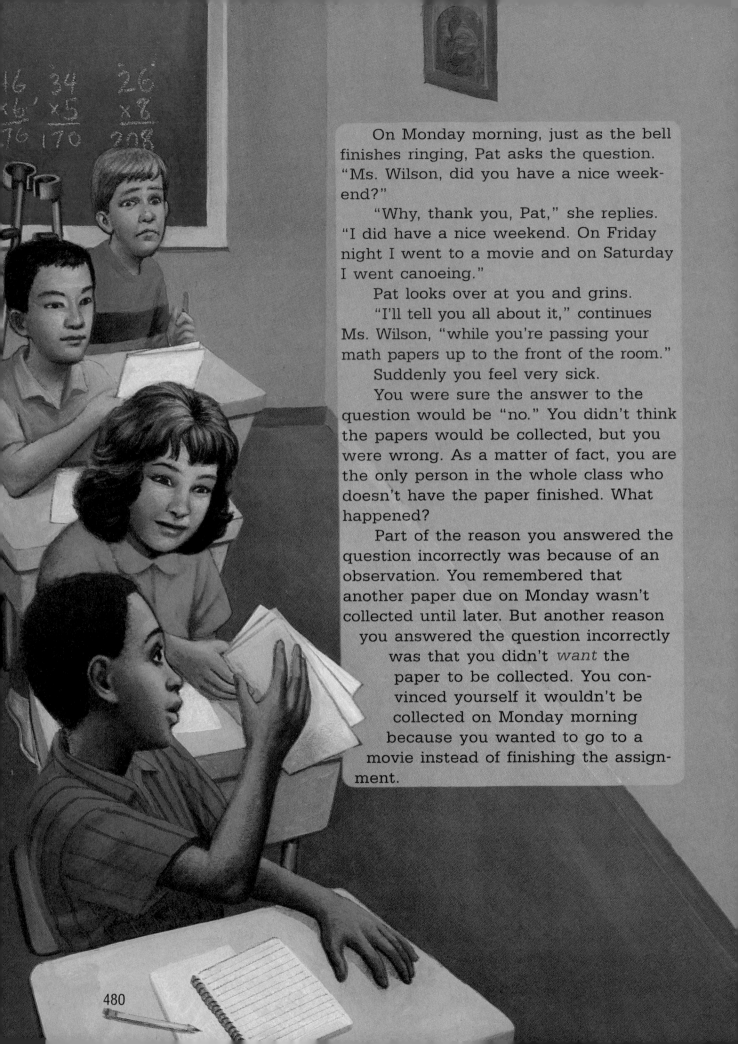

On Monday morning, just as the bell finishes ringing, Pat asks the question. "Ms. Wilson, did you have a nice weekend?"

"Why, thank you, Pat," she replies. "I did have a nice weekend. On Friday night I went to a movie and on Saturday I went canoeing."

Pat looks over at you and grins.

"I'll tell you all about it," continues Ms. Wilson, "while you're passing your math papers up to the front of the room."

Suddenly you feel very sick.

You were sure the answer to the question would be "no." You didn't think the papers would be collected, but you were wrong. As a matter of fact, you are the only person in the whole class who doesn't have the paper finished. What happened?

Part of the reason you answered the question incorrectly was because of an observation. You remembered that another paper due on Monday wasn't collected until later. But another reason you answered the question incorrectly was that you didn't *want* the paper to be collected. You convinced yourself it wouldn't be collected on Monday morning because you wanted to go to a movie instead of finishing the assignment.

Sometimes we really want the answer to a question to turn out in a certain way. Such a question can be difficult to answer correctly or fairly. Often it is easier to find an answer we like than an answer that is correct.

Carelessly used information, what others think, what we want to happen—none of these are very reliable ways of answering questions. Too many times they lead to wrong answers. Is there a better way? How can you find out whether throwing a dead snake over a tree branch really will bring rain?

There *is* a better way to find answers. Scientists use a series of steps called *the scientific method* to find accurate and reliable answers to their questions.

Good scientists are skeptical, but they keep an open mind. They know that experiments sometimes show that the correct answer to a question is not *always* the one you think it will be!

MEET STEPHEN P. KRAMER

Science has always fascinated Stephen P. Kramer. In college, he studied biology, the science of living things. After graduation, he taught science for four years on a Navajo reservation. Today, Kramer lives in Vancouver, Washington, where he writes and helps care for his two sons. His books combine his training as a biologist and his experience as a teacher. His first book, **Getting Oxygen: What Do You Do If You're Cell Twenty-Two?**, explains how the body gets and uses oxygen. **How to Think Like a Scientist** describes the scientific method, the step-by-step process that scientists use to learn about our world.

MY FLOOR IS SOMEBODY'S CEILING

My floor is somebody's ceiling
And my ceiling is somebody's floor.
So maybe my table is somebody's chair
And maybe my here is somebody's there,
And maybe my circle is somebody's square
And my window is somebody's door.
These are things I have wondered before,
But I think that I won't anymore.
No, I think that I won't anymore.

Jeff Moss

ssoM ffeL

No, I think that I won't anymore.
But I think that I won't anymore.
These are things I have wondered before,
And my window is somebody's door.
And maybe my circle is somebody's square
And maybe my here is somebody's there,
So maybe my table is somebody's chair
And my ceiling is somebody's floor.
My floor is somebody's ceiling

CEILING
SOMEBODY'S
MY FLOOR IS

MEET
PATRICIA LAUBER

PATRICIA LAUBER WROTE HER FIRST BOOK AT THE
URGING OF A FRIEND. LAUBER'S STORIES ABOUT CLARENCE,
HER DOG, WERE SO ENTERTAINING THAT HER FRIEND URGED
HER TO WRITE THEM DOWN. "CLARENCE AND I
BOTH THOUGHT THIS WAS A FINE IDEA, . . ." SAYS LAUBER.

"THE RESULT WAS MY FIRST
BOOK, **CLARENCE THE TV
DOG**." SINCE THEN, LAUBER
HAS WRITTEN MORE THAN
FIFTY BOOKS.

WRITING A NONFICTION
BOOK REQUIRES "A GREAT
DEAL OF RESEARCH," ACCORD-
ING TO LAUBER. SHE READS,
TALKS TO EXPERTS, AND
VISITS KEY PLACES. FOR
**THE NEWS ABOUT
DINOSAURS**, SHE HAD TO
MAKE SURE ALL THE ILLUSTRATIONS IN THE
BOOK WERE SCIENTIFICALLY ACCURATE. MUCH OF
THE ART LAUBER CHOSE WAS DONE BY PALEON-
TOLOGISTS, SCIENTISTS WHO STUDY DINOSAURS.

FOR PATRICIA LAUBER, WRITING IS AN ACT OF
SHARING. "WHEN I AM FULL OF ENTHUSIASM
FOR A SUBJECT, I HAVE A STRONG
DESIRE TO SHARE IT WITH
OTHER PEOPLE."

THE NEW DINOS

S ABOUT AURS

BY PATRICIA LAUBER

inosaurs were discovered in the early 1800s. Until then, no one had even guessed that once there were dinosaurs.

Scientists studied the big teeth and bones they had found. They wondered what kind of animals these belonged to. Finally they decided the animals were reptiles—relatives of today's crocodiles, turtles, snakes, and lizards. In 1841 the animals were named *dinosaurs,* meaning "terrible lizards."

Dinosaur hunters dug for bones. They found giant dinosaurs, dinosaurs the size of chickens, and many in-between sizes. They gave each kind a name. They fitted bones together and made skeletons. After a hundred or more years, this work seemed to be ending. Scientists began to think they had discovered nearly every kind of dinosaur that ever walked the earth.

Baryonyx Walkeri

THE NEWS IS: The work was far from finished. Today new kinds of dinosaurs are found all the time. And scientists think there must be hundreds more that they haven't discovered yet. Four of the new kinds they have found are *Baryonyx, Mamenchisaurus, Deinonychus,* and *Nanotyrannus.*

▲ *Mamenchisaurus* was a giant plant-eating dinosaur, 72 feet long. Its 33-foot neck is the longest of any known animal. The dinosaur is named for the place in China where it was found.

▲ *Nanotyrannus* was a pygmy tyrannosaur, a small relative of *Tyrannosaurus rex*. Its name means "pygmy tyrant." This small meat-eating dinosaur looked like its big relative but was only one-tenth as heavy and one-third as long—it weighed about 1,000 pounds and was 17 feet long. *Nanotyrannus* was discovered in a museum, where it had earlier been mistaken for another meat-eater, a gorgosaur, also known as *Albertosaurus.* Here its jaws are about to close on a smaller dinosaur.

Deinonychus was found in Montana. It was fairly small, about 9 feet long, and walked on its hind legs. Each hind foot had a big claw, shaped like a curved sword. The dinosaur's name means "terrible claw." Like other meat-eaters, *Deinonychus* spent much of its time resting or sleeping and digesting its last meal. This pair has just awakened, hungry and ready to hunt. ▼

ost reptiles walk with their knees bent and their feet wide apart. Scientists used to think dinosaurs must have walked the same way. They pictured dinosaurs as slow and clumsy, waddling along with their tails dragging on the ground. So that was how dinosaurs were made to look in books and museums.

▲ **For many years, people thought of dinosaurs as slow-moving and slow-witted. That is how they appear in this 1870s painting by Benjamin Waterhouse Hawkins. He was the first artist to work closely with scientists who were studying dinosaurs.**

THE NEWS IS: Dinosaurs didn't look like that at all. They were good walkers. They held their tails up. And many kinds were quick and nimble. Today's scientists have learned this by studying dinosaur footprints.

When dinosaurs walked in mud or wet sand, they left footprints. Most of these tracks washed or oozed away. But in some places the tracks hardened. Later they were buried under mud or sand that turned to rock. The tracks were preserved in the rock—they became fossils.

Today dinosaurs are shown as lively and active. These huge, horned plant-eaters are driving off *Albertosaurus*, a fierce meat-eater. ▼

By Gregory S. Paul © Gregory S. Paul 1988

Tracks show that dinosaurs walked in long, easy strides. Their legs and feet were under their bodies, not out to the side. Their bodies were high off the ground. Big plant-eaters walked at 3 or 4 miles an hour. Some small meat-eaters could run as fast as 35 or 40 miles an hour.

◀ At least some dinosaurs could swim. *Apatosaurus* has tried to escape a pack of *Allosaurus* by taking to the water— but the meat-eaters can swim, too.

◀ *Camarasaurs* (foreground) and *camptosaurs* are crossing a recently flooded area and leaving footprints. Preserved in rock, such tracks have revealed much about dinosaurs.

The biggest dinosaurs belonged to the group of plant-eaters named sauropods. Among them were *Mamenchisaurus, Diplodocus, Brachiosaurus, Apatosaurus,* and *Camarasaurus.* They were the longest, tallest, heaviest land animals that ever lived. They had legs like tree trunks, long tails, and long necks that ended in small heads.

Earlier scientists thought these giants spent their lives in shallow lakes or swamps, where water helped support their heavy bodies. Some scientists wondered if sauropods were able to walk on land at all.

Sauropods were very much at home on dry land. They may have spent some of their time in water, but they didn't live there. Their bones and footprints have been found in places that were dry part of the year and rainy part of the year. They have been found in places where forests of evergreens grew in the days of dinosaurs.

Footprints show that sauropods walked in long strides on all four feet. They may have reared up on their hind legs, using their tails for balance, to feed from the tops of trees.

Giant animals need giant amounts of food. A large sauropod must have eaten several hundred pounds of plant food a day. Perhaps sauropods traveled about, following the greening of forests as rainy seasons came and went.

▲ Sauropods were at home on dry land, where they used their long necks to reach into treetops for food. Shown here are *Camarasaurus* (left), *Barosaurus* (center), and *Apatosaurus* (right).

Like all sauropods, *Brachiosaurus* (left) and *Barosaurus* (right) moved easily on land, which was helpful when they met meat-eaters such as *Ceratosaurus* (center). ▼

▲ Sauropods probably traveled long distances to new sources of food.

Early dinosaur hunters discovered that many kinds and sizes of dinosaurs once roamed the earth.

Today's dinosaur hunters are discovering how dinosaurs lived—how they moved and traveled and fed and defended themselves. They are learning what dinosaurs were like before they hatched. They are even learning about dinosaur senses and voices.

The part of a skull that holds the brain is called a braincase. It shows the size and shape of the brain. It shows which parts of the brain were highly developed. In dinosaurs these parts were ones that receive information from the senses. Dinosaurs had good eyesight and a keen sense of smell. They also had a keen sense of hearing.

By Eleanor M. Kish. Courtesy of the National Museum of Natural Sciences, National Museums of Canada

◀ Most dinosaur skin rotted away after the animals died. So we may never know what colors dinosaurs really were. But scientists feel sure that dinosaurs did have markings of various colors, just as today's animals do. Stripes, for example, would have helped a duckbill to blend into the broad-leaved forest, making it hard for a meat-eater to see. Meat-eaters may have had markings that helped to conceal them when they stalked their prey.

◀ Dinosaurs were alert. Their keen senses helped meat-eaters to find prey and plant-eaters to learn of danger.

501

A splash of color would call attention to the spiny neck frill of this horned dinosaur, which may have frightened meat-eaters. ▶

By Douglas Henderson © (collection of Phil Tippett)

Still other bones show that dinosaurs had voices. Young dinosaurs may have squeaked and squealed. Bigger dinosaurs may have croaked, tootled, barked, bellowed, bayed, or made sounds like a tuba.

With all the new discoveries, perhaps it seems there's not much left to learn about dinosaurs.

Scientists will be finding new dinosaurs and learning about dinosaur lives for years to come. And when they do, their discoveries will be reported in the news.

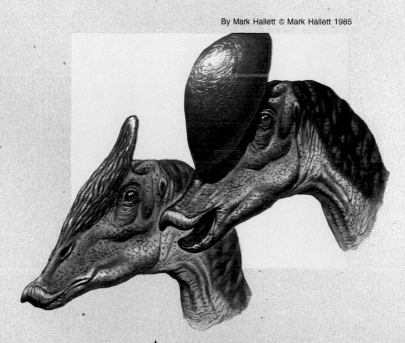

▲ Some dinosaurs may have had hollow pouches on their heads, which could be blown up and used to scare off enemies or to attract mates.

fossils

Older than
books,
than scrolls,

older
than the first
tales told

or the
first words
spoken

are the stories

in forests that
turned to
stone

in ice walls
that trapped the
mammoth

in the long
bones of
dinosaurs—

the fossil
stories that begin
Once upon a time

Lilian Moore

I Love the Look of Words

Popcorn leaps, popping from the floor
of a hot black skillet
and into my mouth.
Black words leap,
snapping from the white
page. Rushing into my eyes. Sliding
into my brain which gobbles them
the way my tongue and teeth
chomp the buttered popcorn.

When I have stopped reading,
ideas from the words stay stuck
in my mind, like the sweet
smell of butter perfuming my
fingers long after the popcorn
is finished.

I love the book and the look of words
the weight of ideas that popped into my mind
I love the tracks
of new thinking in my mind.

MAYA ANGELOU

EINSTEIN

Meet Seymour Simon

Since 1968, Seymour Simon has been writing children's books on science topics ranging from paper airplanes to optical illusions. More than forty of these books have been named Outstanding Science Trade Books for Children. But it wasn't until 1980 that he began writing his Einstein Anderson fiction series. In these books, Simon combines mystery, science, and "bad puns." "The reader gets a chance to solve the puzzle," Simon points out, "and, I hope, gets a chance to learn something about science as well."

A former science teacher, Simon still finds joy in helping students learn. He loves to hear from readers who have tried an experiment in one of his books. Sharing a reader's discovery, he says, is "as much fun as the first time I found something out for myself."

ANDERSON

two stories by Seymour Simon
illustrations by Mary Thelen

THE INCREDIBLE SHRINKING MACHINE

THE IMPOS

Margaret Michaels was Einstein's good friend and arch rival. Science was their favorite subject. Einstein and Margaret were always talking about important things like atoms, planets, and who was the best science student.

Margaret's mother didn't quite know what to make of her daughter. Mrs. Michaels had wanted Margaret to take ballet classes on Saturday mornings. Margaret had insisted that she wanted to be in the Saturday Science Experimenters Club.

Mrs. Michaels thought that animals were nice when they were outside of her house. Margaret thought that animals were nice both outside and inside the house. She had a pet springer spaniel named Nova, two pet cats named Orville and Wilbur, a pet gerbil named Sammy, and assorted tropical fish. She hadn't named them yet.

SIBLE TRICK

"Children," Ms. Taylor said, "the school fair is scheduled for next Friday. There will be a used-book sale, a cookie and cake sale, and the usual kinds of booth activities, such as bobbing for apples. All the money earned from the fair will be used to help pay expenses for our school's long weekend at Big Lake State Park later this month."

Mrs. Michaels liked to listen to classical music. Margaret liked to listen to jazz. Mrs. Michaels was a member of the Sparta Choral Singing Society. Margaret couldn't sing a note in tune. But despite all the differences between them, Mrs. Michaels was very proud of her daughter's doings and boasted about her whenever she had the chance.

Margaret had left to visit her aunt for a week as soon as school was let out for the summer. Einstein knew that Margaret was back and wondered why she hadn't called him. Finally he decided to call and find out.

"Hello, Margaret, what's happening? How is your aunt? How come you didn't call?"

Ms. Taylor paused as the class started to buzz. Everyone was looking forward to the fair and also to the weekend at Big Lake. Ms. Taylor, Einstein's sixth grade teacher, waited a few minutes and then called on the class to quiet down.

"I want to appoint a committee to decide on our class booth at this year's fair. Try to come up with something

"Einstein," Margaret said, "I was just about to call you. Aunt Bess drove me home two days ago and stayed to visit my parents. She's going to drive back tomorrow, and she said it would be O.K. if I invited a friend to her house for the week-end. She's a biology professor at State University and has all kinds of science stuff at her house that you might like to see. How would you like to go?"

different. The class that earns the most money with its booth will go up to Big Lake a day early. Now who would like to serve on the committee? Hands, please."

Many children raised their hands to volunteer. Ms. Taylor chose six children, including Pat Burns and his pal Herman. She chose neither Einstein nor Margaret.

Einstein was about to refuse because his family was going to the beach on Sunday, when Margaret continued.

"Also, I have a science puzzle to show you at Aunt Bess's that even the great Einstein Anderson can't solve."

Well, that changed everything. Einstein couldn't turn down a science challenge from Margaret, so he agreed to go. He spent the rest of the day playing

Later, during lunch recess, Margaret was talking to Einstein. "I wonder why Ms. Taylor didn't choose either of us for that committee," she said. "Does she really expect Pat the Brat or Herman to come up with an original idea?"

baseball with some classmates and wondering about the puzzle that Margaret had mentioned.

Einstein and Margaret were driven by Aunt Bess early in the morning on Saturday. They arrived at Remsen, a town near the State University, just after 8:00 A.M. Aunt Bess's house was in a sort of clearing surrounded by trees. Instead of first going inside, Margaret led Einstein behind the house and down a twisting path in the woods.

Hidden from the house at the end of the path was a small shack with a bright yellow door. The early-morning sun shone directly on the yellow door and made it look almost like gold.

"Well, it's only fair that everyone gets a chance," Einstein replied. "And maybe Ms. Taylor thinks that scientists can't come up with a contest that's fun."

"I guess that's so," Margaret said glumly. "You haven't even cracked one joke all day long. Maybe too much science makes you lose your sense of humor."

"Lose my sense of humor!" exclaimed Einstein. "Not very likely! I'm just like the scientist who invented spaghetti. I can use my noodle to come up with an idea for a booth that will be the hit of the fair."

"Look, noodle head," Margaret said sweetly, "talk is cheap. Let's see you come up with a *science* booth that is funny and attractive. The committee is supposed to report tomorrow on their idea for a booth. Why don't you come up with your own idea? If it's better than the committee's idea, I'm sure the class will go along with it."

Margaret unlocked the yellow door and motioned Einstein inside. Einstein noticed that the single room they entered had no other doors and only one small window. The only objects in the room were a large stone table and a small black box sitting on the table.

"Einstein, look over the stone table closely," Margaret said. "It was put together right in this room. You can see that it is too big to pass through the door or the window. You would have to break it into little pieces to get it out of the room."

Best idea! by Einstein Anderson

"I accept your challenge," said Einstein. "Science *can* be fun. In the meantime, let's go and eat an astronaut's favorite meal. Launch."

The next day the committee was giving their ideas about a booth for their class. They had elected Pat the Brat chairman because he had

Little Box

Big Table

volunteered for it. Pat said that he would make a good chairman. Besides, he pointed out, looking at his fist, he was also the strongest kid in the class. No one else on the committee was prepared to argue the point.

"Here's what we decided to do," Pat reported to the class. "We're going to have a fortune-telling booth. I'm going to dress up with a turban, and we'll get a crystal ball. Then we'll charge ten cents apiece to tell people's fortunes."

"But, Pat, what do you know about telling fortunes?" Ms. Taylor asked.

"I could make them up," said Pat. "Who's going to know the difference?"

"Sure," called out Einstein, "Pat could dress up like a lady and we could call him Miss Fortune."

Pat glared at Einstein. "O.K., wise guy," he said. "You got a better idea for a booth?"

"It just so happens I have," answered Einstein. "Suppose our class has The Booth of the Impossible Trick. You have to pay a dime to try it out, and if you can do the trick you win a dollar."

Einstein checked the table carefully. He could see that what Margaret said was true. You would need a bulldozer to break up that old stone table.

"I'm now going to switch on my incredible shrinking machine," said Margaret. She flipped a switch on the side of the little black box. Nothing much happened except that the black box sort of burped once and then was quiet.

"But who's going to try to do an impossible trick?" asked Pat.

"That's the good part," said Einstein. "The trick sounds like it's easy to do, but it's really impossible. We should get lots of people who'll try to win."

"That's stupid," said Pat. "How can a trick sound easy if it's really impossible?"

"Do you want to try it?" asked Einstein.

"Do I have to pay you a dime to try?" Pat asked suspiciously.

"No, this is for free," said Einstein. "All you have to do is bend over and touch your toes without bending your knees."

"What!" said Pat. "That's easy. I'll bet you a dime I can do that."

"There's just one more thing, Pat," Einstein said. "You have to begin with your back and your feet touching a wall. Your feet have to remain against the wall as you bend."

"So what?" said Pat. "I'm strong. I can touch my toes anywhere."

"Sorry," said Einstein, "but it can't be done."

Margaret motioned Einstein to follow her out. "We'll have to leave the room so as not to shrink ourselves," she said. "But when we come back in a few hours, the table will be gone without a trace. The incredible shrinking machine will have reduced it down to the size of an atom."

the Switch

the BOX

Margaret led Einstein back to Aunt Bess's house. For the rest of the day Einstein and Margaret experimented with chemical indicators such as litmus and brom thymol blue. They used a microscope to look at the protozoa in a drop of pond water. They fed food pellets to Aunt Bess's laboratory white mice. Lunch for Einstein and Margaret was peanut butter and jelly sandwiches.

Aunt Bess started an outdoor barbecue going late in the afternoon. They had grilled hamburgers, newly picked corn, a fresh tomato salad, and watermelon for dessert. It was all delicious and they didn't finish washing and straightening up till eight o'clock.

Can you solve the puzzle: *How does Einstein know that Pat cannot touch his toes without bending his knees when his feet are against a wall?*

Pat stood up against the front wall of the classroom and laughed. "Can you imagine?" he said. "Einstein is telling me that I can't touch my toes. Maybe he thinks I'm as weak as he is."

Pat started to bend over, but he quickly lost his balance. "Let me try that again," he said. Again Pat bent over and nearly fell down. He tried to do it several more times and then said in disgust, "That's impossible. No one can do it."

"That's just what I told you, Pat," said Einstein. "The trick sounds easy, but it's really impossible."

"Einstein, that's really a great idea," Ms. Taylor said. "I think it will make a terrific booth at the fair. Everyone

It was twilight when Margaret led Einstein back by a different path to the shack. They arrived just as the setting sun shone directly on the yellow door, turning it golden, just as it had done in the morning.

Margaret unlocked the door and they went inside. The room looked almost the same: one door, one small window, and one small black box. But the big stone table was gone. Nothing, not even a chip of stone, remained on the floor.

At first Einstein couldn't believe his eyes. Margaret might really stump him this time. How could that big stone table just disappear? Had Margaret really invented a shrinking machine?

Margaret smiled at the look on Einstein's face. "Well," she asked, "what do you think of my incredible shrinking machine?"

Einstein was quiet for a few minutes. Then his face changed and he began to laugh. He pushed back his glasses, which had slipped down. "You almost had me there for a minute, Margaret," he said. "I think I know what happened to the table. And if I'm correct, there is no such thing as an incredible shrinking machine."

will want to try it out. We can put the tryout place behind a curtain so that no one can see it's impossible to do."

Margaret raised her hand. "I agree with you, Ms. Taylor," she said. "It really is a great idea. Science can

be fun. But why is the trick impossible? Can you explain it to us?"

"Certainly, Margaret," replied Ms. Taylor. "The trick is impossible because . . . er . . . Would you please explain the trick, Einstein?"

Can you solve the puzzle:
What do you think happened to the table?

"The key to the puzzle," Einstein began his explanation, "is the sun."

"The sun!" Margaret exclaimed. "What does the sun have to do with the shrinking machine?"

"You know that the sun rises in the east in the morning and sets in the west in the evening," Einstein explained. "Yet both the rising sun and the setting sun shone directly on the yellow door. That's impossible."

"So what's the answer?" Margaret asked.

"Sure," said Einstein. "It's all a matter of your center of gravity. That's the point where all your weight is concentrated. If your center of gravity is directly over your feet, then you're O.K. But if your center of gravity moves to a point outside your feet, then you fall over."

"But then how can you touch your toes at other times?" asked Ms. Taylor.

"Well, when you bend over freely, you shift your upper body weight forward and move your lower body weight backwards at the same time. That keeps your center of gravity from moving outside your feet. But with a wall at your back, you can't shift your

"Simple," Einstein said. "There must be two doors and two rooms in the shack, one in back and one in front. The sun shone on one door in the morning and on the other door in the afternoon. You must have taken me into one room in the morning but into the other room in the afternoon. The first room contained the stone table. The other room didn't have anything in it."

"You're right," said Margaret.

They left the shack and started back to the house. "I see that I made one mistake," Margaret said, shaking her head.

"What's that?" Einstein asked.

"I should have shown you my incredible shrinking machine on a cloudy day."

"Right," said Einstein. "Your machine had me in the dark for a while. But it was the sun that let me see the light."

lower body weight backwards. All your weight moves forward. So you fall over when you try to touch your toes."

"That's wonderful, Einstein," Margaret said to him later. "I'm sorry I called you a noodle head yesterday."

"It did me some good," said Einstein. "As Frankenstein said when he was hit by a bolt of lightning, 'Thanks, I needed that.'"

"You certainly haven't lost your sense of humor," Margaret said. "Unfortunately!"

BE A MATH SLEUTH

Science sleuth Einstein Anderson always uses his noodle to solve tricky problems. Now it's your turn! Use your noodle to solve these math puzzles. In a few cases, you'll need some paper and a pencil, too.

A *palindrome* is a word that is spelled the same backward and forward. *Noon* is a palindrome. So is *aha!* Numbers can be palindromes, too. The most recent palindromic year was 1991. What are the next *two* palindromic years?

LOOK BOTH WAYS

clue in the clock

Copy this clock face onto a sheet of paper. Then draw a line dividing your clock face in half so that the sum of the numbers in each half is the same. (The sum is part of the title of a famous Alfred Hitchcock movie mystery.)

Use the keypad on this telephone to decode this message. Because each number can stand for three different letters, this may be a trying experience.

4 2!   4 2!   8 3 7 9   "7 4 6 6 3 9!"

BREAK THE CODE!

Magic Mystery SQUARE

The sum of every row, column, and diagonal in a magic square is the same number. Copy this magic square onto a sheet of paper. Then fill in numbers to complete it. You can only use each number (one to nine) once.

2	7	6
	3	

THE FAMILY FORTUNE

Imagine that Lord and Lady Riches died under suspicious circumstances, leaving their large fortune to their children. There are nine sons. Each son has one sister. How many suspects, er, children are there altogether?

A "PET-ICULAR" PROBLEM

Imagine that Encyclopedia Brown, supersleuth, had two pets. His dog was three times as old as his cat. Two years later, though, the dog was only *twice* as old as his cat. How old were Encyclopedia's pets in each case?

Mastermind a math puzzle of your own. See if your friends can solve your puzzle.

525

MAGNET

This small

Flat horseshoe

Is sold for

A toy: we are

Told that it

Will pick up pins

And it does, time

After time; later

It lies about,

Getting its red

Paint chipped, being

Offered pins less

Often, until at

Last we leave it

Alone: then

It leads its own

Life, trading

Secrets with

The North Pole,

Reading

Invisible messages

From the sun.

Valerie Worth

WILLIE BEA
and the Time the
MARTIANS LANDED

by VIRGINIA HAMILTON
illustrations by NEAL McPHEETERS

On the eve of Halloween in 1938, a radio play entitled *The War of the Worlds* announces that alien creatures have landed. Willie Bea and her family are among the thousands of people who believe the announcement.

Panic spreads quickly that October night. Willie Bea's town is abuzz with reports that Martians have landed at the Kelly Farm. Willie Bea's friend Toughy Clay even claims to have seen them!

Willie Bea doesn't exactly believe that *Martians* have landed—she thinks the aliens are from the planet Venus. The lines in Willie Bea's hand form a pattern called the "Star of Venus," and Willie Bea imagines that this is a sign that the visitors are from Venus—and that she can communicate with them.

Willie Bea convinces Toughy Clay to come with her and find the aliens. They set out on stilts, wearing capes of sheets over their Halloween costumes.

They strode the dark world, stilting. Willie Bea and Toughy Clay were out in the countryside. They were along roads, and through the fields whenever it was possible for them to get over fences.

The velveteen night and the distant, cold stars were what they could see traveling with them. They imagined they were alone on earth. Willie Bea could feel the loneliness in her heart and soul, and more than once she wished she was home.

Why'd I start this dumb, fool journey? she wondered.

They both imagined beings from another planet just out of sight in the dark.

Toughy Clay didn't dare turn around to check their backs, for fear he would see something beyond belief and fall. "You ever think what's gone happen if one of us fall off these dang stilts?" he whispered loudly to Willie Bea.

But she was thinking hard, and when she answered, it was not about one of them falling. "The evening star of Venus could be falling down on us this very minute," she told him.

"You think so?" he said anxiously.

"Sure," she said, "and maybe that Mars is falling down, too. They say it is red and *mean,* boy!"

Wonder what is really going on, she thought. And if the United States army can't stop them space men, what will happen to *us?* And why come everything is so awful quiet all around?

She felt strange, as if they were being watched. She was about to warn Toughy and tell him to shut off the flashlight. The light bobbed along with them. It was a weak light, batteries wearing out. It barely lit the side of the road. But it was what they had and a comfort in the dark.

Suddenly, there was a burst of flames close to a fence in a field they were passing. The flames grew rapidly into a huge bonfire. The fire flowed up and licked a pile of brush and brambles, crackling and sizzling hotly.

A gun went off with a roar. It was such a shock, all that fire and then the shot.

"Am I hit?" Toughy cried. He lost his grip on the flashlight, but he kept his balance. "Whoa! Somebody shootin' at us!"

"Shhhh!" Willie Bea said. "Be quiet!"

The flashlight clattered and rolled on the road. It broke open and its light went out. They would have to leave it. There was no way to get down and then back on the stilts again.

"Halt! Who goes there!" a rasping voice yelled.

A man came toward them from the bonfire. He leaned on the fence and aimed his shotgun right at them.

"Here he comes!" Toughy whimpered.

Willie Bea's heart thudded and skipped. She lost her breath; got it back, ragged and gasping.

"It's us. We're only kids!" she managed to call out.

"Well, balls-a-fire! I almost 'bout to give you some buck-shot," said the man. "What chu kids doin' out chare!"

A woman who looked to be his wife came up beside him. "An' so tall—stilts!" she said.

"Don' chu know they is Martians spreadin' they sin all over this land?" said the farmer. "Get on in your home!"

He was a skinny farmer. There were some young kids about half Willie Bea's age around the fire now. She didn't recognize them or the farmer from this far side of town.

"We're on our way now," she hollered across. "But have you seen anything?"

"How can I see anythin' when you make me light up muh far-er fer nothin'?" hollered the farmer. "Git on away from here 'fore I git my dandurf up! Now git!"

Willie Bea and Toughy
went, striding as fast as their legs
and arms propelling the stilts would take
them, their capes bouncing.

"No!" hollered the farmer after them. His
children and wife commenced shouting. "That's the
wrong way! You're headin' the direction of that Kelly farm.
That's where the Martians is. . . ."

But Willie Bea and Toughy were gone. They were in the
dark, invisible in the night.

Her hands and face were cold now.

So cold! she thought. Glad for the capes of sheets!

Out here where there were only cornfields, the cold
seemed to sift down from the sky into the ground and come up
again. Willie Bea longed to stop and just take stock of things.
Her muscles were mighty sore, holding on so tightly to the
stilts. Her fingers cramped her, and her legs were stiff and
chilled. They were starting to ache.

"Maybe we oughtn't to come out here," she said softly. All
was so still around them. "Toughy, maybe we ought to just go
on back."

Toughy strode ahead of her. They had slowed somewhat,
for thick trees along the road blocked out the bonfire light
behind them. They crossed onto a narrower gravel strip with
fields on either side. Gravel was tricky beneath their stilts.
Willie Bea saw that there was no fence on either side of the
gravel road.

"This is a private road," Toughy told her.

"Whose private?" she asked him.

"It's the Kelly private," Toughy said. "Cuts right through the
corn, and they own it. Can say who walk and stride on it, too."

Toughy had never been on the Kelly road before. But he recognized it from the years of stories he had heard about the farm.

"Are we that close? Keep your voice *down*," she whispered.

"Look there," Toughy said. He stood, shifting back and forth to keep his balance.

Willie Bea shifted, too. But she was better at balancing than Toughy was. Just arm pressure and flexing leg muscles was all that was necessary. And once in a while moving the stilts an inch or two. "Look at what?" she said.

"There. Come over here," Toughy said.

She came up beside him. And what she saw made her feel like someone had shut down all her tiredness. Had turned off the cold of her hands and face. She didn't realize she was shivering, but the cold had got way under the hobo costume she had made.

They were on the private Kelly road and it had risen over a hillock. At first Willie Bea looked down at the reach of land.

"Is it the ice-skating lake?" she asked in the softest voice. Who could tell anything in this deep night?

"Uh-uh," Toughy said. "I hear the lake is on the other side of the house. Here is only the fields on each side of the private road."

"Well, I'm glad of that," Willie Bea said.

She thought to look up, gazing across and beyond the black land-reach to where there had to be some sort of hill. Over there, situated high and handsome, was the biggest house Willie Bea had ever seen. It was enormous. And it was lit up like a carnival, like a birthday cake.

"Havin' a Halloween ball?" she asked in awe.

She thought she heard strains of music coming from the mansion.

"Think they just own a lot of light," Toughy said. "Think they must be listenin' to their Victrola phonograph."

They don't even know the Venus ones are here! Willie Bea thought.

"Did you hear that?" she said. "Did you hear them laughing over there, them Kellys?" she asked Toughy. Her voice was dreamy and faraway.

"No," he said. "They don't act like they care about Martians, though."

"Not Martians," Willie Bea said. "They are from Venus."

"That's what you said before. But how you know that?" he asked her.

"Aunt Leah read my palm and she found in it the Star of Venus. Aunt Leah says it is a sign of great good luck."

"You sure?" Toughy asked. But he knew anything Leah Wing told was true. Everyone knew that Leah Wing was the best fortune lady ever did live among the people. And rich, like the Kellys.

"So you lookin' for the Venus ones. So, see what they have to say to you?" Toughy asked.

Willie Bea nodded in the dark. "I don't know what-all will happen," she said in a misty voice. She never took her eyes from that Kelly mansion of enchantment. "But maybe it will stop the attack from them. Maybe if they see there's somebody here that has the Star of Venus . . ." Her voice seemed to drift off on the air.

"I don't know," Toughy murmured. He imagined it could be true. In the deep dark of Halloween night, the Kelly farm was a magic kingdom. Invading men from Venus were *boldacious* monsters, close about. Watch out! Anything could be true.

"Where'd you see the monster?" Willie Bea asked. "Was it over there? You can see some big, dark trees by the light from those windows."

Toughy shifted uneasily on his stilts. He cleared his throat, about to tell his lie again, when Willie Bea said, "Come on! We'll follow the road closer."

It was deep, dark going, and their stilts made grating sounds on the gravel. When they were down there, it didn't feel or look much different than on the rise. It was cold. The cornfields looked full of tall rows of dark.

"There's no lake that I can tell," Willie Bea said.

"I told you. Say the lake is on the other side of the house," Toughy said.

"Well, you don't have to yell," Willie Bea told him.

"I'm not yelling!" he yelled back.

They were both yelling. Noise, a deep rumbling, was coming out of the ground. Willie Bea couldn't hear herself breathe, or think.

"What's that?" she hollered at Toughy.

"Don't know. Can't tell where it is or what it is!" he hollered.

It was getting closer. Willie Bea thought she saw something. Like the blackest night moving.

"You see that?" she thought she yelled. Her mouth moved, but she couldn't hear what came out. "Toughy!" she screamed.

"Willie Bea!" he was screaming back. "Willie Bea!"

Now they could guess what the noise was. The great black dark that moved was one of the monsters. It was a rolling, ear-splitting, outlandish alien. And huge.

The thing must have turned a corner in front of them from behind the house, somehow. It had turned toward them and they saw its evil eye.

An awful, white, wicked, round eye. It could have been its heat ray, but it didn't hurt them. It was just blinding.

"Wait! I got the Star!" cried Willie Bea.

The great black dark came straight for them. And another huge blackness came on behind it. Giants as tall as houses, tall as trees, on the move.

Another one came after the second. Two of them march-
ing, rolling behind the first. They spread out to the left of the
first one. Their blinding eyes outlined the first one. Illumi-
nated it for Willie Bea to see plainly that it was a deadly,
monstrous alien.

"It's true! It's an invasion!" Toughy was yelling. "Run.
Run, Willie Bea!"

Willie Bea couldn't hear him. She couldn't move. She was
transfixed by the monsters. The first one's neck wasn't in the
center of its body, where it should have been. It was on the
right *side* of it! The long neck was like a wide stovepipe jut-
ting out of its side. Its head that fitted on its neck was *all*
V-shaped.

Suddenly, it seemed that the first monster spoke to her.
She was staring into its awful eye, into its noise. The darkness moving one by one was overpowering.

All went quiet inside Willie Bea. She no longer heard the
monster's roaring noise. Its sound of voice was right with her,

like it was all around in her head. It seemed to be right by her, right in her ear.

"Huh?" Willie Bea said, staring wildly into the evil eye.

"Willie Bea, I come here, too. I got here late. I was looking for you. Heard you shouting." Spoken loud and as clear as a bell in her ear.

The white eyes of the monsters coming on held her hypnotized. She thought she told them, "Look. I hold the Star of Venus in my palm. Turn off your rays. Don't fight. We only want to be friends!" She held up her palm for them to see.

"Willie Bea, we'd better get back. You coming back with me?"

The first monster was now to the left side of the road. Its head on the side, on its long neck, was coming right at her.

"Oh, no, I can't go back to Venus with *you!*" she told it.

"You're just scared and tired. Follow me close behind."

The second monster was passing along beside the gravel road. Willie Bea looked up at its head.

"No! Get away!" she hollered.

Then she was backing away from the third monster. She thought its light was bearing down. "You leave me be!" She flailed her arms backward and one stilt leg slipped in the gravel. She twisted, trying to untangle herself from the foot wedges. She was falling. Something grabbed at her. She saw the last monster's head turn in her direction. Its light was full on her. It was coming for her.

Willie Bea, falling. And something, someone had hold of her, was falling with her. She hit the ground, falling hard on part of someone. Something struck her a glancing blow on the forehead.

All went dark for Willie Bea. The dark filled with glowing comets and stars. Great planets of Venus and Mars. All such colors of worlds, pumpkin yellow and orange in a Halloween universe.

Willie Bea opened her eyes on an alien standing over her. She thought she saw its V-shaped mouth: "Willie Bea! Are you hurt?"

"No. I won't go back with you, either," she told it. "I like my own world."

"You hit your head. It knocked you silly," the alien said.

Willie Bea's head started hurting. Suddenly, she felt cold all over. Her legs were aching. Her hand with its Star felt numb as she came to.

She saw a great light. It was upon her and the someone who stood over her.

"Where . . . ?" was all she could think to say.

She heard fast footfalls on the gravel. She lifted her head and was blinded by the white monster-light. The monster made its roaring sound, but it wasn't moving now.

"What happened?" it hollered, sounding frightened. "What are you kids doing where we are harvesting? Did we hit someone? . . . Oh, little child!"

Willie Bea saw a man in the light. He knelt beside her. "Did the combines scare you, child? We might've run you over!"

Willie Bea was damp and clammy from the gathering cold and mist. Tired and confused, she closed her eyes. Her insides flopped and the inky night of a dizzying universe returned.

Where a giant black cat sat on a pumpkin world. Where aliens were Kelly kings. They took away the Star in her palm. Willie Bea was so small, so unimportant. They made her polish their V-shaped crowns of gold.

MEET VIRGINIA HAMILTON

When Virginia Hamilton was a child, she loved to listen to the stories her relatives told when they got together. Some of these stories told of family history. Others were wonderful tales of mystery and magic. The stories grew and changed with each telling and were passed along from one generation to the next.

Virginia Hamilton believes the rich family storytelling in her childhood shapes her writing. "I am a teller of tales," she explains, "in part, because of the informal way I learned from Mother and her relatives. . . ."

Hamilton often roots her books in a real event from history. She creates characters and details to make the story come alive for readers today. *Willie Bea and the Time the Martians Landed,* for example, shows how a small-town Ohio girl with an active imagination responds to an actual 1938 radio broadcast that frightened many people.

Like Willie Bea, the young Virginia Hamilton was a bright, imaginative girl from a close-knit Ohio family. Today, Hamilton is the widely praised author of many books for young readers as well as a collector of folk tales, myths, and legends.

IDENTIFIED FLYING OBJECTS!

by Margaret McKelway

AHNIGHITO, one of the largest meteorites ever found, attracts a crowd at the American Museum of Natural History in New York City.

Invaders from space are heading for earth! But don't worry. Similar invaders have been pelting the planet since its birth. Flying objects fill the solar system. If you've seen a shooting star you've seen a small invader from space. Big things fall to earth, too. Read on to find out more.

FLASHY FLIERS

After the main characters of the solar system formed—the sun and the planets and their moons—a lot of building material was left over. It's still there, and sometimes pieces of it come close enough to earth to give us clues about the universe. These pieces are the comets and the asteroids.

Comets probably put on the most dazzling show. Huge chunks of frozen ice and dust, comets usually stay at the frigid outer edges of the solar system. But sometimes a comet plunges toward the sun. As it nears the sun's warmth, its nucleus, or body, begins to vaporize into gas, which escapes as a dusty tail.

A comet's journey around the sun can take from just a few years to several million. During each orbit the

comet leaves a trail of dust. As the earth passes through the dust, particles hit earth's atmosphere. Most burn up as streaks of light called meteors. Some—about 50 tons a day—fall harmlessly to the earth's surface.

In the past comets have hit earth. Many scientists believe that some comets may have brought the materials from which life developed.

FAR-OUT STUFF ◀
Mineral crystals gleam like gems inside a slice of meteorite. Meteorites are rocks from space that have landed on earth. While in space, they are called meteoroids.

LIGHT SHOW ▲
Two lucky stargazers spot a shower of meteors, or shooting stars. Meteors are meteoroids that appear as streaks of light as they hit the earth's atmosphere and begin to vaporize.

ROCK 'N ROLLERS

Orbiting the sun in a broad belt between Jupiter and Mars are chunks of stone or metal or both, called asteroids. They range in size from boulders to mountains or bigger. Sometimes they collide and shatter. Fragments fly in all directions. Some fragments fall into orbits that pass inside the moon's orbit around earth. Smaller pieces, called meteoroids, usually vaporize as meteors. Those that reach the surface are known as meteorites.

ASTRO-POTATO? ▲
Space probe Galileo traveled past this 35-mile-long asteroid in 1994. Many asteroids have odd shapes, but few have moons like the tiny one to the right in this photograph.

ROCKY ROAD ▶
Asteroids—chunks of rock or metal or both—circle the sun, most in a ring called the asteroid belt. Within the belt asteroids often crash together and shatter. Asteroid pieces spin out of the belt and fall into other orbits.

Neptune

Uranus
Pluto

ASTEROID BELT

Mars

Saturn

Mercury
Sun
Venus
Earth

Jupiter

DIG IT! ▲
In this artist's vision of the future, a miner searches for precious metal ore on a large asteroid. Earth is visible in the distance, beyond the moon. Asteroids may offer an endless supply of resources and energy for future residents of earth.

IMPACTS!

Rarely, a huge asteroid or comet crashes to earth. It's happened before. Craters scar all the continents. But don't expect a major crash in your lifetime. Huge meteorites that, upon impact, form craters like the one above almost never hit the earth. Even the smaller ones that make it to earth more frequently rarely strike or injure people. But just in case, scientists are keeping an eye on the skies. They're already at work on plans to deflect any meteoroid that might threaten earth.

BIG BLAST ▲
Astro-geologist Eugene Shoemaker stands on the rim of Meteor Crater in Arizona. He and other scientists think a 300,000-ton meteorite crashed here 50,000 years ago with the force of a 15-megaton bomb.

GIANT KILLER ◄
What wiped out the dinosaurs? Here's one theory: Sixty-five million years ago an asteroid six miles across slammed into earth, leaving a huge depression now called Chicxulub Crater. The impact vaporized rocks, sending dust into the air. Shock waves may have set off volcanoes on the opposite side of the planet. For years dust and ash blocked the sun, and the earth grew cold. Animals that couldn't adapt to the sudden change, including dinosaurs, died.

The map shows other large impact sites in North America where smaller meteorites hit.

CANADA

Manicouagan, Quebec

UNITED STATES

Haviland, Kansas

Odessa, Texas

Meteor Crater, Arizona

Gulf of Mexico

MEXICO

Chicxulub Crater

The sun is an orange dinghy
       sailing across a calm sea.

It is a gold coin
       dropped down a drain in heaven.

It is a yellow beach ball
       kicked high into the summer sky.

It is a red thumb-print
       on a sheet of pale blue paper.

It is the gold top from a milk bottle
       floating on a puddle.

Wes Magee

WHAT IS...

Dramatic images of the sun often appear in Mexican art, as shown in these suns made of tinware, baked clay, and painted wood.

THE SUN?

READING RESOURCES

CONTENTS

she lacked. If the procedure is successful, the genetically engineered blood cells will pump out normal levels of the crucial enzyme and restore the girl's immune system to full health.

The specific disorder the girl suffers from is adenosine deaminase (ADA) deficiency, which results from a lack of the ADA gene, which makes an enzyme needed to clean up dangerous metabolic byproducts in the body.

The experimental procedure was developed by Dr. R. Michael Blaese of the National Cancer Institute, Dr. W. French Anderson of the National Heart, Lung and Blood Institute, and Dr. Kenneth W. Culver.

Inventions and Discoveries

Invention	Date	Inventor	Nation.
Adding machine	1642	Pascal	French
Adding machine	1885	Burroughs	US
Aerosol spray	1926	Rotheim	Norwegian
Air brake	1868	Westinghouse	US
Air conditioning	1911	Carrier	US
Air pump	1654	Guericke	German
Airplane, automatic pilot	1912	Sperry	US
Airplane, experimental	1896	Langley	US
Airplane jet engine	1939	Ohain	German
Airplane with motor	1903	Wright bros.	US
Airplane, hydro	1911	Curtiss	US
Airship	1852	Giffard	French
Airship, rigid dirigible	1900	Zeppelin	German
Arc welder	1919	Thomson	US
Autogyro	1920	de la Cierva	Spanish
Automobile, differ- ential gear	1885	Benz	German
Automobile, electric	1892	Morrison	US
Automobile, exp'mtl	1864	Marcus	Austrian
Automobile, gasoline	1889	Daimler	German
Automobile, gasoline	1892	Duryea	US
Automobile magneto	1897	Bosch	German
Automobile muffler		Maxim, H.P.	US
Automobile self-starter	1911	Kettering	US
Babbitt metal	1839	Babbitt	US
Bakelite	1907	BaekelandBelg	US
Balloon	1783	Montgolier	French
Barometer	1643	Torricelli	Italian
Bicycle, modern	1885	Starley	English
Bifocal lens	1780	Franklin	US
Block signals, railway	1867	Hall	US
Bomb, depth	1916	Tait	US
Bottle machine	1895	Owens	US
Braille printing	1829	Braille	French
Burner, gas	1855	Bunsen	German
Calculating machine	1833	Babbage	English
Camera— see also Photography			
Camera, Kodak	1888	Eastman, Walker	US
Camera, Polaroid Land	1948	Land	US
Car coupler	1873	Janney	US
Carburetor, gasoline	1893	Maybach	German
Card time recorder	1894	Cooper	US
Carding machine	1797	Whittemore	US
Carpet sweeper	1876	Bissell	US
Cassette, audio	1963	Philips Co	Dutch
Cassette, videotape	1969	Sony	Japanese
Cash register	1879	Ritty	US
Cathode ray oscilloscope	1897	Braun	German
Cathode ray tube	1878	Crookes	English
CAT scan (computerized tomography)	1973	Hounsfield	English
Cellophane	1908	Brandenberger	Swiss
Celluloid	1870	Hyatt	US
Cement, Portland	1824	Aspdin	English

Invention	Date	Inventor	Nation.
Chronometer	1761	Harrison	English
Circuit, integrated	1959	Kilby, Noyce Texas Instr	US
Clock, pendulum	1657	Huygens	Dutch
Coaxial cable system	1929	Atlel, Espen- sched	US
Coke oven	1893	Hoffman	Austrian
Compressed air rock drill	1871	Ingersoll	US
Comptometer	1887	Feit	US
Computer, automatic sequence	1944	Aiken et al.	US
Computer, mini	1960	Digital Corp.	US
Condenser microphone (telephone)	1916	Wente	US
Corn, hybrid	1917	Jones	US
Cotton gin	1793	Whitney	US
Cream separator	1878	DeLaval	Swedish
Cultivator, disc	1878	Mallon	US
Cystoscope	1878	Nitze	German
Diesel engine	1895	Diesel	German
Disk, compact	1972	RCA	US
Disk, floppy	1970	IBM	US
Disk player, compact	1979	Sony, Philips Co.	Japanese, Dutch
Disk, video	1972	Philips Co.	Dutch
Dynamite	1866	Nobel	Swedish
Dynamo, continuous current	1871	Gramme	Belgian
Dynamo, hydrogen cooled	1915	Schuler	US
Electric battery	1800	Volta	Italian
Electric fan	1882	Wheeler	US
Electrocardiograph	1903	Einthoven	Dutch
Electroencephalograph	1929	Berger	German
Electromagnet	1824	Sturgeon	English
Electron spectrometer	1944	Deutsch, Elliott, Evans	US
Electron tube multigrid	1913	Langmuir	US
Electroplating	1805	Brugnatelli	Italian
Electrostatic generator	1929	Van de Graaff	US
Elevator brake	1852	Otis	US
Elevator, push button	1922	Larson	US
Engine, automatic transmission	1910	Fotinger	German
Engine, coal-gas 4-cycle	1876	Otto	German
Engine, compression ignition	1883	Daimler	German
Engine, electric ignition	1883	Benz	German
Engine, gas, compound	1926	Eickemeyer	US
Engine, gasoline	1872	Brayton, Geo	US
Engine, gasoline	1889	Daimler	German
Engine, steam, piston	1705	Newcomen	English
Engine, steam, piston	1769	Watt	Scottish
Engraving, half-tone	1852	Talbot	US

(continued)

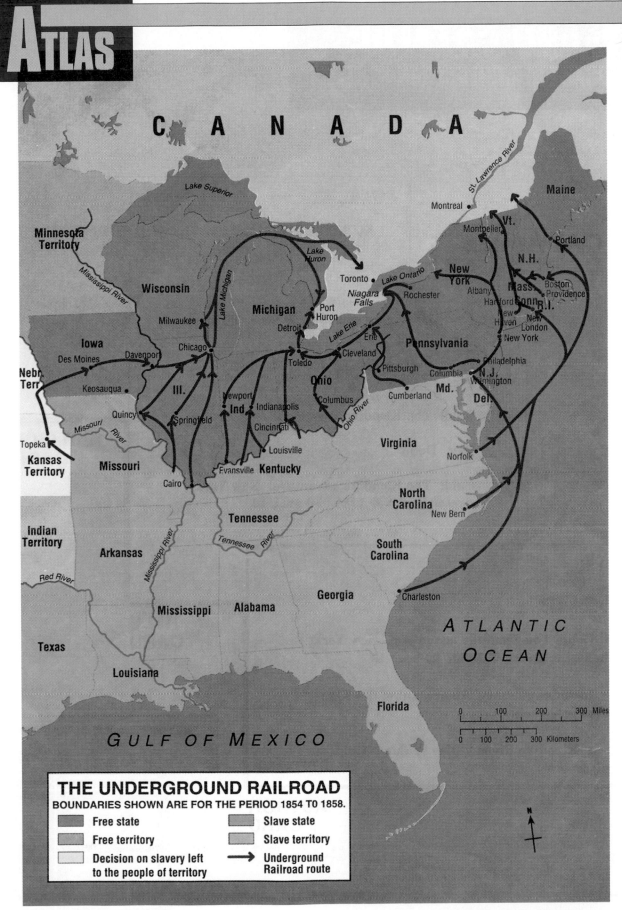

CANADA

Lake Superior

Minnesota
Territory

Lake Huron

Montreal

St. Lawrence River

Maine

Wisconsin

Lake Michigan

Michigan

Port Huron

Toronto

Lake Ontario

Niagara Falls

Rochester

Montpelier

Vt.

Portland

N.H.

Milwaukee

Detroit

Lake Erie

New York

Albany

Mass.

Boston
Providence

R.I.

Iowa

Chicago

Toledo

Cleveland

Erie

Pennsylvania

Hartford

Conn.

Des Moines

Davenport

New
Haven

New
London

Nebr.
Terr.

Keosauqua

Ill.

Newport

Indianapolis

Ohio

Columbus

Pittsburgh

Columbia

Philadelphia

New York

N.J.

Wilmington

Quincy

Springfield

Ind.

Cincinnati

Louisville

Ohio River

Cumberland

Md.

Del.

Topeka

Missouri River

Cairo

Evansville

Kentucky

Virginia

Norfolk

Kansas
Territory

Missouri

Indian
Territory

Mississippi River

Tennessee

Tennessee River

North
Carolina

New Bern

Arkansas

Red River

South
Carolina

Georgia

Charleston

ATLANTIC

OCEAN

Mississippi

Alabama

Texas

Louisiana

Florida

GULF OF MEXICO

| 0 | 100 | 200 | 300 Miles |

| 0 | 100 | 200 | 300 Kilometers |

N

THE UNDERGROUND RAILROAD

BOUNDARIES SHOWN ARE FOR THE PERIOD 1854 TO 1858.

- Free state
- Slave state
- Free territory
- Slave territory
- Decision on slavery left to the people of territory
- → Underground Railroad route

CARD CATALOG AND LIBRARY CLASSIFICATION SYSTEMS

CATALOG CARDS

J 971.91

KLONDIKE RIVER VALLEY (YUKON)--GOLD DISCOVERIES

Ray, Delia

  Gold! The Klondike adventure. New York: Lodestar Books © 1989. 90 pp. ; ill.

SUBJECT CARD

J 971.91

  Gold! The Klondike adventure.

  Ray, Delia

  Gold! The Klondike adventure. New York:
Lodestar Books © 1989. 90 pp. ; ill.

TITLE CARD

J 971.91

  Ray, Delia

  Gold! The Klondike adventure. New York:
Lodestar Books © 1989. 90 pp. ; ill.

  Includes glossary. An account of the Klondike gold rush.

  1. Klondike River Valley (Yukon)--Gold discoveries.

AUTHOR CARD

A-Bi	D-Em
Bj-Bz	En-F
C-Ch	G-Hos
Ci-Cz	Hot-I

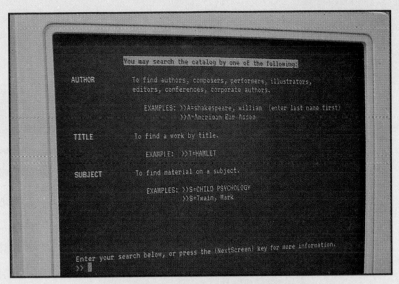

COMPUTERIZED FORM OF THE CARD CATALOG

LIBRARY CLASSIFICATION SYSTEMS

000–099 Generalities
100–199 Philosophy
200–299 Religion
300–399 Social Sciences
400–499 Language
500–599 Pure Sciences
600–699 Technology (Applied Sciences)
700–799 The Arts
800–899 Literature and Rhetoric
900–999 General Geography, History, and Related Disciplines

DEWEY DECIMAL CLASSIFICATION SYSTEM (DDC)

A General Works
B Philosophy – Religion
C History – Auxiliary Sciences
D History and Topography (except America)
E-F American History
G Geography, Anthropology, Folklore, Manners and Customs, Recreation
H Social Sciences
J Political Sciences
K Law of the United States
L Education
M Music and Books on Music
N Fine Arts
P Language and Literature
Q Science
R Medicine
S Agriculture – Plant and Animal Industry
T Technology
U Military Science
V Naval Science
W Bibliography and Library Science

LIBRARY OF CONGRESS CLASSIFICATION SYSTEM (LC)

J-Ken	Pe-Q	Ta-Tim
Keo-L	R-Rom	Tin-V
M-Nos	Rom-Sm	Wa-Wis
Not-Pa	Sn-Sz	Wit-Z

People Who Like to Build

WORKER	PART OF BUILDING
Architect	Entire building
Carpenter	Entire building
Construction Supervisor	Entire building
Developer	Entire building
Estimator	Entire building
Expeditor	Entire building
Plumber	Entire building
Stonemason	Outside of building

It takes many people to construct a building or to renovate an old one. Maybe a career in building is something you'd like to try. This is only a handful of the many job opportunities available in the building profession.

WORKER'S ROLE	EDUCATION	ENVIRONMENT
Designs and plans building to be built and renovated	College degree; graduate work	Office and construction site; mostly indoors
Works with wood to construct building and its parts	High school not mandatory; must be 17 years old to join 4-year apprentice program	Construction site; indoors and outdoors
Manages and oversees crew at the construction site	High school diploma; extensive on-the-job construction experience	Construction site; indoors and outdoors
Obtains and provides money for project; schedules and manages all operations	High school diploma; extensive management experience	Office and construction site; mostly indoors
Figures out how much building will cost to build	High school diploma; technical or junior college training available	Office and construction site; mostly indoors
Buys building materials	High school diploma; technical or junior college training available	Office and wholesalers' offices; mostly indoors
Assembles and installs pipe systems to carry water	High school diploma recommended; 4–5 years apprenticeship	Office and construction site; mostly indoors
Works with stone to create outside of building	High school not mandatory; technical or junior college training available	Office and construction site; mostly outdoors

EARTH

ERA	CENOZOIC (Age of Mammals)	MESOZOIC (Age of the Dinosaurs)
Millions of Years Ago	0–65	65–250
Climate Conditions	Cold, then warming to present conditions	Warm, dry
Earth Events	Periodic ice ages; Grand Canyon, Alps, and Himalayas form	Continents separate; Rocky and Andes mountains form
Plant Life	Modern; first grasses; first cultivated plants	Cone-bearing plants; first flowering plants, oaks, maples
Animal Life	Humans appear; diverse mammals appear; many mammals become extinct	Many dinosaurs; first birds and mammals; dinosaurs become extinct

SQUIRREL

HUMANS

MAMMOTH

APATOSAURUS

TYRANNOSAURUS REX

TRICERATOPS

COELOPHYSIS

HISTORY

PALEOZOIC (Age of Fish)	PRECAMBRIAN
250-570	570-5,000 billion
Warm and humid, then gradually drier and cooler	Cool
Appalachian and Ural mountains form; continents drift and collide	First glaciers; volcanoes active; continents were joined as one land
First land plants; mosses; cone-bearing plants	Blue-green algae
First animals with shells and skeletons; first fishes and amphibians (animals that live in water and on land); first reptiles and insects	Simple, one-celled worm-like animals; jellyfish and jellyfish-like animals

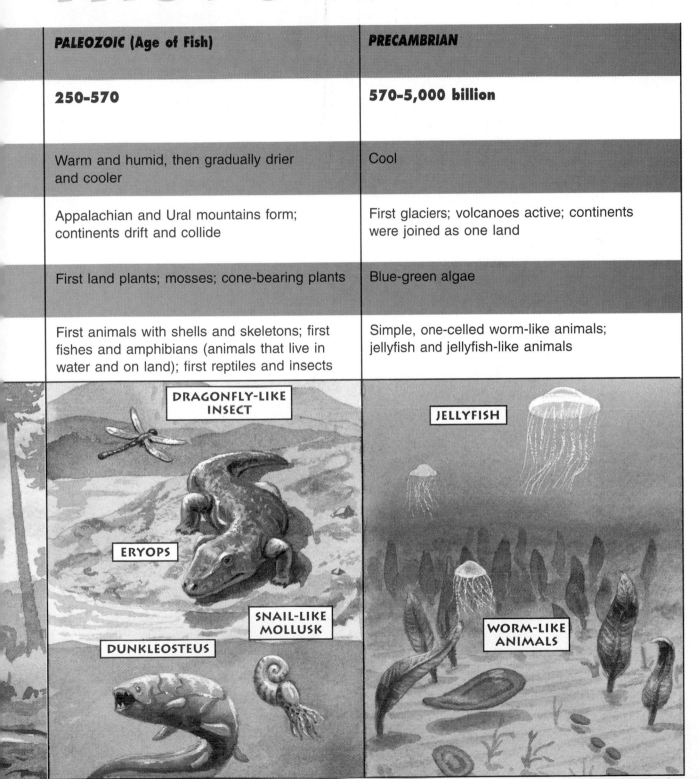

DRAGONFLY-LIKE INSECT

ERYOPS

SNAIL-LIKE MOLLUSK

DUNKLEOSTEUS

JELLYFISH

WORM-LIKE ANIMALS

Layers of Earth

No one has ever dug deep enough into Earth to reach the outer or inner core, or even the mantle.

Crust
Earth's outermost layer ranges from 4–43 miles (6–60 kilometers) thick.

Mantle
This layer of rocks is 1,800 miles (2,900 kilometers) thick. The top of the mantle is partly fluid.

Outer Core
A layer of liquid metal 1,400 miles (2,200 kilometers) thick lies under the mantle.

Inner Core
Earth's center is a solid ball of iron and nickel 750 miles (1,200 kilometers) thick.

THREE KINDS OF BRIDGES

HOW THEY TRANSMIT LOADS

 Load   Support   Downward Force

BEAM BRIDGE

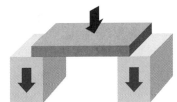

ARCH BRIDGE

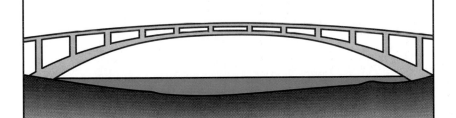

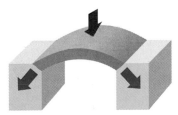

SUSPENSION BRIDGE

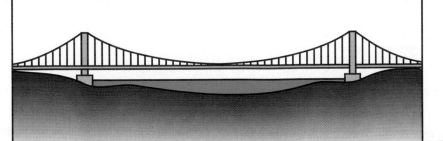

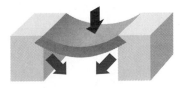

DICTIONARY

guide words

main entry

sculpture **1.** The art of carving or making figures or designs that occupy space. Sculpture usually is done by carving stone, wood, or marble, modeling in clay, or casting in bronze or another metal. **2.** The figure or design that is made in this way. That statue is a beautiful piece of *sculpture. Noun.*
—To carve, model, or cast figures or designs. The artist *sculptured* a lion. *Verb.*
  sculp·ture (skulp′chər) *noun, plural*
  sculptures; *verb,* **sculptured,**
  sculpturing.

definition

verb forms

scurry To go or move in a hurry. The children *scurried* after their parents.
  scur·ry (skûr′ē) *verb,* **scurried, scurrying.**

scurvy A disease that is caused by a lack of vitamin C. A person with scurvy feels very weak and has bleeding gums. Scurvy can be prevented by eating vegetables and fruits that contain a large amount of vitamin C.
  scur·vy (skûr′vē) *noun.*

pronunciation

scythe A tool with a long curved blade and a long bent handle. It is swung from side to side to mow or cut grasses and crops by hand.
  scythe (sīth) *noun, plural* **scythes.**

SD Postal abbreviation for *South Dakota.*

S.D. or **S. Dak.** An abbreviation for *South Dakota.*

SE or **S.E.** An abbreviation for *southeast.*

sea **1.** The large body of salt water that covers almost three fourths of the earth's surface; ocean. **2.** A large part of this body of salt water, usually partly enclosed by land. **3.** The movement of the water of the ocean; wave or waves. The crew struggled to keep the ship afloat in the rough *seas.* **4.** An overwhelming amount or number. A *sea* of soldiers stormed the fort. Another word that sounds like this is **see.**

homophone

idiom

  • **at sea.** **1.** Out on the ocean. We were *at sea* for a week. **2.** Confused; bewildered. I was *at sea* about what to do.
  • **to go to sea.** **1.** To become a sailor. They joined the navy and *went to sea.* **2.** To begin a voyage at sea. They *went to sea* a week ago.
  sea (sē) *noun, plural* **seas.**

sea anemone A sea animal that is shaped like a tube and that attaches itself to rocks and other objects.

seaboard The land on or near the sea. California is on the Pacific *seaboard.*
  sea·board (sē′bôrd′) *noun, plural* **seaboards.**

part of speech

seacoast Land that is near the sea or bordering the sea.
  sea·coast (sē′kōst′) *noun, plural* **seacoasts.**

seafaring **1.** Making a living by working at sea. The *seafaring* merchant visited many lands. **2.** Of or having to do with the sea or sailors. The sailor told *seafaring* tales.
  sea·far·ing (sē′fâr′ing) *adjective.*

syllable division

seafood Saltwater fish or shellfish used for food.
  sea·food (sē′füd′) *noun, plural* **seafoods.**

plural

sea gull A white and gray bird with long wings that lives near the sea. Look up **gull** for more information.

sea horse A kind of fish with a head that looks like that of a horse. It has a curling tail that it uses to hold onto underwater plants.

compound word

seal¹ A sea animal that lives in coastal waters and has flippers instead of feet. Seals spend some of their time on land. Seals are mammals.
  seal (sēl) *noun, plural* **seals** or **seal.**

sea horse

illustration

seal² **1.** A design that is stamped on wax, paper, or other soft material or a picture of such a design. A seal is used to show who owns something or that something is genuine. **2.** Something that closes tightly and completely. The *seal* of this envelope is a flap with glue on it. **3.** The condition of being closed tightly. The *seal* on the jar was so tight that we had to put the top under hot water to loosen it. **4.** A stamp or sticker. Some kinds of seals are sold to raise money for a cause, and people who buy seals usually put them on letters and packages. *Noun.*
—**1.** To close tightly and completely. Please *seal* the envelope. The worker *sealed* the cracks in the wall with plaster before painting. **2.** To settle or decide. The two neighbors *sealed* their agreement by shaking hands. **3.** To place a seal on. The diploma was stamped and *sealed* by the college. *Verb.*
  seal (sēl) *noun, plural* **seals;** *verb,* **sealed, sealing.**

homographs

example sentence

sea lion One of several large seals that are found in the Pacific Ocean.

at; āpe; fär; câre; end; mē; it; īce; pierce; hot; ōld; sông, fôrk; oil; out; up; ūse; rüle; pùll; tûrn; chin; sing; shop; thin; this; hw in white; zh in treasure. The symbol ə stands for the unstressed vowel sound in about, taken, pencil, lemon, and circus.

pronunciation key

647

DICTIONARY OF THE ENGLISH LANGUAGE

chaleco salvavidas	**1.** life jacket	lancha de motor	**13.** motorboat
canoa	**2.** canoe	deslizador de vela	**14.** windsurfer
remo/paleta (de agua)	**3.** paddle	veleta	**15.** sailboard
bote de vela	**4.** sailboat	bote de paseo	**16.** cabin cruiser
timón	**5.** rudder	canoa de los esquimales	**17.** kayak
orza de deriva/quilla	**6.** centerboard	bote/lancha/botecito	**18.** dinghy
botalón/botavara	**7.** boom	anclaje/bolla	**19.** mooring
mástil	**8.** mast	flotador inflable	**20.** inflatable raft
vela	**9.** sail	escálamo/horquilla	**21.** oarlock
esquiador	**10.** water-skier	remo	**22.** oar
sirga/cuerda de remolque	**11.** towrope	bote de remo	**23.** rowboat
motor exterior	**12.** outboard motor		

A PICTURE DICTIONARY IN SPANISH AND ENGLISH

HOW TO TREAD WATER

Treading water is a simple way of keeping your head above water. Nonswimmers have been known to stay afloat for as long as 12 hours by using this method. The human body acts as its own life preserver when the lungs are filled with air. Here's what to do:

1. Keep calm. If you panic and struggle, you may swallow water. This will cause you to cough and choke, expelling air from your lungs.

2. Open and close your legs in a scissors-like motion, keeping a steady rhythm.

3. At the same time, keep your arms going in a steady back-and-forth movement in front of you. With your elbows slightly bent and palms out, move your hands away from each other (the arms will follow); then, with palms facing, bring your hands together again.

4. With your head above water, you will now be able to inhale through your mouth to fill your lungs with air.

5. Continue these treading movements in a steady, relaxed manner until help arrives.

SIDE VIEW

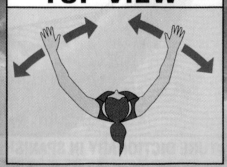

TOP VIEW

KNOTS

OVERHAND KNOT

An overhand knot is a simple knot made in a single piece of rope. It is used as a "stopper."

1. Make a loop in the rope.

2. Pass the end of the rope lying under the loop over and down through the loop.

3. Pull both ends of the rope.

You can also make an overhand knot by holding one end of the rope in your right hand and the other in your left.

1. Place the rope on a table, with the ends about 20 inches apart. Then fold your arms, one hand over and one under the opposite forearm.

2. Bend over and pick up an end of the rope with each hand.

3. Still holding the rope, unfold your arms and pull.

SQUARE KNOT

A square knot, also called a reef knot, is used to bind or fasten. To practice making this knot, use two pieces of rope and work on a table or other flat surface.

1. Make a long "U" with rope A.

2. With rope A to your left, pass one end of rope B over the end of the "U."

3. Working left, pass rope B under the upper leg of the "U."

4. Still working left, pass rope B over both legs of the "U."

5. Now working right, pass rope B first under the lower leg of the "U," then over the end of the "U."

6. With both ends of rope A in the left hand and both ends of rope B in the right hand, pull the ropes tight.

46   coin

COINS OF THE OLD WORLD

GREEK DECADRACHM
(5th century B.C.)

ITALIAN TESTONE
(16th century)

ROMAN DENARIUS
(1st century A.D.)

JUDEAN
WIDOW'S MITE
(1st century A.D.)

ISLAMIC FATIMID
(11th century)

SPANISH PIECES OF EIGHT

ENGLISH PENNY
(14th century)

BYZANTINE NOMISMA

VENETIAN DUCAT
(13th century)

coin (koin), a stamped or embossed disk that is generally made of metal and used as money. Coins are necessary for completing small, everyday financial transactions, and the minting of them is an important function of national governments. Unlike paper currency, which merely represents value, coins have a value in themselves.

Most modern coins bear designs and words that are impressed into the surface of the coin during minting. In the typical minting operation the metal to be used is melted and cast into bars. The bars are divided into coin strips of regulated thickness. The strips are fed to a cutting machine, where carbon-steel dies punch out blank coins. The coins are then milled by a machine that raises their edges above the surface. This process makes it easier to stack the coins and also minimizes surface wear. Finally, the coins are fed to a hydraulic press that imprints symbols and words under tremendous pressure. At the same time the rims of the more valuable coins receive a pattern of indentations to prevent people from shaving off bits of the metal.

History

In early civilizations, goods were acquired by barter, or the direct exchange of one commodity for another. When coins became the principal medium of exchange, such metals as gold, silver, bronze, copper, lead, and iron were used to mint them. The first known coins were introduced in Lydia in Asia Minor and in China about the 8th century B.C. The Lydian coins, probably issued by private rather than by state sources, were made of a natural alloy of gold and silver, known as electrum. Governments soon assumed the responsibility for authorizing and producing coins. By the end of the 6th century B.C., gold and silver coins were being minted in many Greek city-states. As Athens became

the commercial center of the Aegean Sea area, its coins were used and imitated throughout the region.

The first Roman coins were made of bronze, and they date from about the 4th century B.C. Gold and silver were used during the period of the later Roman Empire. After the fall of Rome in the 5th century A.D., Byzantine and Merovingian gold coins and, later, Carolingian silver coins were used extensively in European trade centers. With the breaking up of the Carolingian Empire various cities and states made their own coins, which were mostly crude thin silver pieces. As Genoa and Venice rose in commercial importance in the 12th century, Italian coins became the predominant medium of exchange.

The early American colonists used Indian wampum as money. Wampum consisted of small shell beads made into belts. The value of wampum was not based on the worth of its material as much as on the labor required to produce the belts. In the colonial period European coins were circulated in America, but their value fluctuated from colony to colony and from one locality to another. In 1652 the Massachusetts Bay colony produced the first coins minted in America. During the American Revolution the Continental Congress issued coins made of pewter, silver, and brass.

The U.S. Mint was established in Philadelphia in 1792, and its first coins were circulated the following year. In the American Civil War the Confederacy printed paper money because of the shortage of metal to make coins. After the war, bank notes, checks, drafts, and other forms of paper currency increased in use, while metal currency continued to decline. In 1933 the United States discontinued entirely the use of gold coins in domestic and foreign commerce. It is still legal, however, for coin collectors to save them and to exchange them with other collectors.

AMERICAN COINS OF THE PAST
(Both sides of each coin are shown.)

PINE TREE SHILLING

$20 GOLD PIECE

FUGIO CENT

CONFEDERATE
HALF-DOLLAR

COMMEMORATIVE
ISABELLA QUARTER

Coins have always reflected the degree of prosperity enjoyed by the nations issuing them. The Romans often devaluated their coins to pay their debts with "cheap" money during financial crises. Similar depreciation of coins was common at various times in all later European states. It occurred whenever rulers resorted to reminting coins at a reduced ratio of gold and silver to make up for the lack of available funds. In more modern times the silver content of British coins was decreased with the decline of the British Empire after World War I. By 1947 British "silver" coins had lost all their silver content and were being made of a mixture of copper and nickel, called cupronickel.

Coin Design

The earliest coins were seldom imprinted with words, but most of them bore symbols on both their observe, or front and reverse, back sides. Generally, the designs represented animals, religious subjects, military heroes, or civil authorities. The head of the goddess Athena was frequently depicted on Athenian coins. Roman coins commemorated great victories or bore a representation of the head of an emperor or of a god. Many ancient coins are outstanding for their artistic qualities. Syracuse, a trade center in Sicily, produced some of the most beautiful coins, and certain of its skilled craftsmen and artists have become known to generations through the coins they designed.

Through the ages the coins of all countries typically have carried the profile of a present or past chief of state and a motto. Many U.S. coins bear a representation of the head of a former President. The date of issue and the denomination appear on all U.S. coins, and almost all coins bear such inscriptions as "Liberty," "In God We Trust," and *E Pluribus Unum*," a Latin phrase meaning "one from many."

Coin Collecting

There are an estimated 400,000 numismatists, or coin collectors, in the United States. The prime consideration in determining the worth of a coin is supply and demand. The condition of a coin also affects its value. A coin that shows little or no surface wear is far more valuable than another of the same year that shows signs of considerable handling or wear. Ancient coins are often valuable regardless of condition.

In large collections, coins are usually wrapped individually and kept in trays stored in metal cabinets. Smaller collections and display pieces are kept in specially designed albums and folders. Many albums include cutout spaces for inserting a series of related coins. An important part of collecting is the ability to recognize counterfeit coins. Counterfeits usually make a dull sound when they are dropped on a hard surface, and many of them feel greasy. They also have irregular edges, and some of them can be easily cut with a knife. Many numismatists collect only the coins of a specific country, and some collect coins regardless of origin. Other collectors specialize in tokens, commemorative medals, and paper money in addition to the coins of one or more countries.

Books for Further Study
How to Build a Coin Collection by Fred Reinfeld and Burton H. Hobson (Sterling, 1977).
The Coin Atlas: The World of Coinage from Its Origins to the Present Day by Joe Cribb and others (Facts on File, 1990).
Collecting Coins for Pleasure & Profit: A Comprehensive Guide and Handbook for Collectors and Investors by Barry Krause (Betterway Publications, 1991).
Standard Catalog of World Coins by Chester L. Krause and Clifford Mishler (Krause, published annually).

CLASSIC GAMES—SPECIAL EDITIONS

Use the order form below to order your sets of special edition games created exclusively for Classic Games.

--------------------------------DETACH HERE--------------------------------

ORDER FORM

ITEM	ITEM #	PRICE	ITEM	ITEM #	PRICE
Marbles (Bagged Set)	001	$5.95	Parcheesi	006	$9.95
Marbles (Boxed Set)	002	$9.95	Tiddlywinks	007	$3.95
Checkers	003	$9.95	Jacks	008	$2.95
Chess	004	$9.95	Backgammon	009	$9.95
Checkers & Chess—Travel Set	005	$9.95			

Please Print

NAME _Tiffany Baker_

ADDRESS _245 Evans Road_

CITY _Chicago_   STATE _IL_   ZIP _00000-0000_   PHONE _000 555-6432_

ITEM #	QTY.	NAME OF ITEM	PRICE EACH	TOTAL PRICE
001	1	Marbles (Bagged)	$5.95	$5.95
004	1	Chess	9.95	9.95
005	1	Checkers and Chess	9.95	9.95
008	2	Jacks	2.95	5.90

Packing & Delivery

For Orders of: Add:

Up to $20	$4.00
Up to $30	$5.00
Up to $40	$6.00
Up to $50	$7.00
$50 to $75	$9.00
$75 to $100	$11.00
$100 & Up	$13.00

Payment Information
(Check one.)

SUBTOTAL	$31.75
PACKING & DELIVERY	6.00
TAX: ADD LOCAL SALES TAX IF DELIVERED IN CA	
TOTAL ORDER	$37.75

Check enclosed ___

Please charge
my credit card ✓

Credit Card Type _Master_

Credit Card # _0000-0000-0000-0000_

Signature of cardholder _Sarah Baker_

Expiration date _2/97_

Print name of cardholder _Sarah Baker_

SEND TO:
Classic Games
295 Dominguez Avenue
Ardmore, CA 00000-0000

OUR GUARANTEE
If you're not happy with any item for any reason, you may return it for a full refund.

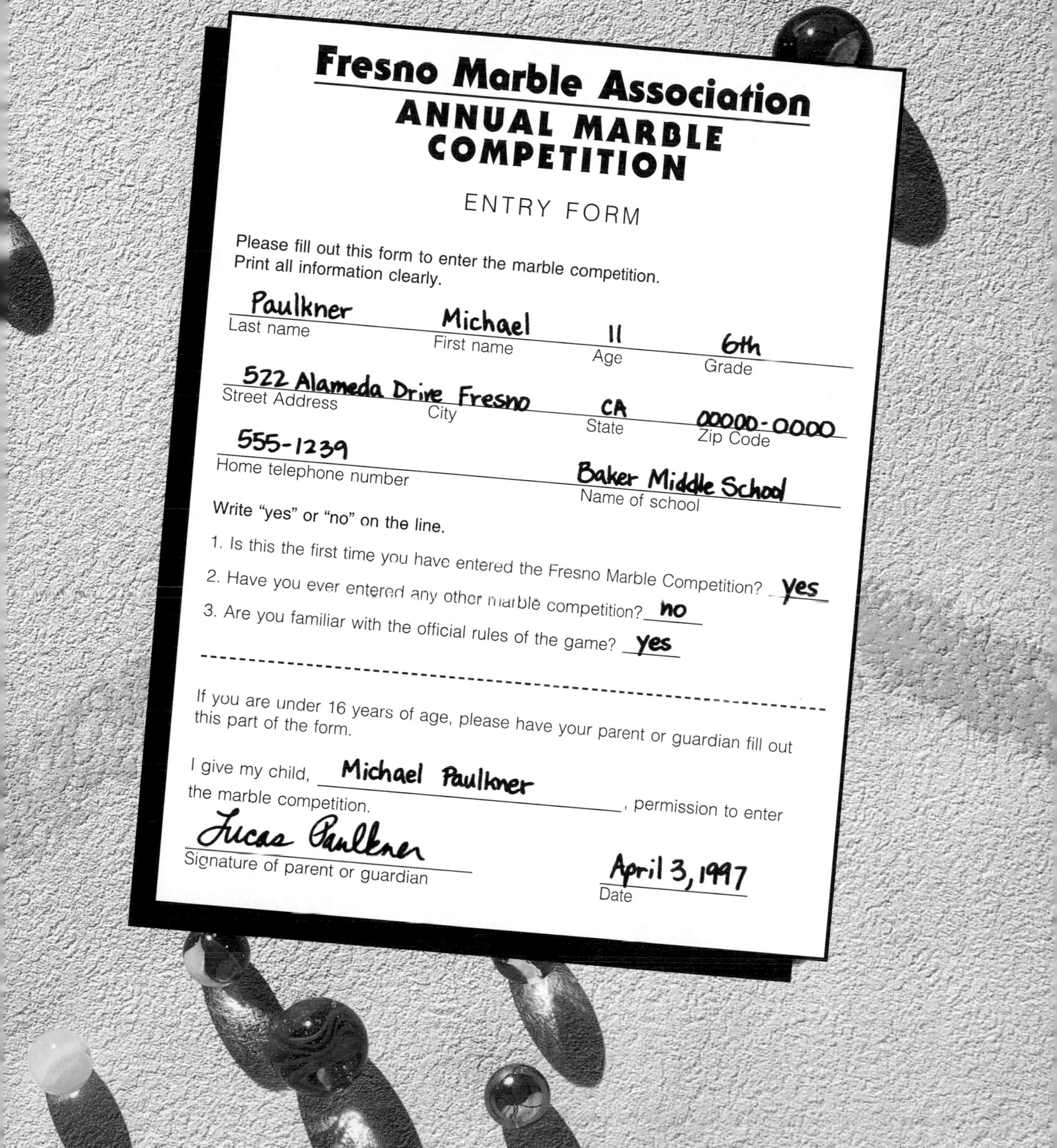

Fresno Marble Association
ANNUAL MARBLE COMPETITION
ENTRY FORM

Please fill out this form to enter the marble competition.
Print all information clearly.

Paulkner
Last name

Michael
First name

11
Age

6th
Grade

522 Alameda Drive Fresno
Street Address　　　　City

CA
State

00000-0000
Zip Code

555-1239
Home telephone number

Baker Middle School
Name of school

Write "yes" or "no" on the line.

1. Is this the first time you have entered the Fresno Marble Competition? **yes**

2. Have you ever entered any other marble competition? **no**

3. Are you familiar with the official rules of the game? **yes**

- -

If you are under 16 years of age, please have your parent or guardian fill out
this part of the form.

I give my child, **Michael Paulkner** , permission to enter
the marble competition.

Lucas Paulkner
Signature of parent or guardian

April 3, 1997
Date

The United States: A Growing Nation

Population Growth of Three Western States

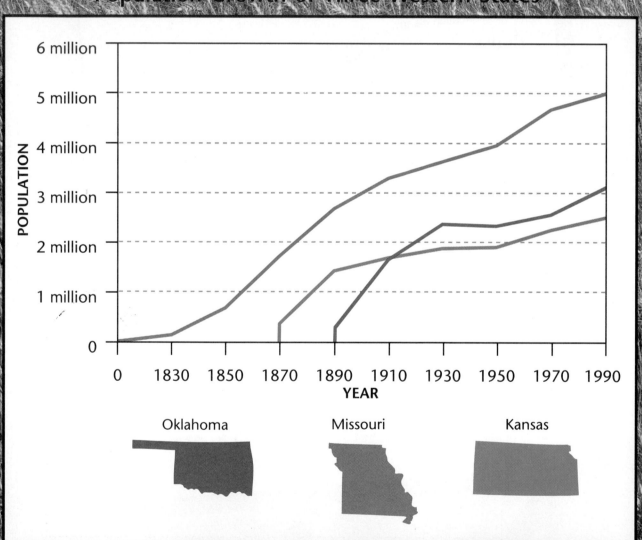

Population: East and West

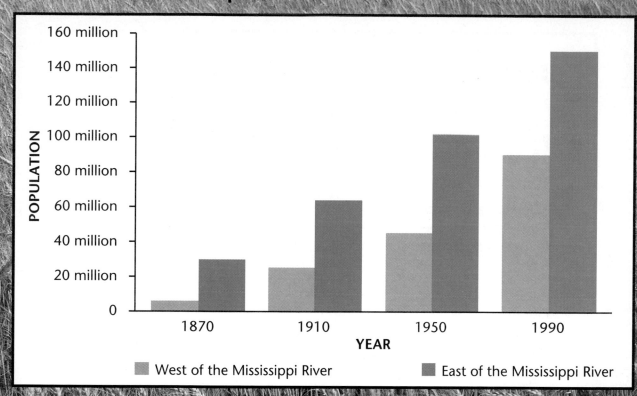

West of the Mississippi River

East of the Mississippi River

Rural and Urban Population Growth, 1870–1940

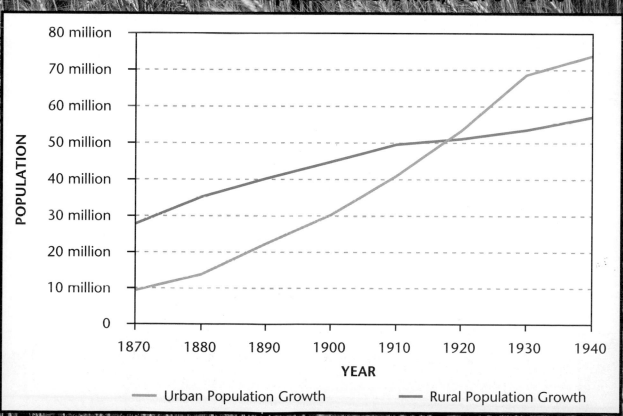

Urban Population Growth

Rural Population Growth

Index

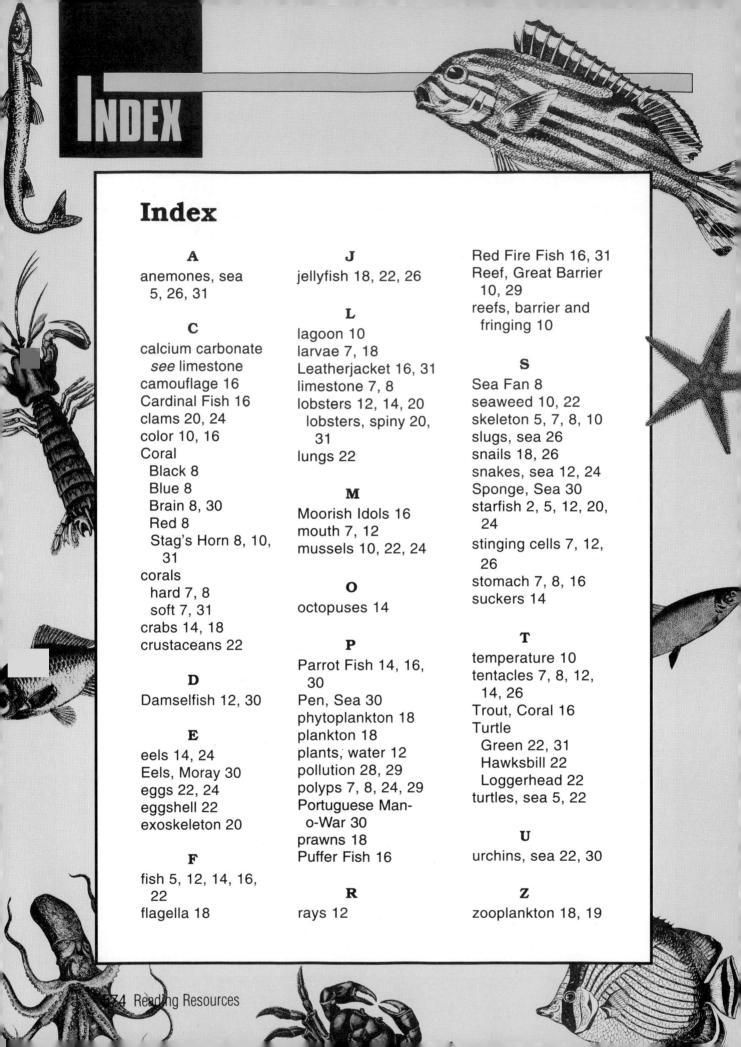

LABELS

The Food We Eat

Hanson's Farms
Grated Beets
Nutrition Facts

Serving Size 1/2 cup (120g)
Servings Per Container 4

Amount Per Serving	
Calories 40	**Calories from Fat 0**

	% Daily Value*
Total Fat 0g	0%
Saturated Fat 0g	0%
Cholesterol 0mg	0%
Sodium 300mg	13%
Total Carbohydrate 8g	3%
Dietary Fiber 2g	8%
Sugars 5g	
Protein 1g	

* Percent Daily Values based on 2,000 calorie diet.

INGREDIENTS: BEETS, WATER, SALT
NO PRESERVATIVES

Bellissimo!
Tomato and Basil Sauce
Nutrition Facts

Serving Size 1/2 cup (124g)
Servings Per Container 8

Amount Per Serving	
Calories 110	**Calories from Fat 50**

	% Daily Value*
Total Fat 6g	9%
Saturated Fat 1.5g	8%
Cholesterol 4mg	1%
Sodium 450mg	19%
Total Carbohydrate 10g	3%
Dietary Fiber 2g	8%
Sugars 4g	
Protein 4g	

* Percent Daily Values based on 2,000 calorie diet. Your daily values may be higher or lower depending on your calorie needs.

INGREDIENTS: TOMATOES, TOMATO PUREE, HIGH FRUCTOSE CORN SYRUP, OLIVE OIL, GARLIC, PARMESAN CHEESE, BASIL, BLACK PEPPER
No Preservatives added.

Adolfo Rotini Pasta
Nutrition Facts

Serving Size 2 oz. (56g)
Servings Per Container 8

Amount Per Serving	
Calories 210	**Calories from Fat 10**

	% Daily Value*
Total Fat 1g	2%
Saturated Fat 0g	0%
Polyunsaturated Fat 0.5g	
Cholesterol 0mg	0%
Sodium 30mg	1%
Total Carbohydrate 40g	13%
Dietary Fiber 2g	8%
Sugars 2g	
Protein 9g	
Iron	8%
Thiamine	30%

* Percent Daily Values based on 2,000 calorie diet. Your daily values may be higher or lower depending on your calorie needs.

INGREDIENTS: SEMOLINA, NIACIN, IRON, THIAMIN, MONONITRATE, RIBOFLAVIN.

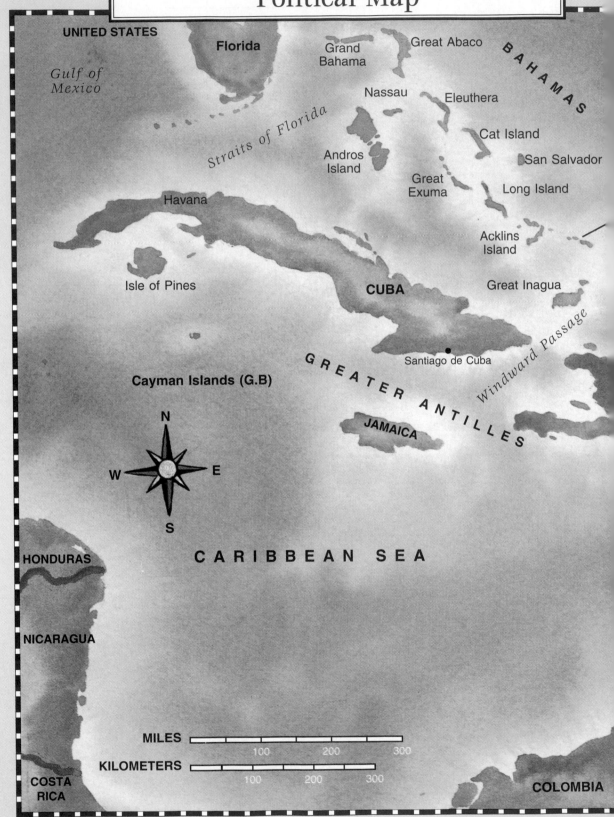

Central America and the Caribbean: Political Map

UNITED STATES

Florida

Gulf of Mexico

Grand Bahama

Great Abaco

B A H A M A S

Nassau

Eleuthera

Cat Island

San Salvador

Straits of Florida

Andros Island

Great Exuma

Long Island

Havana

Acklins Island

Isle of Pines

CUBA

Great Inagua

G R E A T E R A N T I L L E S

Santiago de Cuba

Windward Passage

Cayman Islands (G.B)

N

W   E

S

JAMAICA

HONDURAS

C A R I B B E A N   S E A

NICARAGUA

MILES

100   200   300

KILOMETERS

100   200   300

COSTA RICA

COLOMBIA

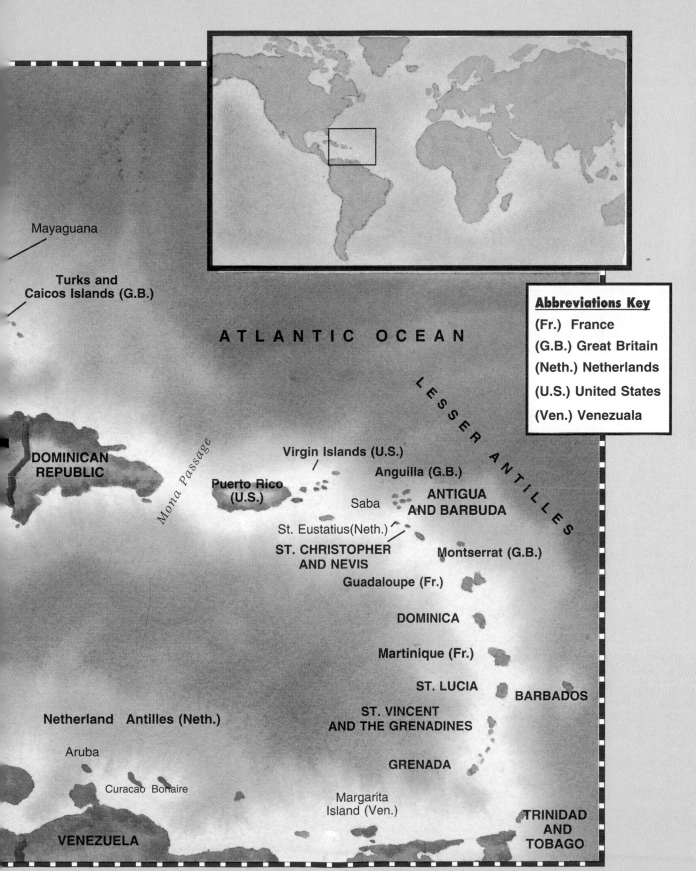

Mayaguana

Turks and
Caicos Islands (G.B.)

ATLANTIC OCEAN

Abbreviations Key
(Fr.) France
(G.B.) Great Britain
(Neth.) Netherlands
(U.S.) United States
(Ven.) Venezuala

LESSER ANTILLES

DOMINICAN
REPUBLIC

Mona Passage

Puerto Rico
(U.S.)

Virgin Islands (U.S.)

Anguilla (G.B.)

Saba

ANTIGUA
AND BARBUDA

St. Eustatius(Neth.)

ST. CHRISTOPHER
AND NEVIS

Montserrat (G.B.)

Guadaloupe (Fr.)

DOMINICA

Martinique (Fr.)

ST. LUCIA

BARBADOS

Netherland Antilles (Neth.)

ST. VINCENT
AND THE GRENADINES

Aruba

GRENADA

Curacao Bonaire

Margarita
Island (Ven.)

TRINIDAD
AND
TOBAGO

VENEZUELA

MAPS

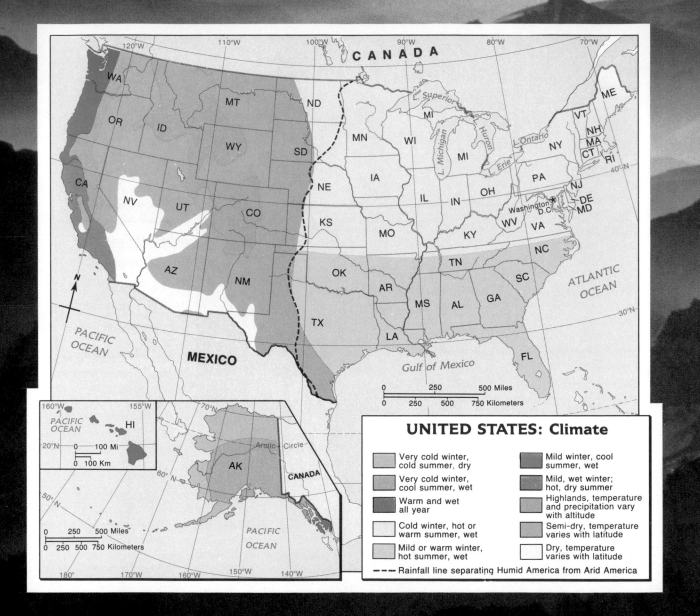

UNITED STATES: Climate

- Very cold winter, cold summer, dry
- Very cold winter, cool summer, wet
- Warm and wet all year
- Cold winter, hot or warm summer, wet
- Mild or warm winter, hot summer, wet
- Mild winter, cool summer, wet
- Mild, wet winter; hot, dry summer
- Highlands, temperature and precipitation vary with altitude
- Semi-dry, temperature varies with latitude
- Dry, temperature varies with latitude
- - - - Rainfall line separating Humid America from Arid America

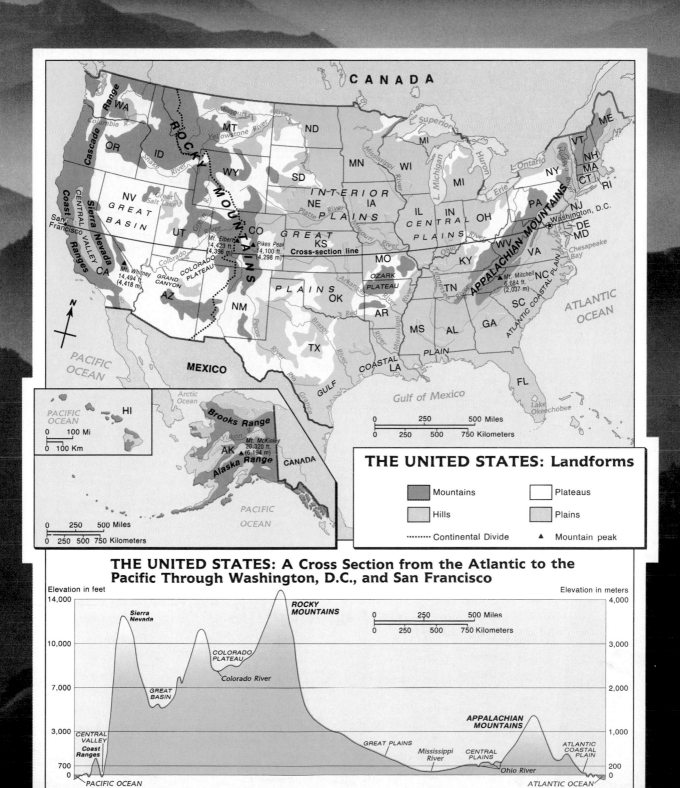

THE UNITED STATES: Landforms

- Mountains
- Hills
- Plateaus
- Plains
- ········· Continental Divide
- ▲ Mountain peak

THE UNITED STATES: A Cross Section from the Atlantic to the Pacific Through Washington, D.C., and San Francisco

The Blue and Gold

The Warbleton School Newspaper — Hunterville, California

Spring 1996

Omar Sanchez To Receive Special Award

by Judy Cator
Student Reporter

This year Warbleton leads city-wide when it comes to one student who cares about the community. The Hunterville Chamber of Commerce will honor a Warbleton fifth-grader for helping to launch a new city program to recycle plastic toys. His name is Omar Sanchez.

The recycling program, which may be the only community operation in the country that deals with toys, is now in full effect throughout Hunterville. However, it never would have come to pass if Omar had not become concerned about the problem of plastic waste. "I began noticing a lot of toys in the garbage around my neighborhood," he said. "As soon as they break or their owner outgrows them, they get tossed."

Omar's awareness of the problem came from a class project on recycling. For the project he had prepared a report on the ways in which plastics, paper, glass, and aluminum products are recycled and reused to make new products. After writing to the Departments of Sanitation of several cities, he discovered that recycling efforts differ from city to city and town to town.

Omar decided to look into our town's recycling program to see how effective it really is. For over 3 months he kept track of several trash cans in several different neighborhoods. He listed the different kinds of plastic, metal, glass, or paper being thrown away, and kept note of which of these were being recycled. He found out that plastic toys made up a significant portion of trash that could be recycled. The only problem was that Hunterville had no laws requiring the recycling of plastic toys.

It took 3 more months of gathering

statistics, several letters to the town council, and the support of prominent adults in the city for Omar's plan to go into effect. The town council had to form a special committee to investigate the costs of recycling plastic toys. Although some were made from the same kind of plastic as food containers already being recycled, other kinds of toy plastic required special processing.

When the problems about recycling toys were revealed, 6 council members spoke out against the project, saying it would be too costly. That's when Omar went back to work. With the help of his father, who is a chemist at Bradley Labs, he helped create a proposal that would lower the budget on recycling toys and presented it by himself to the Council.

It was finally decided that toys for recycling could be sorted in Hunterville, but that a part of them would be shipped to a plant in nearby Mill Creek on a weekly basis. The new plan will cost taxpayers some money. An additional $48,000 will be needed to add plastic toys to the list of recyclable products.

"I think the extra cost is worth it," said Omar. "Recycling toys will teach the kids who play with them to think about what making them costs us and the environment. It might make the cost of the toys lower as well."

Omar will be honored by a special dinner and award ceremony on April 23. We at Warbleton are planning to honor him as well. On May 15 a special assembly hosted by our student officers will be held in the auditorium. There, Omar will explain how he developed his plan for recycling toys.

Way to go, Omar!

Maypole Day Will be a Spring "Riot"

By Bobby Santiago

Letisha Foster and Billie Schwartz, who head the Maypole Day planning committee, are promising to make this year's Maypole Day celebrations even "wilder" than last year's. Those of you who came to last year's party in the rear playground probably remember the good times had by all. There were one-legged races, a students vs. teachers touch-football game, and an open-air barbecue. But this year, Letisha and Billie say they will add disco to the mix.

There will be seven student D.J.'s, picked by Letisha Foster, Billie Schwartz, and the rest of the Maypole Day planning committee. The committee is taking applications now. There will also be a team of teacher judges to give awards to the best dancers in hip hop, free-style, and line dancing.

As if all this were not enough, Barnaby's Fabrics has donated 600 inches of surplus ribbon for the Maypole Dance. Over 70 ribbons of different colors will be hung from the flag pole. We'll wind them around it to the accordion music of Susan Hammond, a Warbleton fifth-grader.

Volunteer barbecue chef-assistants, servers, and clean-up people are needed for this event. So if you're interested, sign up in Ms. Hardy's room between 8:00 A.M. and 3:00 P.M. any day this week.

See you there!

CONTENTS

In My Opinion

Let's Help Out

As the editors of The Blue and Gold we feel that students at Warbleton School should get involved in the community. Omar Sanchez did a great job setting up a recycling project and should be an example for all of us. But don't think that to make a difference you have to do something as ambitious as Omar Sanchez's project. There are a lot of fun ways to get involved.

A great way is to help out at the The Huntsville Senior Center, behind the school on Oak Drive. Many Senior Citizens helped us out at the Winter Carnival last month, and now they need help organizing and setting up their annual Crafts Fair. They need people to set up and decorate the auditorium the week before the Fair. On Saturday and Sunday they need help selling food and drinks and cleaning up afterwards.

They were a great help to us last month, so let's return the favor and lend a hand with the Crafts Fair in a few weeks. The Center needs volunteers year round too, as many residents don't have families in the area and want someone to spend time with them a few days a week. You can help them write letters, play a game, go for a walk, or just talk. Sign up on the activities board to help, and get involved!

Editorial

Sports

A Basketball Miracle

Blue Caps Rally

Last month's game between the Blue Caps and the RedShirts left everybody breathless. Word had it that the RedShirts had stepped up their practice after school. No one thought the Blue Caps would stand a chance.

At the end of the third quarter, it looked like the predictions were about to come true. The RedShirts had a 12-point lead. The score was 33 to 21. The Blue Caps looked discouraged. Then Anderson passed it to Colon at the beginning of the last quarter. Colon got close to the hoop and put it home. After that the Blue Caps rallied, creaming the Redshirts by a margin of 9. The final score was Blue Caps 44, RedShirts 35.

The Blue and Gold
CLASSIFIEDS

TO SELL

Antique Comic Collection. Mint Condition. Over 200 comics going back to 1949. Singles, series, or entire collection. Price negotiable. Call Marcy at 555-8989.

Miniature Railroad. Full set, only slightly used. Bought for $239 new. Your price: $110. Bill 555-4445.

Terrarium. Fish-tank style. Already planted and doing great! Several sizes and kinds. Not much maintenance needed. I make them and sell them. I can tell you how to keep the plants healthy. From $10 to $50. Terence 555-2390.

TO TRADE

CD-Rom's. I've got 8 CD-Rom Games. Willing to trade them for ones I haven't tried. Mac compatible. Beth 555-9666.

Stamps from all over the world. Special Editions. A one-year collection. Show me yours. Let's trade! Call Peter 555-4690.

Marionette. This guy is cute! Hiking shorts, a little cap. You control the strings. It was a present, brought from Austria. Would like to trade him for an American doll with wardrobe. Barbara 555-5111.

Marble Collection. Cat's-Eyes, Clears, Blacks, and More! Also like to play marbles. Call me Saturday and bring your collection. We'll swap and play. Barnaby 555-8690.

WANTED

Bike Parts Needed. I repair bikes and then give them to people who need them. Call if you have tires, handlebars, wheels, or gears to sell. Nothing is in too bad a condition! Can also pay small amounts for complete bikes in need of repair. Call Justin. 555-9870

Food and Volunteers. We're a one-kitchen operation making meals for the needy. We could use coldcuts, fruit, beverages, or any other food donations. We also need some help putting it all together! 555-1111.

SERVICES

Tutors. Having trouble with one of your subjects? Don't despair. We're a team of student volunteers who tutor after school in Mr. Barkley's room. Call Patti at 555-9128.

ADVENTURES IN LIFE SCIENCE

Volume 34	September 1997	Number 9

IN THIS ISSUE

COVER STORY

Janet Beasley has devoted her life to studying the habits of the Red Panda.

ADVENTURES
IN LIFE SCIENCE

Volume 34
September 1997
Number 9

Publisher
Fabio Montalve

Editor-in-Chief
Madeleine Lewin

Editorial Director
Doreen Farber

Editor
Juan Robless

Associate Editor
Carmen Johnson

Assistant Editor
Polly Lou Paglia

Research
Jasmin Murti
Peter Bluestone
Doris Schwartz

Design
Albert Lu

Circulation
Bruce Jones

Advertising
Suzanne Youngstone

RECIPES

Liza's Famous Spoon Bread

Serves 8

Ingredients

2 cups water
1 cup yellow cornmeal
3 tablespoons butter
1 teaspoon salt
3 eggs
1 cup milk

Steps

1. Preheat oven to 375° F.
2. Heat water to boiling.
3. Add cornmeal slowly, stirring constantly until thick and smooth. Stir in butter and salt. Cool to lukewarm.
4. Add eggs and milk. Beat for 2 minutes.
5. Pour into a greased casserole and bake 35 minutes, or until golden brown. Serve immediately with butter.

SCHEDULES

NORTH ELEMENTARY SCHOOL
AFTER-SCHOOL ACTIVITIES SCHEDULE

OCTOBER

SUNDAY	MONDAY	TUESDAY	WEDNESDAY	THURSDAY	FRIDAY	SATURDAY
					1 3:00 Football Practice	**2**
3	**4** 3:00–5:00 Supervised Playground / 3:00 Football Practice / 6:30 Annual Parent-Teacher-Student Banquet (Cafeteria)	**5** 3:00 Football Practice / 3:30 Play Rehearsal	**6** 3:00 Football Practice / 3:30 Girl's Athletic Club (Room 105)	**7** 3:30 Play Rehearsal	**8** **In-Service Day** No School	**9**
10	**11** **Columbus Day** No School	**12** 3:00 Football Practice / 3:15 Brownies (Room 110)	**13** 3:00 Football Practice / 3:30 Play Rehearsal	**14** 3:00 Pep Rally (Gym) / 3:30 Football Game – North Tigers vs Grant Cougars (Grant School)	**15** 3:30 Play Rehearsal / 3:45 All-School Bicycle Race (City Park)	**16** 10:00 Science Club Field Trip to Burnam Woods (meet at North School for bus)
17	**18** 3:00–5:00 Supervised Playground / 3:00 Football practice	**19** 3:00 Play Rehearsal (Dress Rehearsal)	**20** 3:00 Football Practice / 3:15 Art Club (Room 110)	**21** 7:00 Performance: "The Ugly Duckling" (Auditorium)	**22** 3:00 Football Practice	**23**
24	**25** 3:00–5:00 Supervised Playground / 3:00 Football practice / 3:30 Science Club (Room 110)	**26** 3:00 Football Practice / 3:15 Cub Scouts (Room 110)	**27** 3:00 Football Practice / 3:30 Film Festival: "Around the World in 80 Days" (Auditorium)	**28** 3:00 Pep Rally (Gym) / 3:30 Football Game – North Tigers vs Central Indians (North School)	**29** 3:30 Halloween Party (Gym)	**30**
31 **Halloween**						

A Radio Schedule of Yesteryear

Two Views

SATURDAY

9:00 - 9:30 P.M.
KSNN 1280 . . Terry and the Pirates
WPRT 1460 . . . . Buster Brown
KWLX 710 . . . . National News
WHLR 95 . . . . . . The Garden Club

9:30 - 10:00 P.M.
KSNN 1280 . . . . Dick Tracy
WPRT 1460 . . . . Fishing News
KWLX 710 . . . . Ma Perkins
WHLR 95 . . . . Superman

10:00 - 10:30 P.M.
KSNN 1280 . . . . . . The Farm News
WPRT 1460 . . Classical Music Time
KWLX 710 . . . . Henry Aldrich
WHLR 95 . . . . . . The Green Hornet

10:30 - 11:00 P.M.
KSNN 1280 . . . . Let's Pretend
WPRT 1460 . . . War of the Worlds
(Rebroadcast)
KWLX 710 . . . . . . Twenty Top Hits
WHLR 95 . . . . The Shadow

SATURDAY	9:00 P.M.	9:30 P.M.	10:00 P.M.	10:30 P.M.
WHLR 95	The Garden Club	Superman	The Green Hornet	The Shadow
KWLX 710	National News	Ma Perkins	Henry Aldrich	Twenty Top Hits
WPRT 1460	Buster Brown	Fishing News	Classical Music Time	War of the Worlds (Rebroadcast)
KSNN 1280	Terry and the Pirates	Dick Tracy	The Farm News	Let's Pretend

TECHNOLOGY

Send It E-Mail!

When you click this icon, your e-mail is sent. No envelope or stamp is required!

This is where you type the "address" of the person you want to e-mail. E-mail addresses tell the computers on the Internet where your friend's computer is.

The subject tells your friend what your e-mail is about before it is opened. It is like a title for your message.

Clicking on this icon calls up a list of people to whom you often send e-mail.

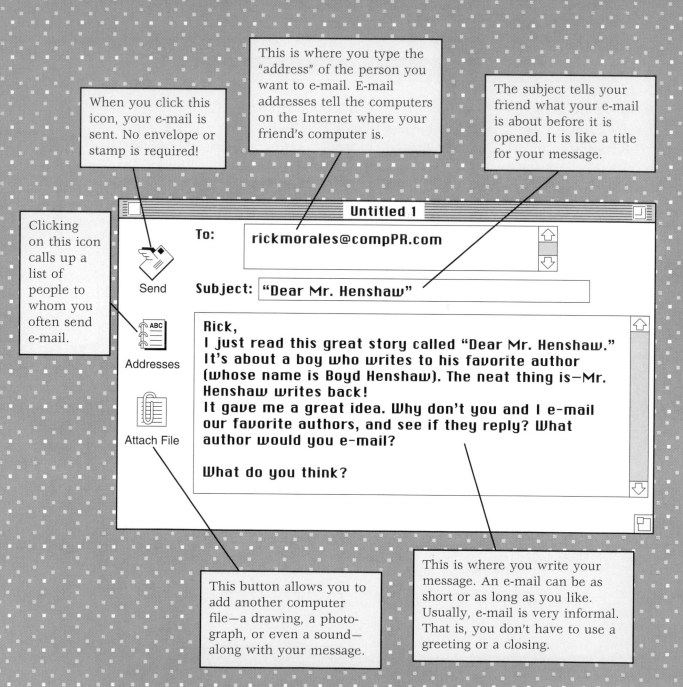

Untitled 1

To: rickmorales@compPR.com

Send

Subject: "Dear Mr. Henshaw"

Addresses

Rick,
I just read this great story called "Dear Mr. Henshaw."
It's about a boy who writes to his favorite author
(whose name is Boyd Henshaw). The neat thing is—Mr.
Henshaw writes back!
It gave me a great idea. Why don't you and I e-mail
our favorite authors, and see if they reply? What
author would you e-mail?

What do you think?

Attach File

This button allows you to add another computer file—a drawing, a photograph, or even a sound—along with your message.

This is where you write your message. An e-mail can be as short or as long as you like. Usually, e-mail is very informal. That is, you don't have to use a greeting or a closing.

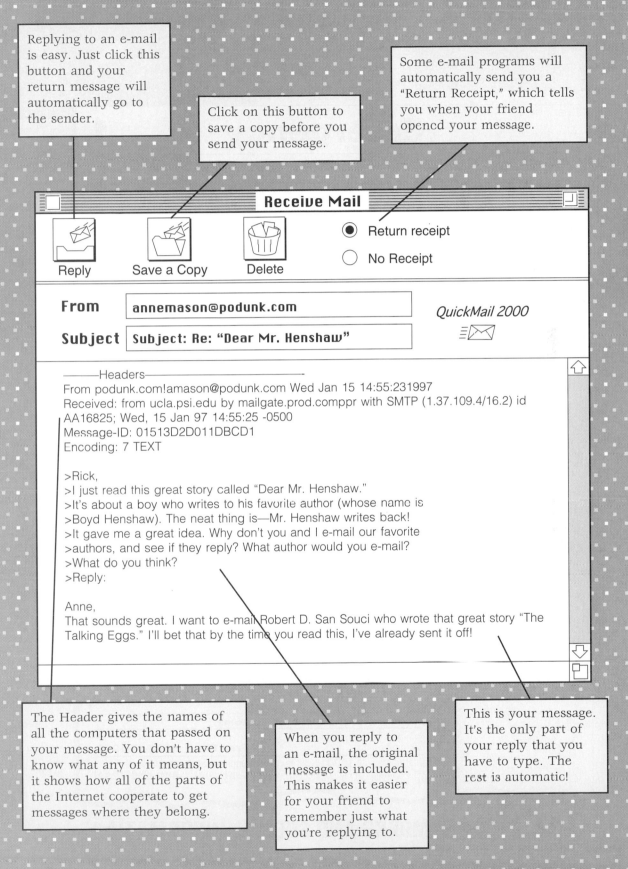

Replying to an e-mail is easy. Just click this button and your return message will automatically go to the sender.

Click on this button to save a copy before you send your message.

Some e-mail programs will automatically send you a "Return Receipt," which tells you when your friend opened your message.

Receive Mail

Reply   Save a Copy   Delete

◉ Return receipt
◯ No Receipt

From annemason@podunk.com

QuickMail 2000

Subject Subject: Re: "Dear Mr. Henshaw"

————Headers————————
From podunk.com!amason@podunk.com Wed Jan 15 14:55:231997
Received: from ucla.psi.edu by mailgate.prod.comppr with SMTP (1.37.109.4/16.2) id
AA16825; Wed, 15 Jan 97 14:55:25 -0500
Message-ID: 01513D2D011DBCD1
Encoding: 7 TEXT

>Rick,
>I just read this great story called "Dear Mr. Henshaw."
>It's about a boy who writes to his favorite author (whose name is
>Boyd Henshaw). The neat thing is—Mr. Henshaw writes back!
>It gave me a great idea. Why don't you and I e-mail our favorite
>authors, and see if they reply? What author would you e-mail?
>What do you think?
>Reply:

Anne,
That sounds great. I want to e-mail Robert D. San Souci who wrote that great story "The Talking Eggs." I'll bet that by the time you read this, I've already sent it off!

The Header gives the names of all the computers that passed on your message. You don't have to know what any of it means, but it shows how all of the parts of the Internet cooperate to get messages where they belong.

When you reply to an e-mail, the original message is included. This makes it easier for your friend to remember just what you're replying to.

This is your message. It's the only part of your reply that you have to type. The rest is automatic!

Emergency 1

Emergency Numbers

East Oakland

Fire	**555-2323**
Police (Alternate number 555-2616)	**555-2452**
Sheriff (Night 555-2412)	**555-2501**
Ambulance	**555-2104**

Other Emergency Numbers

Police Control Center	**1 + 800-555-6633**
Highway Patrol	**1 + 555-2562**
FBI	**1 + 000-555-8181**
If no answer call	**1 + 000-555-6100**

Special Information

TDD Customers

Services for Hearing Impaired Customers:

TDD/TTY customers call for new or additional service and repair service

or

If you would like additional information on how your directory listing can indicate you communicate with a TDD or to obtain information on special rates for TDD calls within your Southwestern Bell Telephone service area, please call Customer Assistance Bureau.

Toll Free Dial 1-555-2326

For operator assistance	**Toll Free Dial 1-800-555-1155†**
†Teletype number	

Products for the Disabled Customer:

For voice, motion, sight or hearing products	**Toll Free Dial 1-800-555-1222**
Customers with TDD/TTY call for new or additional service and repair service	**Toll Free Dial 1-800-555-3232**

EMERGENCY NUMBERS AND SPECIAL INFORMATION

48 Drew–Eklund

Drew Ralph 301 Main 555-4516
Drew Stephen 1130 Oakmore......................555-1812
Drew Wanda 1250 Oakmore.......................555-3692
Dryden Jill 309 W 32..................................555-2332
DUANE'S AUTO SERVICE
   Main & W 54..**555-3155**
Duffey—See also Duffy
Duffey Irene 102 W Victoria........................555-2767
Duffey Malcolm 205 Sunset........................555-2207
Duffey Margaret 205 Sunset......................555-2208
Duffield Kyle 113 Mill Dr............................555-5190
Duffold Allen 814 College Dr......................555-4898
Duffy—See also Duffey
Duffy Nancy 1305 Lake Rd 555-5388
Dunn Zelma 425 W 4.................................555-2244
Dunlap Sharon 1451 M~~~~~~~~~~555-9792

EAGLE PRODUCTS
   750 Pinehurst **555-6284**
Eagle Robert 39 Lake Rd............................555-4015

Eames Oliver 1112 Main.............................555-3657
Eaton Richard
   204 Broadway.....................................555-6306
EAVES DR JAMES
   213 Main **555-3685**
    Residence 16 Mill............................555-3510
Ebert Allen 1009 Westway.........................555-2879
Econo Lodge 176 S Range.........................555-2424
Edmond Thelma 415 Cedar........................555-3931
EDMOND VICTOR MD
   304 Price Ave.....................................**555-6518**
Edwards Con~~~~ 98 Ash ~~~~~~~~~555-4721

WHITE PAGES

523   Clothes – Coal

CREATIVE CLOWNS
Clown Entertainment for all Occasions
Bob and Betty

Casper..**555-4387**

YEAR-ROUND ENTERTAINERS
MUSIC – PUPPETS – MAGIC
PARTIES – PICNICS

200 Alameda in Barstow..................**555-0462**

CLUBS

A+ AUTO CLUB

Emergency Road Service....................**555-8888**
710 W Palmer Cheyenne......................**555-7800**
21 Montana Douglas **555-7600**
8601 Cross Drive Laramie...................**555-7900**

Alliance Francaise 681 Jewell 555-5437
Ardmore Tennis Club
   7431 N Pearl Casper........................555-9887
Botany Garden Club
   721 N Bowles...................................555-6571

Meadowlands Spa 455 Quincy..........555-6887
Mountain Hiking Club
   7500 N Brighton Rd 555-4551
MURFORD COMMUNITY CLUB
Facilities for
Receptions • Meetings • Dinners
"Meet you at Murford's"
531 Lowell Boulevard..................**555-4300**

Oxford Garden Club 555-6270
Pinetree Golf Club.............................555-6571
   E Pecos at Orchard Rd 555-3542
Polish Club of Casper
   1340 Old Bannock Rd 555-8593
River Social Club 4328 35 Ave 555-5346
Rotary of Barstow 777 E 11...................555-3885
Stadium Club Barnes Stadium................555-7677
Timberline Trails 9801 N Emerson 555-4651
University Club Beck Bldg......................555-5346
Valley Sports Center 331 Orlando Drive...555-5346
Women's Club of Barstow
   678 E Madison 555-5346

COAL

ATLANTIC & PACIFIC COAL IND
   ~~Henderson Rd~~............555-4300

GLOS

This glossary can help you to pronounce and find out the meanings of words in this book that you may not know.

The words are listed in alphabetical order. Guide words at the top of each page tell you the first and last words on the page.

Each word is divided into syllables. The way to pronounce each word is given next. You can understand the pronunciation respelling by using the key at right. A shorter key appears at the bottom of every other page.

When a word has more than one syllable, a dark accent mark (′) shows which syllable is stressed. In some words, a light accent mark (′) shows which syllable has a less heavy stress.

Glossary entries are based on entries in *The Macmillan/McGraw-Hill School Dictionary 1*.

a at, bad	**d** dear, soda, bad
ā ape, pain, day, break	**f** five, defend, leaf, off, cough, elephant
ä father, car, heart	**g** game, ago, fog, egg
âr care, pair, bear, their, where	**h** hat, ahead
e end, pet, said, heaven, friend	**hw** white, whether, which
ē equal, me, feet, team, piece, key	**j** joke, enjoy, gem, page, edge
i it, big, English, hymn	**k** kite, bakery, seek, tack, cat
ī ice, fine, lie, my	**l** lid, sailor, feel, ball, allow
îr ear, deer, here, pierce	**m** man, family, dream
o odd, hot, watch	**n** not, final, pan, knife
ō old, oat, toe, low	**ng** long, singer, pink
ô coffee, all, taught, law, fought	**p** pail, repair, soap, happy
ôr order, fork, horse, story, pour	**r** ride, parent, wear, more, marry
oi oil, toy	**s** sit, aside, pets, cent, pass
ou out, now	**sh** shoe, washer, fish, mission, nation
u up, mud, love, double	**t** tag, pretend, fat, button, dressed
ū use, mule, cue, feud, few	**th** thin, panther, both
ü rule, true, food	**th** this, mother, smooth
** u̇** put, wood, should	**v** very, favor, wave
ûr burn, hurry, term, bird, word, courage	**w** wet, weather, reward
ə about, taken, pencil, lemon, circus	**y** yes, onion
b bat, above, job	**z** zoo, lazy, jazz, rose, dogs, houses
ch chin, such, match	**zh** vision, treasure, seizure

abandoned Left behind; no longer used or lived in. The porch of the *abandoned* house is overgrown with vines.
    a•ban•doned (ə ban′dənd) *adjective.*

accurate Being correct, exact, or precise. The newspaper stories about the accident were not *accurate.*
    ac•cu•rate (ak′yər it) *adjective.*

achievement Something accomplished or carried out. The invention of the telephone was a great *achievement.*
    a•chieve•ment (ə chēv′mənt) *noun, plural* **achievements.**

admission 1. The price a person must pay to enter. The *admission* to the park was one dollar. **2.** The act of allowing to enter. Who is in charge of the *admission* of patients to that hospital?
    ad•mis•sion (ad mish′ən) *noun, plural* **admissions.**

admission

advantage Something that is helpful or useful; benefit. Being tall is an *advantage* for a basketball player.
• **to take advantage of. 1.** To use in a helpful or beneficial way; benefit by. We *took advantage of* the excellent opportunity to learn French. **2.** To use or treat in an unfair or selfish way. Don't *take advantage of* your friend's willingness to be helpful.
    ad•van•tage (ad van′tij) *noun, plural* **advantages.**

afford 1. To have enough money to pay for. Can you *afford* a new car? **2.** To be able to spare or give. They couldn't *afford* the time to help us. **3.** To be able to do without causing harm. I can't *afford* to skip breakfast.
    af•ford (ə fôrd′) *verb,* **afforded, affording.**

Albertosaurus (al bûr′tə sôr′əs).

alien 1. A being from some place outside of the earth or its atmosphere. The movie was about *aliens* who tried to take over the earth. **2.** A person who is not a citizen of the country in which he or she lives; foreigner.
    al•ien (āl′yən *or* a′lē ən) *noun, plural* **aliens.**

Allosaurus (al′ə sôr′əs).

anchor A heavy metal device that is attached to a ship by a chain or cable. When an *anchor* is dropped overboard, it digs into the ground below the water and keeps the ship from drifting.
• **at anchor** held fast by an anchor.
    an•chor (ang′kər) *noun, plural* **anchors.**

Apatosaurus (ə pat′ə sôr′əs).

apiece For or to each one; each. These red pencils are fifteen cents *apiece.*
    a•piece (ə pēs′) *adverb.*

Appalachians A mountain range reaching from Canada to Alabama.
   Ap•pa•la•chi•ans (ap′ə lā′chē ənz) *noun, plural.*

approve 1. To have or give a favorable opinion. My parents don't *approve* of my staying up very late. **2.** To consent or agree to officially; authorize. The town recently *approved* the construction of a public swimming pool.
   ap•prove (ə prüv′) *verb,* **approved, approving.**

aquatic Growing or living in or near water. Most frogs are *aquatic* animals.
   a•quat•ic (ə kwat′ik *or* ə kwot′ik) *adjective.*

arctic Having to do with the ice-covered region surrounding the North Pole.
   arc•tic (ärk′tik) *adjective.*

arctic

arrest 1. To seize and hold by authority of the law. The police officer *arrested* the suspect. **2.** To stop or hold. We hope to *arrest* pollution in our country.
   ar•rest (ə rest′) *verb,* **arrested, arresting.**

artificial Made by people, not by nature; not natural.
   ar•ti•fi•cial (är′tə fish′əl) *adjective.*

assemble To come or bring together. A crowd began to *assemble*.
   as•sem•ble (ə sem′bəl) *verb,* **assembled, assembling.**

asteroid Any of the thousands of small planets that revolve around the sun. Most are between the orbits of Mars and Jupiter.
   as•ter•oid (as′tə roid′) *noun, plural* **asteroids.**

astonish To surprise very much; amaze. The news that I had won the contest *astonished* me.
   as•ton•ish (ə ston′ish) *verb,* **astonished, astonishing.**

Ate The word for "father" in the language of the Lakota people.
   A•te (ä ta′) *noun.*

athletic Of or having to do with games, sports, or activities that take strength, skill, and speed.
   ath•let•ic (ath let′ik) *adjective.*

atmosphere 1. The layer of gases that surrounds the Earth. The *atmosphere* is made up of oxygen, nitrogen, carbon dioxide, and other gases. **2.** Character or mood. Our house has a happy *atmosphere*.
   at•mos•phere (at′məs fîr′) *noun, plural* **atmospheres.**

attempt To make an effort; try. The kitten *attempted* to follow the squirrel up the tree.
   at•tempt (ə tempt′) *verb,* **attempted, attempting.**

at; āpe; fär; câre; end; mē; it; īce; pîerce; hot; ōld; sông; fôrk; oil; out; up; ūse; rüle; pull; tûrn; chin; sing; shop; thin; this; hw in white; zh in treasure. The symbol ə stands for the unstressed vowel sound in about, taken, pencil, lemon, and circus.

attract To draw by gaining the attention or admiration of. The beautiful scenery in these mountains *attracts* many tourists.

> **at•tract** (ə trakt′) *verb,* **attracted, attracting.**

attractive Having a quality that attracts people; appealing; pleasing. He looked very *attractive* in his new suit.

> **at•trac•tive** (ə trak′tiv) *adjective.*

auction To sell at a public sale at which articles or property are sold to the person who offers the most money. *Verb.*
—A public sale at which things are auctioned. *Noun.*

> **auc•tion** (ôk′shən) *noun, plural* **auctions;** *verb,* **auctioned, auctioning.**

auction

authority 1. A good source of information or facts. That professor is an *authority* on the life of Abraham Lincoln. 2. The power or right to make decisions, command, act, or control. The captain has *authority* over all the sailors on a ship.

> **au•thor•i•ty** (ə thôr′i tē) *noun, plural* **authorities.**

automatically 1. By itself. The dishwasher operates *automatically.* 2. Without a person's control. Digestion is an action of the body that occurs *automatically.*

> **au•to•mat•i•cal•ly** (ô′tə mat′ik lē) *adverb.*

avalanche The swift, sudden fall of a mass of snow, ice, earth, or rocks down a mountain slope. The *avalanche* completely covered the village with mud.

> **av•a•lanche** (av′ə lanch′) *noun, plural* **avalanches.**

B

bachelor A man who has never been married.

> **bach•e•lor** (bach′ə lər) *noun, plural* **bachelors.**

backwoods Heavily wooded areas far from centers of population. We didn't expect to find a cabin hidden away in the *backwoods.*

> **back•woods** (bak′wudz′) *noun, plural.*

Barosaurus (bar′ə sôr′əs).

Baryonyx (bar′ē on′iks).

bashful Embarrassed and shy around people. The *bashful* child hid behind the chair when the babysitter arrived.

> **bash•ful** (bash′fəl) *adjective.*

basis The part that something rests on or depends on; foundation. The idea that toads give you warts has no *basis* in fact.

> **ba•sis** (bā′sis) *noun, plural* **bases** (bā′sez).

beloved Loved very much. The friendly dog was *beloved* by the whole neighborhood.
be•lov•ed (bi luv′id *or* bi luvd′) *adjective.*

big top The main tent of a circus.
big top (big top) *noun, plural* **big tops.**

blurt To say suddenly or without thinking. I was sorry after I *blurted* out the secret.
blurt (blûrt) *verb,* **blurted, blurting.**

board To get a room to sleep in and meals for pay. I *boarded* with a family in France last summer.
board (bôrd) *verb,* **boarded, boarding.**

border 1. To lie on the edge of. California *borders* Oregon. 2. To put an edging on. The handkerchief was *bordered* with lace.
bor•der (bôr′dər) *verb,* **bordered, bordering.**

Brachiosaurus (bra′ke ō sôr′ s *or* brak′ə ō sôr′əs).

Brontosaurus A huge plant-eating dinosaur.
bron•to•sau•rus (bron′tə sôr′əs) *noun, plural* **brontosauri** *or* **brontosauruses.**

brontosaurus

bruise To cause an injury that does not break the skin but makes a bluish or blackish mark on it. *Verb.* —A mark made by such an injury. *Noun.*
bruise (brüz) *noun, plural* **bruises;** *verb,* **bruised, bruising.**

burglar A person who breaks into a house, store, or other place to steal something. *Burglars* broke into the hotel room and stole some valuable jewels.
bur•glar (bûr′glər) *noun, plural* **burglars.**

C

calypso An improvised song, originally from the British West Indies, usually dealing with subjects that are humorous or of current interest.
ca•lyp•so (kə lip′sō) *noun, plural* **calypsos.**

Word History

The music known as **calypso** takes its name from Calypso, a sea nymph in Greek mythology. Calypso fell in love with the hero Ulysses when, in his wanderings, he visited her island. He remained with her for seven years.

---

at; āpe; fär; câre; end; mē; it; īce; pîerce; hot; ōld; sông; fôrk; oil; out; up; ūse; rüle; púll; tûrn; chin; sing; shop; thin; <u>th</u>is; hw in white; zh in treasure. The symbol ə stands for the unstressed vowel sound in about, taken, pencil, lemon, and circus.

Camarasaurus (kam′ə rə sôr′əs).

Canowicakte (chä no′wa chäk ta).

canvas A strong, heavy cloth made of cotton, flax, or hemp. It is used to make things that must be strong and last for a long time. Tents, sails, coats, and boat covers are made of *canvas.*
> **can•vas** (kan′vəs) *noun, plural* **canvases.**

captive Held prisoner. The *captive* lion was kept in a cage.
> **cap•tive** (kap′tiv) *adjective.*

capture **1.** To succeed in showing or expressing something. The story *captures* what it is like to be an only child. **2.** To attract and hold. The film's strange title *captured* my interest.
> **cap•ture** (kap′chər) *verb,* **captured, capturing.**

carnival A fair or festival that has games, rides, and other amusements. A special roller coaster was built just for the city's spring *carnival.*
> **car•ni•val** (kär′nə vəl) *noun, plural* **carnivals.**

carnival

cemetery A place where the dead are buried.
> **cem•e•ter•y** (sem′ə ter′ē) *noun, plural* **cemeteries.**

Ceratosaurus (se rat′ə sôr′əs).

certificate A written statement that is accepted as proof of certain facts. Your birth *certificate* tells when and where you were born.
> **cer•tif•i•cate** (sər tif′i kit) *noun, plural* **certificates.**

Chan A Japanese form of address for a child, used following the name.
> **Chan** (chän) *noun.*

Chano (chä′nō).

civilization A condition of human society in which government, art, and science are highly developed. Civilization is often characterized by the use of writing and the growth of cities. In school we study the *civilization* of ancient Egypt.
> **civ•i•li•za•tion** (siv′ə lə zā′shən) *noun, plural* **civilizations.**

clammy Cold and damp. They walked through the *clammy* basement.
> **clam•my** (klam′ē) *adjective.*

collision The act of crashing against each other. The two bicycle riders had a *collision,* but neither one was hurt.
> **col•li•sion** (kə lizh′ən) *noun, plural* **collisions.**

conceal To put or keep out of sight; hide. Don't forget to *conceal* the house keys under the porch. I *concealed* my disappointment by smiling.
> **con•ceal** (kən sēl′) *verb,* **concealed, concealing.**

concentrate To bring together into one place. The population of our country is *concentrated* in the cities.
> **con•cen•trate** (kon′sən trāt′) *verb,* **concentrated, concentrating.**

congratulate To give good wishes or praise for someone's success or for something nice that has happened. We *congratulated* them on doing such a good job on their science project.
> **con•grat•u•late** (kən grach′ə lāt′) *verb,* **congratulated, congratulating.**

consent To give permission or agree to. My parents would not *consent* to my going camping by myself, so they went camping with me.
> **con•sent** (kən sent′) *verb,* **consented, consenting.**

constitution The basic principles used to govern a state, country, or organization. The people voted for numerous changes in their state's *constitution*.
> **con•sti•tu•tion** (kon′sti tü′shən) *noun, plural* **constitutions.**

contrary 1. Liking to argue and oppose. That *contrary* child never agrees with what other people say. **2.** Entirely different; opposite. My younger cousin's ideas about sports and music are *contrary* to my own. **• on the contrary.** Just the opposite of what has been said. You are not a clumsy dancer; *on the contrary,* you are very graceful.
> **con•trar•y** (kən trâr′ē *or* kon′trer ē *for definition 1;* kon′trer ē *for definition 2) adjective.*

contrast To show differences that are based on comparing. The teacher *contrasted* life in a big city and life on a farm. *Verb.*
—A difference. There is a great *contrast* between the weather at the North Pole and the weather in the tropics. *Noun.*
> **con•trast** (kən trast′ *for verb;* kon′trast *for noun) noun, plural* **contrasts;** *verb,* **contrasted, contrasting.**

convenience Ease and comfort. I like the *convenience* of canned foods.
> **con•ven•ience** (kən vēn′yəns) *noun, plural* **conveniences.**

cramp¹ To cause a sharp pain in a muscle. Holding the pencil tightly for so long *cramped* my hand. *Verb.*
—A sharp pain in a muscle that suddenly gets tight. A *cramp* in the leg forced the runner to leave the race. *Noun.*
> **cramp** (kramp) *noun, plural* **cramps;** *verb,* **cramped, cramping.**

cramp² To limit; confine. The tiny amount of space on the boat *cramped* us.
> **cramp** (kramp) *verb,* **cramped, cramping.**

crank A part of a machine that has a handle attached to a rod. When the handle is turned, the rod turns with it and makes the machine work. The storekeeper turned the *crank* of the store's awning to lower it. *Noun.*
—To turn a *crank* so that something will work. *Verb.*
> **crank** (krangk) *noun, plural* **cranks;** *verb,* **cranked, cranking.**

credit 1. Praise or honor. The person who did most of the cooking deserves *credit* for the dinner. **2.** Belief in the truth of something; faith. Nobody gave full *credit* to the strange story. **3.** Trust in a person to pay a debt later. Several stores have given me *credit*.
> **cred•it** (kred′it) *noun, plural* **credits.**

---

at; āpe; fär; câre; end; mē; it; īce; pîerce; hot; ōld; sông; fôrk; oil; out; up; ūse; rüle; pùll; tûrn; chin; sing; shop; thin; this; hw in white; zh in treasure. The symbol ə stands for the unstressed vowel sound in about, taken, pencil, lemon, and circus.

crinkle To form or cause to form wrinkles or ripples; wrinkle; crumple. The paper *crinkled* in the fire and then burst into flame.
    crin•kle (kring'kəl) *verb,* **crinkled, crinkling.**

critical Finding something wrong with things. You were *critical* of every plan that we suggested.
    crit•i•cal (krit'i kəl) *adjective.*

crutch A support that assists a person in walking. A crutch is a pole that usually has a padded part at the top that fits under the arm so a person can lean on it.
    crutch (kruch) *noun, plural* **crutches.**

crutch

current A part of the air or of a body of water that is moving along in a path. The rubber raft was caught in the *current* and carried out to sea.
    cur•rent (kûr'ənt) *noun, plural* **currents.**

cycle 1. A series of events that happen one after another in the same order, over and over again. Spring, summer, autumn, and winter are the *cycle* of the four seasons of the year. **2.** A bicycle, tricycle, or motorcycle.
    cy•cle (si'kəl) *noun, plural* **cycles.**

D

dangle To hang or swing loosely. Some old kite string *dangled* from a branch of the tree.
    dan•gle (dang'gəl) *verb,* **dangled, dangling.**

data Individual facts, figures, and other items of information. These *data* from the computer don't seem to be accurate.
    da•ta (dā'tə *or* dat'ə) *noun, plural.*

dawdle To waste time; linger.
    daw•dle (dô'dəl) *verb,* **dawdled, dawdling.**

decade A period of ten years.
    dec•ade (dek'ād) *noun, plural* **decades.**

decipher To figure out the meaning of something that is difficult to read or understand. No one could *decipher* the scribbled handwriting.
    de•ci•pher (di sī'fər) *verb,* **deciphered, deciphering.**

defend 1. To guard against attack or danger; protect. A goalie's job is to *defend* the goal against the opposing team. **2.** To speak or act in support of. The lawyer agreed to *defend* the man.
    de•fend (di fend') *verb,* **defended, defending.**

Deinonychus (di non'ə kəs).

delivery 1. The act of carrying or taking something to the proper place or person. The mail carrier makes a mail *delivery* every day except Sundays and holidays. **2.** A way of speaking or singing. The singer's *delivery* was loud.
    de•liv•er•y (di liv'ə rē) *noun, plural* **deliveries.**

Delphine (del fēn´).

demolish To tear down or destroy. The workers *demolished* the old factory to make way for a new office building.
    de•mol•ish (di mol´ish) *verb*, **demolished, demolishing.**

demolish

deposit To put or set down; place. The shopper *deposited* the groceries on the kitchen table.
    de•pos•it (di poz´it) *verb*, **deposited, depositing.**

despair A complete loss of hope. The family was filled with *despair* when the fire destroyed their house.
    de•spair (di spâr´) *noun*.

destruction Great damage or ruin. The earthquake caused widespread *destruction*.
    de•struc•tion (di struk´shən) *noun*.

developer A person who builds houses or other buildings on an area of land.
    de•vel•op•er (di vel´ə pər) *noun*, *plural* **developers.**

development 1. A group of houses or other buildings on a large area of land. The houses often look alike and are built by one builder. **2.** The act or process of bringing or coming gradually into being. The *development* of a spacecraft that could reach the moon took many years.
    de•vel•op•ment (di vel´əp mənt) *noun*, *plural* **developments.**

digest To break down food in the mouth, stomach, and intestines. When we *digest* food, we change it into a form that can be absorbed and used by the body.
    di•gest (di jest´ *or* dī jest´) *verb*, **digested, digesting.**

Diplodocus (di plod´ə kəs).

disaster An event that causes much suffering or loss. The flood was a *disaster*.
    dis•as•ter (di zas´tər) *noun*, *plural* **disasters.**

discount An amount subtracted from the regular price. I bought a suit on sale at a 25 percent *discount*.
    dis•count (dis´kount) *noun*, *plural* **discounts.**

distinguish To know or show that there is a difference between certain things.
    dis•tin•guish (di sting´gwish) *verb*, **distinguished, distinguishing.**

distressed Having or showing pain, sorrow, or misery. The *distressed* woman asked the police for help.
    dis•tressed (di strest´) *adjective*.

at; āpe; fär; câre; end; mē; it; īce; pîerce; hot; ōld; sông; fôrk; oil; out; up; ūse; rüle; pùll; tûrn; chin; sing; shop; thin; this; hw in white; zh in treasure. The symbol ə stands for the unstressed vowel sound in about, taken, pencil, lemon, and circus.

district An area that is a special part of a larger area. That store is in the business *district* of the city.
    dis•trict (dis′trikt) *noun, plural* **districts.**

District, the The District of Columbia, the location of the capital of the United States.
    Dis•trict (dis′trikt) *noun.*

division 1. One of the parts into which something is split up; a group or section. Our baseball team belongs to the Eastern *Division.* **2.** The process of dividing two numbers to show how many times one number contains the other. We were learning multiplication and *division* in our math class.
    di•vi•sion (di vizh′ən) *noun, plural* **divisions.**

document A written or printed statement that gives official proof and information about something.
    doc•u•ment (dok′yə mənt) *noun, plural* **documents.**

Doña Josefa (don′yä ho sā′fä).

donate To give; contribute. The family *donated* their old clothes to people who needed them.
    do•nate (dō′nāt) *verb,* **donated, donating.**

Doshita? Japanese for "What is wrong?"
    Do•shi•ta (dosh′tə′).

drawbridge A kind of bridge that can be raised or moved so that ships can pass under it. They raised the *drawbridge* so that the tall sailboat could pass.
    draw•bridge (drô′brij′) *noun, plural* **drawbridges.**

drizzle To rain steadily in fine, misty drops. We had expected a downpour, but it only *drizzled. Verb.* —A fine, misty rain. *Noun.*
    driz•zle (driz′əl) *verb,* **drizzled, drizzling;** *noun, plural* **drizzles.**

drought A long period of time when there is very little rain, or no rain at all.
    drought (drout) *noun, plural* **droughts.**

Earp, Wyatt A lawman and gunfighter in the American West in the 1800s.
    Wy•att Earp (wī′ət ûrp)

elegant Rich and fine in quality. The museum has a display of *elegant* costumes.
    el•e•gant (el′i gənt) *adjective.*

emerge

emerge 1. To come into view. The sun *emerged* from behind a cloud. **2.** To come out; become known. New facts about the case *emerged* during the trial.
    e•merge (i mûrj′) *verb,* **emerged, emerging.**

enchantment The state of being delighted, charmed, or fascinated. **en•chant•ment** (en chant′mənt) *noun, plural* **enchantments.**

entertain 1. To keep interested and amused. The clown *entertained* the children. **2.** To have as a guest. They often *entertain* people in their house in the country. **en•ter•tain** (en′tər tān′) *verb,* **entertained, entertaining.**

erect To build. A new apartment house will be *erected* on that lot. *Verb.*
—Upright; raised. The dog's ears became *erect* when its owner whistled. *Adjective.* **e•rect** (i rekt′) *verb,* **erected, erecting;** *adjective.*

eureka A word used as an exclamation upon the sudden discovery of something or the solving of a problem. **eu•re•ka** (yu̇ rē′kə) *interjection.*

Word History

Eureka comes from the Greek word *heureka,* which means "I have found (it)." The Greek scientist Archimedes supposedly said this when he discovered a method for determining the purity of gold.

---

exhaustion The condition of being very weak or tired. The runner's *exhaustion* was caused by a twenty-mile run. **ex•haus•tion** (eg zôs′chən) *noun.*

expense 1. Money spent to buy or do something; cost. My family cannot afford the *expense* of a new car. **2.** A cause or reason for spending money. Building the swimming pool was a big *expense.* **ex•pense** (ek spens′) *noun, plural* **expenses.**

expression 1. The act of putting thoughts or feelings into words or actions. These flowers are an *expression* of our thanks to you. **2.** An outward show; look. The students all had *expressions* of surprise on their faces after the magician performed the trick. **ex•pres•sion** (ek spresh′ən) *noun, plural* **expressions.**

flail To wave or swing, especially violently or quickly. I *flailed* my arms at the bees swarming around me. **flail** (flāl) *verb,* **flailed, flailing.**

flexible 1. Able to bend without breaking; not stiff. **2.** Able to change or adjust when necessary. **flex•i•ble** (flek′sə bəl) *adjective.*

fossil The hardened remains or traces of an animal or plant that lived long ago. The *fossils* that we found were imprints of ancient leaves and seashells in rock. **fos•sil** (fos′əl) *noun, plural* **fossils.**

fragile Easily broken; delicate. That china cup is very *fragile.* **frag•ile** (fraj′əl) *adjective.*

---

at; āpe; fär; câre; end; mē; it; īce; pîerce; hot; ōld; sông; fôrk; oil; out; up; ūse; rüle; pu̇ll; tûrn; chin; sing; shop; thin; this; hw in white; zh in treasure. The symbol ə stands for the unstressed vowel sound in about, taken, pencil, lemon, and circus.

G

gigantic Like a giant; huge and powerful. A *gigantic* whale swam under the ship.
    gi•gan•tic (jī gan′tik) *adjective.*

gigantic

glory Great praise; honor; fame. They both did the work, but only one got the *glory*.
    glo•ry (glôr′ē) *noun, plural* **glories.**

graffiti Words or drawings on walls, fences, sidewalks, and so forth.
    graf•fi•ti (grə fē′tē) *noun, plural.*

Word History

The word **graffiti** has a long history. It comes from the Italian word *graffiare,* which means "to scratch." The Italian word goes back to the Latin word *graphium,* meaning "stylus," or an instrument used for writing on soft materials, such as wax. The Latin word, in turn, comes from the Greek word *graphein,* which means "to write."

---

gratitude A feeling of thanks for a favor one has received or for something that makes one happy. Our neighbors were full of *gratitude* for the help that we gave them.
    grat•i•tude (grat′i tüd′ *or* grat′i tūd′) *noun.*

gravity 1. The force that pulls things toward the center of the earth. Gravity is the force that causes objects to fall when they are dropped. Gravity causes objects to have weight. **2.** Serious nature. Because of the *gravity* of the situation, troops were sent in.
    grav•i•ty (grav′i tē) *noun, plural* **gravities.**

Great Depression The period of hard times in the United States that began in 1929 and lasted throughout the 1930s. During the *Great Depression,* many people lost their jobs and many businesses closed.
    Great De•pres•sion (grāt di presh′ən) *noun.*

Great Plains A large region east of the Rocky Mountains, reaching from Canada to Texas, and consisting primarily of flat or rolling, mostly treeless plains.
    Great Plains (grāt plānz) *noun.*

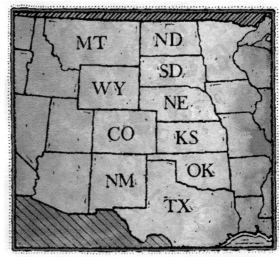
Great Plains

grope 1. To feel about with the hands. The child *groped* for the light switch in the dark room. **2.** To search for something in a blind or uncertain way. The students *groped* for the right answer while the teacher waited for someone to raise a hand.
　grope (grōp) *verb,* **groped, groping.**

guarantee 1. To give a promise to repair or replace something or to give back the money for it, if anything goes wrong with it before a certain time has passed. The company *guarantees* this dishwasher for one year. **2.** To make sure or certain. Having that band play will *guarantee* that the dance will be a success.
　guar•an•tee (gar′ən tē′) *verb,* **guaranteed, guaranteeing.**

Gulf of Mexico The large body of water mostly surrounded by the United States and Mexico.
　Gulf of Mex•i•co (gulf əv mek′si kō′) *noun.*

heritage Something that is handed down from earlier generations or from the past; tradition. The right to free speech is part of the American *heritage.*
　her•it•age (her′i tij) *noun, plural* **heritages.**

historian A person who knows a great deal about the story or record of what has happened in the past.
　his•to•ri•an (hi stôr′ē ən) *noun, plural* **historians.**

hoist To lift or pull up. We *hoisted* the flag up the pole.
　hoist (hoist) *verb,* **hoisted, hoisting.**

honorable Bringing honor or distinction; creditable.
　hon•or•a•ble (on′ər ə bəl) *adjective.*

House of Representatives One of the two lawmaking groups that make up the United States Congress.
　House of Rep•re•sent•a•tives (hous əv rep′ri zen′tə tivz) *noun.*

House of Representatives

hover To stay close by. The reporters *hovered* around the candidate while waiting to ask their questions.
　hov•er (huv′ər *or* hov′ər) *verb,* **hovered, hovering.**

at; āpe; fär; câre; end; mē; it; īce; pîerce; hot; ōld; sông; fôrk; oil; out; up; ūse; rüle; pu̇ll; tûrn; chin; sing; shop; thin; **th**is; hw in **wh**ite; zh in trea**s**ure. The symbol ə stands for the unstressed vowel sound in **a**bout, tak**e**n, penc**i**l, lem**o**n, and circ**u**s.

I

incorrect Not right or correct; not proper. You must do this problem over because your answer is *incorrect*.
> **in•cor•rect** (in′kə rekt′) *adjective*. **incorrectly** *adverb*.

injure To cause harm to; damage or hurt. I *injured* myself when I fell.
> **in•jure** (in′jər) *verb*, **injured**, **injuring**.

insistent Demanding attention or notice. The *insistent* ringing of the doorbell woke us.
> **in•sis•tent** (in sis′tənt) *adjective*.

intense 1. Very great or strong, extreme. The heat from the iron was so *intense* that it burned a hole in the cloth. **2.** Having or showing strong feeling, purpose, or effort; concentrated. The worried parent had an *intense* look.
> **in•tense** (in tens′) *adjective*.

intention A purpose; plan. Our *intention* is to wash all the windows before dinner.
> **in•ten•tion** (in ten′shən) *noun*, *plural* **intentions**.

interpret 1. To explain the meaning of. The teacher *interpreted* what the author meant in the poem. **2.** To change from one language to another; translate. Since my friends couldn't speak Spanish, I *interpreted* what my Mexican cousin was saying.
> **in•ter•pret** (in tûr′prit) *verb*, **interpreted**, **interpreting**.

invade To go into or to attack in order to conquer. Enemy troops *invaded* the country.
> **in•vade** (in vād′) *verb*, **invaded**, **invading**.

J

James, Frank and Jesse Two outlaw brothers who robbed banks and trains in and around Missouri in the 1800s.
> **James, Frank and Jesse** (jāmz)

Jericho An ancient Palestinian city in Jordan near the northern tip of the Dead Sea.
> **Jer•i•cho** (jer′i kō′) *noun*.

Jerusalem A historic city in Palestine, the capital of Israel.
> **Je•ru•sa•lem** (jə rü′sə ləm) *noun*.

jut To stick out. The lighthouse is on a piece of land that *juts* into the sea.
> **jut** (jut) *verb*, **jutted**, **jutting**.

K

kernel 1. The whole grain or seed of wheat, corn, and some other plants. When we eat corn on the cob, we are eating the *kernels*. **2.** The central or most necessary part. There was a *kernel* of truth in what our opponent had said. ▲ Another word that sounds like this is **colonel**.
> **ker•nel** (kûr′nəl) *noun*, *plural* **kernels**.

Klondike A region in the Yukon Territory of northwestern Canada.
> **Klon•dike** (klon′dīk′) *noun*.

L

Lakota-oyate (lä kō′tä ō yä′ta′).

landscape The stretch of land that can be seen from a place; view.
land•scape (land′skāp′) *noun, plural* **landscapes.**

lecture 1. To scold. The teacher *lectured* us for not doing our homework. **2.** To give a talk to an audience. The mayor *lectured* on the history of our town.
lec•ture (lek′chər) *verb,* **lectured, lecturing.**

legendary Of or having to do with a story that is passed down through the years that many people believe, but that is not entirely true.
leg•end•ar•y (lej′ən der′ē) *adjective.*

Leigh (lē).

limerick A funny poem five lines long. The following is an example of a *limerick:* There once was a man named Paul/Who went to a masquerade ball./He decided to risk it/And go as a biscuit/But a dog ate him up in the hall.
lim•er•ick (lim′ər ik) *noun, plural* **limericks.**

Word History

The kind of poem called a **limerick,** which has existed since Roman times, takes its name from Limerick, a county and village in Ireland. In the late 1890s, making up these amusing poems became a popular form of entertainment at parties.

Lupe (lü′pā).

M

Mamenchisaurus (mə men′chi sôr′əs).

management The act or process of directing or controlling. The business failed because of bad *management.*
man•age•ment (man′ij mənt) *noun.*

marking A mark or marks; patch or patches of color. The bird had brown and white *markings* on its wings.
mark•ing (mär′king) *noun, plural* **markings.**

microscope A device that is used to look at things that are too small to be seen with the naked eye. It has one or more lenses that produce an enlarged image of anything seen through it. The biologist studied the leaf under a *microscope.*
mi•cro•scope (mī′krə skōp′) *noun, plural* **microscopes.**

microscope

---

at; āpe; fär; câre; end; mē; it; īce; pîerce; hot; ōld; sông; fôrk; oil; out; up; ūse; rüle; pull; tûrn; chin; sing; shop; thin; this; hw in white; zh in treasure. The symbol ə stands for the unstressed vowel sound in about, taken, pencil, lemon, and circus.

---

millionaire A person who has money or property worth a million or more dollars.
> **mil•lion•aire** (mil′yə när′) *noun, plural* **millionaires.**

miniature Much smaller than the usual size. My parents made *miniature* furniture for my doll house. *Adjective.*
—A model or copy of something in a much smaller size. We bought a Statue of Liberty *miniature* as a souvenir of our trip to New York. *Noun.*
> **min•i•a•ture** (min′ē ə chər) *adjective; noun, plural* **miniatures.**

miserably In a very unhappy or wretched way. I failed *miserably* at my first attempt to ice-skate.
> **mis•er•a•bly** (miz′ər ə blē) *adverb.*

monitor To watch over or observe something. Our teacher *monitored* the fire drill. *Verb.*
—**1.** A student who is given a special duty to do. **2.** The screen that a computer uses to display numbers, letters, and pictures. *Noun.*
> **mon•i•tor** (mon′i tər) *noun, plural* **monitors;** *verb,* **monitored, monitoring.**

monstrous Horrible or frightening. The dragon in the story was a *monstrous* creature.
> **mon•strous** (mon′strəs) *adjective.*

mozzarella A soft, white cheese of Italian origin with a mild flavor.
> **moz•za•rel•la** (mot′sə rel′ə *or* mōt′sə rel′ə) *noun.*

Word History
The word **mozzarella** comes from Italy. In Italian, *mozzarella* means "little slices." In cooking, *mozzarella* cheese is often cut up into small pieces so that it will melt quickly.

---

murky Dark and gloomy. We couldn't see beneath the surface of the *murky* water in the pond.
> **murk•y** (mûr′kē) *adjective,* **murkier, murkiest.**

mustache Hair that grows above the upper lip. My grandfather has a big *mustache* that curls up at each end. This word is also spelled **moustache.**
> **mus•tache** (mus′tash *or* mə stash′) *noun, plural* **mustaches.**

N

Nanotyrannus (nan′ō ti ran′əs).

newborn A baby born very recently. A *newborn* baby sleeps most of the time.
> **new•born** (nü′bôrn) *noun, plural* **newborns.**

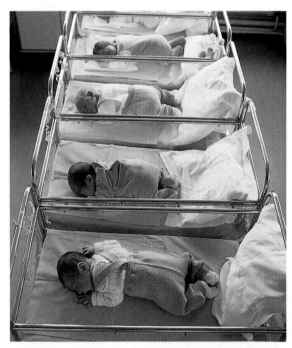

newborns

nimble 1. Light and quick in movement. The circus has *nimble* acrobats. **2.** Quick to understand or respond. In a debate, a *nimble* mind helps.
> **nim•ble** (nim′bəl) *adjective,* **nimbler, nimblest.**

nourish To provide food needed for life and growth. Milk *nourishes* a baby or newborn animal.
> **nour•ish** (nûr′ish) *verb,* **nourished, nourishing.**

O

observation 1. The act or power of noticing. The detective's careful *observation* helped the police to solve the crime. **2.** Something said; comment; remark. I made an *observation* about the weather.
> **ob•ser•va•tion** (ob′zər vā′shən) *noun, plural* **observations.**

offend To cause to be angry or unhappy. I'm sorry that my rude remark *offended* you.
> **of•fend** (ə fend′) *verb,* **offended, offending.**

Ojibway Another spelling of **Ojibwa. 1.** A group of Native Americans formerly living in the Great Lakes region, now living mainly in Minnesota, Wisconsin, and North Dakota. **2.** A member of this group. **3.** The language of this group. *Also,* **Chippewa.**
> **O•jib•way** (ō jib′wa) *noun, plural* **Ojibway** *or* **Ojibways.**

ominous Telling of trouble or bad luck to come; threatening.
> **om•i•nous** (om′e nəs) *adjective.*

onlooker A person who looks on without taking part; spectator. I was only an *onlooker* while my sisters argued.
> **on•look•er** (ôn′lùk′ər) *noun, plural* **onlookers.**

ooze To leak or pass out slowly through small holes or openings; seep.
> **ooze** (üz) *verb,* **oozed, oozing.**

ooze

ore A mineral or rock that is mined for the metal or other substance it contains. ▲ Other words that sound like this are **oar** and **or.**
> **ore** (ôr) *noun, plural* **ores.**

organize 1. To cause to join together in a labor union or other *organization.* **2.** To arrange or put together in an orderly way. Who is in charge of *organizing* the trip to the zoo?
> **or•gan•ize** (ôr′gə nīz′) *verb,* **organized, organizing.**

originate 1. To bring into being; start. Who *originated* the design for this new airplane? **2.** To come into being; begin. The fire *originated* in an old, deserted building.
> **o•rig•i•nate** (ə rij′ə nāt′) *verb,* **originated, originating.**

---

at; āpe; fär; câre; **e**nd; mē; it; īce; pîerce; hot; ōld; sông; fôrk; oil; out; up; ūse; rüle; pùll; tûrn; chin; sing; shop; thin; **th**is; hw in **wh**ite; **zh** in treasure. The symbol ə stands for the unstressed vowel sound in **a**bout, tak**e**n, penc**i**l, lem**o**n, and circ**u**s.

orphanage A place that takes in and cares for children whose parents are dead.
    or•phan•age (ôr′fə nij) *noun, plural* **orphanages.**

overhang To hang out over something; to jut out over. The trees *overhang* the street.
    o•ver•hang (ō′vər hang′) *verb,* **overhung, overhanging.**

P

participate To join with others; take part. Everyone *participated* in the rally.
    par•tic•i•pate (pär tis′ə pāt′) *verb,* **participated, participating.**

patio A paved outdoor space for cooking, eating, and relaxing. Our neighbors dine on their *patio* every weekend.
    pa•ti•o (pat′ē ō′) *noun, plural* **patios.**

patriot A person who loves his/her country and defends or supports it. We studied the lives of many American *patriots.*
    pa•tri•ot (pā′trē ət) *noun, plural* **patriots.**

pave To cover a road or street with a hard surface. The workers were *paving* the street.
    pave (pāv) *verb,* **paved, paving.**

pavement A hard covering or surface for a street, road, or sidewalk. A *pavement* is usually made from concrete or asphalt.
    pave•ment (pāv′mənt) *noun, plural* **pavements.**

payment Money that is given to someone in return for things or work. *Payment* has to be made for the television set when it is delivered.
    pay•ment (pā′mənt) *noun, plural* **payments.**

peddler A person who travels from place to place with goods for sale. I bought an apple for my lunch from a *peddler* on a street corner.
    ped•dler (ped′lər) *noun, plural* **peddlers.**

peddler

pelt[1] To strike over and over again with small, hard things. The children *pelted* each other with snowballs.
    pelt (pelt) *verb,* **pelted, pelting.**

pelt[2] The skin of an animal with its hair, fur, or wool. *Pelts* are used to make clothing and rugs.
    pelt (pelt) *noun, plural* **pelts.**

permission A consent from someone in authority. You should ask your parents for *permission* to stay overnight at my house.
    per•mis•sion (pər mish′ən) *noun.*

persuade To cause to do or believe something by pleading or giving reasons; convince. The principal *persuaded* the students to stop littering the school playground.
    per•suade (pər swād′) *verb,* **persuaded, persuading.**

pier 1. A pillar or other kind of support that is used to hold up a bridge. Modern bridges have steel *piers* to support them. **2.** A structure built out over the water. It is used as a landing place for boats or ships. ▲ Another word that sounds like this is **peer.**
    pier (pîr) *noun, plural* **piers.**

potlatch A feast held by some Native American tribes of the Pacific Northwest at which the host gives away and sometimes destroys valuable objects as a sign of wealth, and to establish his social status.
    pot•latch (pot′lach′) *noun.*

poverty A lack of money; the condition of being poor. That family lives in *poverty.*
    pov•er•ty (pov′ər tē) *noun.*

prehistoric Belonging to a time before people started writing history. Dinosaurs were *prehistoric* animals.
    pre•his•tor•ic (prē′his tôr′ik) *adjective.*

presence 1. The fact of being in a place at a certain time. The *presence* of the growling dog in the room made me nervous. **2.** The area around or near a person. The document had to be signed in the *presence* of a witness.
    pres•ence (prez′əns) *noun.*

previous Coming before; earlier. We were introduced at the *previous* meeting.
    pre•vi•ous (prē′vē əs) *adjective.*

probe To investigate or explore thoroughly. The police *probed* the details of the bank's dishonest practices. *Verb.*
—A tool or device used to test or explore. A doctor might use a *probe* to look into an injured ear. *Noun.*
    probe (prōb) *noun, plural* **probes;** *verb,* **probed, probing.**

prologue An introduction to a play, poem, story, or other literary work.
    pro•logue (prō′lôg′ *or* prō′log′) *noun, plural* **prologues.**

Word History

The word **prologue** comes from the Latin word *prologus,* which means "preface to a play." *Prologus* can be traced back to the Greek *pro-*, meaning "before," and *legein,* meaning "to speak." The Greek word for "something that is spoken before" took on the meaning of "introduction."

prospector A person who explores for gold or other minerals.
    pros•pec•tor (pros′pek tər) *noun, plural* **prospectors.**

prospector

at; āpe; fär; câre; end; mē; it; īce; pîerce; hot; ōld; sông; fôrk; oil; out; up; ūse; rüle; pull; tûrn; chin; sing; shop; thin; this; hw in white; zh in treasure. The symbol ə stands for the unstressed vowel sound in about, taken, pencil, lemon, and circus.

publicity 1. The attention of the public. Most politicians like *publicity.* **2.** Information given out to bring a person or thing to the attention of the public. The *publicity* about the singers brought a large crowd to see them.
pub•lic•i•ty (pu blis′i tē) *noun.*

Q

quench 1. To put an end to by satisfying. I *quenched* my thirst with a long drink of water. **2.** To make something stop burning; put out; extinguish. I *quenched* the fire.
quench (kwench) *verb,* **quenched, quenching.**

R

rascal 1. A mischievous person or animal. That pup is a *rascal.* **2.** A dishonest person; rogue.
ras•cal (ras′kəl) *noun, plural* **rascals.**

rasp To make a harsh, grating sound. The iron gate *rasped* because the hinges were rusty.
rasp (rasp) *verb,* **rasped, rasping.**

reaction An action in response to something that has happened or has been done. What was your parents' *reaction* when they saw your report card?
re•ac•tion (rē ak′shən) *noun, plural* **reactions.**

reasonable 1. Showing or using good sense and thinking; not foolish. A *reasonable* person will always listen to both sides of an argument. **2.** Not too expensive. The grocery store's prices are *reasonable.*
rea•son•a•ble (rē′zə nə bəl) *adjective.*

recital 1. A performance or concert of music or dance. We went to a piano *recital* in the auditorium. **2.** A story or account. Your *recital* of your experiences in Africa was fascinating.
re•cit•al (ri sī′təl) *noun, plural* **recitals.**

recital

reduce 1. To make or become less or smaller in size, number, or degree. Drivers should *reduce* their speed if the road is slippery. **2.** To bring to a lesser form, condition, or position. The forest was *reduced* to ashes by the fire.
re•duce (ri düs′) *verb,* **reduced, reducing.**

reef A ridge of sand, rock, or coral that lies at or near the surface of the ocean or another body of water. If you go scuba diving near a coral *reef* you will see a wide variety of marine animals.
    reef (rēf) *noun, plural* **reefs.**

register To have one's name placed on a list or record. Voters must *register* before they can vote. *Verb.*
—**1.** An official list or record or a book used for this. Guests signed the hotel *register.* **2.** A machine that automatically records and counts. A cash *register* records money it takes in. *Noun.*
    reg•is•ter (rej′ə stər) *noun, plural* **registers;** *verb,* **registered, registering.**

regret To feel sorry about. I *regret* having said unkind things to my friends.
    re•gret (ri gret′) *verb,* **regretted, regretting.**

reject To refuse to accept, allow, or approve. The voters *rejected* the tax plan.
    re•ject (ri jekt′) *verb,* **rejected, rejecting.**

reliable Able to be depended on and trusted. That worker is a *reliable* person who finishes every job on time.
    re•li•a•ble (ri lī′ə bəl) *adjective.*

relieve **1.** To free from discomfort or pain; comfort, help, or aid. I took medicine to *relieve* my cough. **2.** To free from a job or duty. The nurses stayed on duty until they were *relieved.*
    re•lieve (ri lēv′) *verb,* **relieved, relieving.**

reluctantly Unwillingly. She *reluctantly* got into the airplane even though she is afraid of heights.
    re•luc•tant•ly (ri luk′tənt lē) *adverb.*

reptile One of a class of cold-blooded animals with a backbone. Reptiles have dry, scaly skin. They move by crawling on their stomachs or creeping on short legs. Lizards, snakes, alligators, and turtles are *reptiles.*
    rep•tile (rep′təl *or* rep′tīl) *noun, plural* **reptiles.**

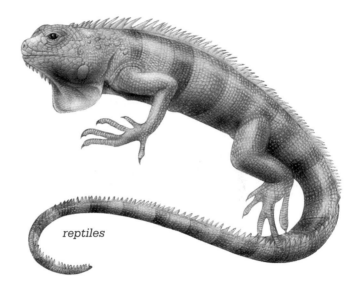

reptiles

reserve **1.** To arrange to have something kept for a particular person or purpose. My parents *reserved* rooms in a hotel. **2.** To keep for oneself. I *reserve* the right to make up my own mind.
    re•serve (ri zûrv′) *verb,* **reserved, reserving.**

restless **1.** Not able to rest. We got *restless* because the speech was so long. **2.** Not giving rest. The patient spent a *restless* night.
    rest•less (rest′lis) *adjective.*

---

at; āpe; fär; câre; **e**nd; mē; **i**t; īce; pîerce; hot; ōld; sông; fôrk; oil; out; up; ūse; rüle; půll; tûrn; **ch**in; si**ng**; **sh**op; **th**in; **th**is; **hw** in **wh**ite; **zh** in trea**s**ure. The symbol ə stands for the unstressed vowel sound in **a**bout, tak**e**n, penc**i**l, lem**o**n, and circ**u**s.

restore 1. To bring back to a former or original state or condition. The old house has been *restored* by its new owners. **2.** To give or put back. The police *restored* the bicycle to its owner.
    re•store (ri stôr′) *verb,* **restored, restoring.**

reveal 1. To make known. Don't *reveal* my secret. **2.** To show; display. The magician opened the lid to *reveal* a bunny.
    re•veal (ri vēl′) *verb,* **revealed, revealing.**

rival A person who is, or tries to be, as good as or better than another. The two students were *rivals* for class president.
    ri•val (rī′vəl) *noun, plural* **rivals.**

Rocky Mountains A group of mountain ranges reaching from New Mexico to Alaska
    Rock•y Moun•tains (rok′ē moun′tənz) *noun.*

rowdy Rude; boisterous; disorderly. The police were called when the crowd became *rowdy.*
    row•dy (rou′dē) *adjective.*

ruby A clear, red precious stone.
    ru•by (rü′bē) *noun, plural* **rubies.**

S

sacred 1. Belonging to a god; having to do with religion. Our choir sings *sacred* music. **2.** Deserving to be treated with great respect. The memory of the dead hero was *sacred* to the town.
    sa•cred (sā′krid) *adjective.*

scheme 1. A plan or plot for doing something. The crooks had a *scheme* for robbing the bank. **2.** An orderly arrangement of related things; design. You can choose the color *scheme* for your room.
    scheme (skēm) *noun, plural* **schemes.**

scratch *Idiom.* **from scratch.** From the beginning; with no resources. When their business failed, they had to start again *from scratch.*
    scratch (skrach) *noun.*

Second Congressional District One of the divisions of a state that elects a member of the House of Representatives.
    Sec•ond Con•gres•sion•al Dis•trict (sek′ənd kən gresh′ə nəl dis′trikt) *noun.*

shack A small, roughly built hut or cabin.
    shack (shak) *noun, plural* **shacks.**

shaky 1. Trembling; shaking. The frightened person answered in a *shaky* voice. **2.** Not firm; unsound. The old bridge is *shaky.*
    shak•y (shā′kē) *adjective,* **shakier, shakiest.**

shoreline The outline or contour of the land along the edge of an ocean, lake, or large river.
    shore•line (shôr′līn′) *noun, plural* **shorelines.**

shoreline

shrivel To shrink, wrinkle, or wither. The plant *shriveled* in the heat.
shriv•el (shriv′əl) *verb,* **shriveled, shriveling.**

silverware Spoons, forks, dishes, or anything else for the table that is made of or coated with silver.
sil•ver•ware (sil′vər wâr′) *noun.*

Sioux Another word for **Dakota.**
1. Any of several groups of Native Americans that once spoke similar languages, and formerly lived on the Great Plains. **2.** A member of one of these groups. **3.** The language of one of these groups.
Sioux (sü) *noun, plural* **Sioux** (sü, süz).

skeptical Having or showing doubt or disbelief.
skep•ti•cal (skep′ti kəl) *adjective.*

sliver A thin, often pointed piece that has been broken, cut, or torn off; splinter. I got a *sliver* of wood in my toe. I'd like a *sliver* of pie.
sliv•er (sliv′ər) *noun, plural* **slivers.**

smear To spread something wet, sticky, or greasy on something else.
smear (smîr) *verb,* **smeared, smearing.**

souvenir Something that is kept because it reminds one of a person, place, or event.
sou•ve•nir (sü′və nîr′ *or* sü′və nîr′) *noun, plural* **souvenirs.**

species A group of animals or plants that have many characteristics in common. Poodles and beagles belong to the same *species.*
spe•cies (spē′shēz) *noun, plural.*

specimen A single person or thing that shows what the whole group is like; sample. I collect *specimens* of different kinds of butterflies.
spec•i•men (spes′ə mən) *noun, plural* **specimens.**

speechless Not able to say anything. You were *speechless* when we yelled "Surprise!"
speech•less (spēch′lis) *adjective.*

stained Having marks or spots. The rug was *stained* where the ink spilled on it.
stained (stānd) *verb.*

stallion An adult male horse.
stal•lion (stal′yən) *noun, plural* **stallions.**

stallion

starvation The act or state of suffering or dying of hunger.
star•va•tion (stär vā′shən) *noun.*

static electricity A quantity of electricity that builds up on an object and does not flow away. *Static electricity* can be created by combing dry hair with a dry comb.
stat•ic e•lec•tric•i•ty (stat′ik i lek tris′ i tē) *noun.*

at; āpe; fär; câre; end; mē; it; īce; pîerce; hot; ōld; sông; fôrk; oil; out; up; ūse; rüle; pùll; tûrn; chin; sing; shop; thin; this; hw in white; zh in treasure. The symbol ə stands for the unstressed vowel sound in about, taken, pencil, lemon, and circus.

G23

stern The rear part of a boat or ship.
stern (stûrn) *noun, plural* **sterns.**

stern

stifle 1. To make breathing difficult
for; smother. The smoke *stifled* the
people in the burning building.
2. To be unable to breath normally;
feel smothered. I opened the
windows because I was *stifling*.
3. To hold back; stop. I *stifled* a
yawn.
  sti•fle (stī′fəl) *verb*, **stifled,
  stifling.**

stride To walk with long steps. We
watched the models *stride* in their
fancy clothes. *Verb.*
—**1.** A long step. My friend has a
quick *stride.* **2.** Progress or
improvement. Science has made
strides in fighting disease. *Noun.*
  stride (strīd) *noun, plural* **strides;**
  verb, **strode, stridden, striding.**

stun 1. To shock. We were *stunned*
by the news. **2.** To make
unconscious. The robin was *stunned*
when it flew into the window.
  stun (stun) *verb*, **stunned,
  stunning.**

submit 1. To present. Please *submit*
your book reports on Monday. **2.** To
yield to some power or authority.
The children *submitted* to their
parents' wishes.
  sub•mit (səb mit′) *verb*,
  submitted, submitting.

subterranean Being, located, or
happening below the surface of
the earth; underground. The train
carries passengers through a
subterranean tunnel.
  sub•ter•ra•ne•an
  (sub′tə ra′ne ən) *adjective.*

summon 1. To ask to come. We
summoned the police to the car
accident. **2.** To stir up; arouse. I
summoned my courage and dove
off the high diving board.
  sum•mon (sum′ən) *verb*,
  summoned, summoning.

survey 1. To look at or study in
detail. The mayor *surveyed* the
damage to the city after the storm.
2. To measure land to fix or find
out its boundaries. They *surveyed*
the property before it was divided
into lots.
  sur•vey (sər vā′) *verb*, **surveyed,
  surveying.**

swerve To turn aside suddenly. The
driver *swerved* to avoid hitting the
dog.
  swerve (swûrv) *verb*, **swerved,
  swerving.**

swollen Made larger by swelling.
I can't get my ring on my *swollen*
finger.
  swol•len (swo′lən) *adjective.*

T

Tahcawin (täk′shô we ä).

tantie In Trinidad, a female relative
who assists in the upbringing of
young children.
  tan•tie (tän tē) *noun.*

Tasinagi (tä′she nä ge).

technique A method or way of bringing about a desired result in a science, art, sport, or profession. The farmer taught me some good *techniques* for planting crops.
  tech•nique (tek nēk´) *noun, plural* **techniques.**

temporary Lasting or used for a short time only. Some students try to find *temporary* jobs for the summer.
  tem•po•rar•y (tem´pə rer´ē) *adjective.*

thief A person who steals. The *thief* broke into the house and stole the television.
  thief (thēf) *noun, plural* **thieves.**

threat A person or thing that might cause harm; danger. The outbreak of flu was a *threat* to everyone in the community.
  threat (thret) *noun, plural* **threats.**

thrive To be successful; do well. This plant *thrives* in the sun.
  thrive (thrīv) *verb,* **thrived, thriving.**

Tonweya (ton wa´yə).

transatlantic Crossing or spanning the Atlantic Ocean. I made a *transatlantic* telephone call.
  trans•at•lan•tic (trans´at lan´tik or tranz´at lan´tik) *adjective.*

treacherous Full of danger; hazardous. Many ships have sunk in those *treacherous* waters.
  treach•er•ous (trech´ər əs) *adjective.*

treatment 1. The care or medicine used to help cure a sick or injured person. Rest was the recommended *treatment.* **2.** The way something or someone is treated. That scratched record has had rough *treatment.*
  treat•ment (trēt´mənt) *noun, plural* **treatments.**

tropical Having to do with or found in the region of the earth that is near the equator. Most monkeys live in *tropical* forests.
  trop•i•cal (trop´i kəl) *adjective.*

tropical

tutor A teacher who gives private lessons to a pupil.
  tu•tor (tü´tər *or* tū´tər) *noun, plural* **tutors.**

Word History
  The word **tutor** comes from the Latin word *tutor,* meaning "defender" or "guardian." In some English universities, the word *tutor* was used for a graduate responsible for a younger student. From this meaning came the sense of "a private teacher."

---

at; āpe; fär; câre; end; mē; it; īce; pîerce; hot; ōld; sông; fôrk; oil; out; up; ūse; rüle; pùll; tûrn; chin; sing; shop; thin; **th**is; hw in white; zh in treasure. The symbol ə stands for the unstressed vowel sound in about, taken, pencil, lemon, and circus.

typical Showing the qualities or characteristics of a certain type. A *typical* movie lasts about ninety minutes.
   typ•i•cal (tip′i kəl) *adjective.*

Tyrannosaurus Rex A huge dinosaur that lived in North America in prehistoric times.
   ty•ran•no•sau•rus rex (ti ran′ə sôr′əs reks) *noun.*

Tyrannosaurus Rex

U

universe Everything that exists, including Earth, the planets, the stars, and all of space.
   u•ni•verse (ū′nə vûrs′) *noun.*

Word History

The word **universe** comes from a Latin word that means "the whole world."

V

vaguely In a way that is not clear or definite. I only *vaguely* know how to get to the theater.
   vaguely (vāg′lē) *adverb.*

vandalize To damage or destroy property willfully.
   van•dal•ize (van′də līz′) *verb,* **vandalized, vandalizing.**

Word History

The word **vandalize** comes from *Vandals,* the name of a group of people who lived in northern Europe more than 1,500 years ago. In the fourth and fifth centuries A.D., the *Vandals* made destructive raids into the areas that are now France, Spain, and Italy. Today, *vandalize* means "to destroy property, especially something of artistic or religious value." A person who vandalizes is called a *vandal.*

---

vaporize To change or be changed into small particles of mist, steam, or smoke that can be seen in the air. When water boils in a pot, it *vaporizes* into the air.
   va•por•ize (vā′pə rīz′) *verb,* **vaporized, vaporizing.**

variety A number of different things. We bought a *variety* of foods at the grocery store.
   va•ri•e•ty (və rī′i tē) *noun, plural* **varieties.**

visible Able to be seen. Their house is *visible* from the road.
   vis•i•ble (viz′ ə bəl) *adjective.*

W

Y

Waŋbli The word for "eagle" in the language of the Lakota people.
Waŋ•bli (wäm ble′) *noun.*

wampum Small, polished beads made from shells and strung together or woven into belts, collars, and necklaces. *Wampum* was used by some Native Americans as money.
wam•pum (wom′pəm) *or* (wôm′pəm) *noun.*

wampum

Yukon A territory in northwestern Canada that borders Alaska.
Yu•kon (ū′kon) *noun.*

Z

zooxanthella A very small, single-celled organism with two whiplike "tails."
zo•o•xan•thel•la (zo′ə zan thel′ə) *noun,* *plural* **zooxanthellae**.

Word History

The word **zooxanthella** comes from the Greek words *zoe,* meaning "life," and *xanthos,* meaning "yellow," and the Latin word ending *-ella,* meaning "small." Literally, then, *zooxanthella* means "a small, yellow living thing."

---

wedge A piece of wood, metal, plastic, or other substance that is thick at one end and narrow at the other. We served a *wedge* of cheese with some crackers.
wedge (wej) *noun,* *plural* **wedges.**

whist A card game for two pairs of players, played with a full deck of fifty-two cards.
whist (hwist *or* wist) *noun.*

---

at; āpe; fär; câre; end; mē; it; īce; pîerce; hot; ōld; sông; fôrk; oil; out; up; ūse; rüle; púll; tûrn; chin; sing; shop; thin; <u>th</u>is; hw in white; zh in treasure. The symbol ə stands for the unstressed vowel sound in about, taken, pencil, lemon, and circus.

ACKNOWLEDGMENTS

The publisher gratefully acknowledges permission to reprint the following copyrighted material:

"The Act" from WILLIAM CARLOS WILLIAMS: COLLECTED POEMS 1939-1962, Volume II. Copyright © 1948 by William Carlos Williams. Reprinted by permission of New Directions Publishing Corp.

"Amazing...But True! Bridges" from AMAZING...BUT TRUE! BRIDGES AND TUNNELS by Laura Allen. SUPERSCIENCE BLUE, January 1995, Volume 6, Number 4, Copyright © 1995 by Scholastic. Reprinted by permission.

"Ben and Me" from BEN AND ME by Robert Lawson. Copyright 1939 by Robert Lawson; © renewed 1967 by John W. Boyd. By permission of Little, Brown and Company.

"The Best Bad Thing" from THE BEST BAD THING by Yoshiko Uchida. Copyright © 1983 by Yoshiko Uchida. Reprinted with permission of Margaret K. McElderry Books, an imprint of Simon & Schuster Books for Young Readers.

Cover permission for THE BIG ROCK by Bruce Hiscock. Copyright © 1988 by Atheneum. Reprinted by permission.

"The Big Storm" by Bruce Hiscock. Copyright (c) 1993 by Bruce Hiscock. Reprinted with permission of Atheneum Books for Young Readers, Simon & Schuster Children's Publishing Division.

"Breaker's Bridge" from THE RAINBOW PEOPLE by Laurence Yep. Text copyright © 1989 by Laurence Yep. Reprinted by permission of HarperCollins Publisher.

"Calvin and Hobbes" from THE ESSENTIAL CALVIN AND HOBBES: A CALVIN AND HOBBES TREASURY by Bill Watterson. Copyright © 1988 by Bill Watterson. Published by Andrews and McMeel Books. Reprinted by permission.

"Change" from RIVER WINDING by Charlotte Zolotow. Copyright © 1970 by Charlotte Zolotow. Reprinted by permission by HarperCollins Publishers.

Book covers for CHRONICLES OF NARNIA by C. S. Lewis. Reproduced with the permission of the Harper Collins Publishing Company.

"City" from COLLECTED POEMS by Langston Hughes, Copyright © 1994 by the Estate of Langston Hughes. Reprinted by permission of Alfred A. Knopf Inc.

"Como un recuerdo/Like a Memory" from JUNTO AL ALAMO DE LOS SINSONTES by Emilio de Armas. Copyright © 1988 Ediciones Casa de las Americas. Published by Ediciones Casa de las Americas. Reprinted by permission.

"Crystal Rowe" from CLASS DISMISSED. Text copyright (c) 1986 by Mel Glenn. Reprinted by permission of Clarion Books/Houghton Mifflin Company. All rights reserved.

"Curious Ben" from KIDS DISCOVER magazine, Volume 4, Issue 9, November 1994. Copyright © 1994 by Kids Discover Magazine. Reprinted by permission.

"Dear Mr. Henshaw" from DEAR MR. HENSHAW by Beverly Cleary. Copyright © 1983 by Beverly Cleary. Used by permission of Morrow Junior Books, a division of William Morrow & Company, Inc.

"The Diary of Martha Baker Wilson" from ALASKA GOLD RUSH DIARY OF MARTHA BAKER WILSON by Grace Esterbrook Fake. Copyright © 1982 by Grace E. Fake.

"Dive to the Coral Reefs" from DIVE TO THE CORAL REEFS: A NEW ENGLAND AQUARIUM BOOK written by Elizabeth Tayntor, Paul Erickson, and Les Kaufman. Copyright © 1986 by the New England Aquarium. Reprinted by permission of Crown Publishers, Inc. Permission also from Mews Books Ltd. for New England Aquarium.

"For Poets" by Al Young. Copyright © 1968 by Al Young. Reprinted with permission of the author.

"For Purple Mountains' Majesty" from THE MALIBU AND OTHER POEMS by Myra Cohn Livingston. Copyright © 1972 by Myra Cohn Livingston. Reprinted by permission of Marian Reiner for the author.

"Fossils" reprinted with permission of Atheneum Books for Young Readers, an imprint of Simon & Schuster Children's Publishing Division, 1969. Simon & Schuster from SOMETHING NEW BEGINS by Lilian Moore. Copyright © 1982 by Lilian Moore.

Book cover for THE GARDEN OF ABDUL GASAZI by Chris Van Allsburg. Copyright © 1979 by Chris Van Allsburg. Reprinted by permission of Houghton Mifflin Co. All rights reserved.

"The Gold Coin" from THE GOLD COIN by Alma Flor Ada. Copyright © 1991 by Alma Flor Ada. Illustrations copyright © 1991 by Neil Waldman. Reprinted with permission from Atheneum Books for Young Readers, an imprint of Simon & Schuster Children's Publishing Division.

"Grandma Essie's Covered Wagon" by David Williams, illustrated by Wiktor Sadowski. Text copyright © 1993 by David Williams. Illustrations copyright © 1993 by Wiktor Sadowski. Reprinted by permission.

Cover use of THE HAPPIEST ENDING by Yoshiko Uchida. Cover by Kinuko Craft and used with permission of the artist.

Jacket illustration from HENRY AND BEEZUS by Beverly Cleary. Illustrated by Frederika Ribes. Text copyright (c) 1952 by Beverly Cleary. By permission of Morrow Junior Books, a division of William Morrow and Company, Inc.

"How It Feels to Fight for Your Life" from HOW IT FEELS TO FIGHT FOR YOUR LIFE by Jill Krementz. Copyright © 1989, 1991 by Jill Krementz, Inc. Reprinted by permission of Little, Brown and Company.

Book cover for HOW IT FEELS WHEN A PARENT DIES by Jill Krementz. Copyright © 1981 by Jill Krementz. Reprinted by permission of Alfred A. Knopf, Inc.

"How to Think Like a Scientist" from HOW TO THINK LIKE A SCIENTIST: ANSWERING QUESTIONS BY THE SCIENTIFIC METHOD by Stephen P. Kramer. Copyright © 1987 by Stephen P. Kramer. Reprinted by permission of HarperCollins Publishers.

"Human-Made Reef Relief" reprint permission and copyright © 1994 by Weekly Reader Corporation. All Rights Reserved.

"I Love the Look of Words" by Maya Angelou, copyright © 1993 by Maya Angelou, from SOUL LOOKS BACK IN WONDER by Tom Feelings. Used by permission of Dial Books for Young Readers, a division of Penguin Books USA Inc.

"Identified Flying Objects" by Margaret McKelway from NATIONAL GEOGRAPHIC WORLD, Number 239, July 1995. Copyright © 1995 by the National Geographic Society. Reprinted by permission.

"The Impossible Trick" from THE GIGANTIC ANTS AND OTHER CASES, the third book of THE EINSTEIN ANDERSON SCIENCE SERIES, by Seymour Simon. Text copyright (c) 1981 by Seymour Simon. By permission of Morrow Junior Books, a division of William Morrow & Company, Inc.

"The Incredible Shrinking Machine" from THE HOWLING DOG AND OTHER CASES, the first book of THE EINSTEIN ANDERSON SCIENCE SERIES, by Seymour Simon. Text copyright (c) 1980 by Seymour Simon. By permission of Morrow Junior Books, a division of William Morrow & Company, Inc.

"It's Our World, Too!" from IT'S OUR WORLD TOO! by Phillip Hoose. Copyright © 1993 by Phillip Hoose. By permission of Little, Brown and Company.

Cover use of A JAR OF DREAMS by Yoshiko Uchida. Cover by Kinuko Craft and used with permission of the artist.

"Jigsaw Puzzle" by Russell Hoban reprinted by permission of Harold Ober Associates, Incorporated. Copyright © 1970 by Russell Hoban.

Book cover for JUMANJI by Chris Van Allsburg. Copyright © 1981 by Chris Van Allsburg. Reprinted by permission of Houghton Mifflin Co. All rights reserved.

"Klondike Fever" from GOLD! THE KLONDIKE ADVENTURE by Delia Ray. Copyright © 1989 by Laing Communications, Inc. Used by permission of Lodestar Books, an affiliate of Dutton Children's Books, a division of Penguin USA, Inc.

Text of "Knoxville, Tennessee" from BLACK TALK, BLACK FEELING, BLACK JUDGMENT by Nikki Giovanni. Copyright (c) 1968, 1970 by Nikki Giovanni. By permission of William Morrow and Company, Inc.

"maggie and milly and molly and may" is reprinted from COMPLETE POEMS: 1904-1962 by e. e. cummings, Edited by George J. Firmage, by permission of Liveright Publishing Corporation. Copyright © 1956, 1984, 1991 by the Trustees for the E. E. Cummings Trust.

"Magnet" from MORE SMALL POEMS by Valerie Worth. Copyright © 1976 by Valerie Worth. Published by Farrar, Straus & Giroux, Inc. Reprinted by permission.

"Making a Difference" by Tracy Williams Cheney and Connie Eden from FALCON MAGAZINE, Volume 3, Number 4, July/August 1995. Copyright © 1995 by Falcon Press Publishing. Reprinted by permission.

"The Marble Champ" from BASEBALL IN APRIL AND OTHER STORIES, copyright © 1990 by Gary Soto. Reprinted by permission of Harcourt Brace & Company.

"Money, Money, Money" from SPIDER Magazine January 1995 Volume 2, Number 1. Copyright © 1995 by Carus Publishing Co.

Book cover for MR. REVERE AND I by Robert Lawson. Copyright 1953 by Robert Lawson. Copyright © renewed by John W. Boyd. By permission of Little, Brown and Company.

"My Adventures at the Center of the Earth" by Ana Maria Shua. Copyright © 1988 by Editorial Sudamericana. Reprinted by permission.

"My Floor Is Somebody's Ceiling" from THE BUTTERFLY JAR by Jeff Moss. Copyright © 1989 by Jeff Moss. Used by permission of Bantam Books, a division of Bantam Doubleday Dell Publishing Group, Inc.

"my friend" by Emily Hearn from HOCKEY CARDS AND HOPSCOTCH by John McInnes & Emily Hearn. Copyright © 1971. Used with permission of Nelson Canada, a Division of Thomson Canada Limited.

"New Providence" from NEW PROVIDENCE: A CHANGING CITYSCAPE by Renata Von Tscharner and Ronald Lee Fleming, The